Engineers of the Renaissance

Bertrand Gille

Engineers of the Renaissance

The M.I.T.Press
Massachusetts Institute of Technology
Cambridge, Massachusetts

Copyright © 1966 by Hermann, Paris

Translated from
Les ingénieurs de la Renaissance
published by Hermann, Paris, in 1964

Library of Congress Catalog Card Number 66–27213
Printed in Great Britain

Contents

List of illustrations

Any study of the engineers of the Renaissance is inevitably dominated and somewhat falsified by the great figure of Leonardo da
Vinci. So many books have been written about him and so much
praise has been meted out to him that his predecessors, and even his
contemporaries, have sunk into oblivion. It is very difficult to
re-establish them. There have been some attempts to strike a correct
balance, but these, it seems, have failed. This view, persistent and
widespread, has led us, after long and patient research, to attempt a
more complete picture of the great movement of ideas that extends
throughout the fifteenth century. We shall end up with a better
understanding of the men whose writings Leonardo may not have
read but whom he certainly met, listened to, and respected.

The first stage in this study has therefore been devoted to the predecessors of Leonardo da Vinci. It has been a thankless and difficult
task, but an absorbing one. Our authors are very little known and
will doubtless long remain so, unless discoveries are made in libraries;
their works, moreover, are badly catalogued. We had to begin by a
systematic examination of the catalogues of the great European
libraries; but their entries in this field are less accurate than one could
wish and even contain obvious errors: omissions or false identifications are quite numerous.

An investigation of this kind requires comparisons between
manuscripts; but since, in contrast to those of Leonardo, these have
frequently not been published and are widely scattered, such comparisons have usually been impossible. It was microfilm alone which
enabled us to make these essential confrontations. With the help of the
Centre national de la recherche scientifique, Ecole pratique des hautes
études, Institut de recherche et d'histoire des textes, Direction des
archives de France, and the unsparing help of individuals, a collection

of microfilms was assembled and a catalogue, naturally provisional, was drawn up and will be found at the end of this book. Real study could not begin until this preliminary work had been undertaken. Despite a wide search, it is probable that many documents have escaped us. The publication of the illustrations with which we have sought to enliven our text may lead to new and interesting identifications. This is the only way in which a definitive history of the great technical movement of the Renaissance may be worked out.

Although the nature of this technical Renaissance became thus progressively clearer to us, took on shape and vigour and considerable breadth, it still remained necessary to identify both its foundations and its effects; it was, in short, impossible to isolate it from its historical context. This double purpose might, at first sight, seem to be a challenge.

It is well known that our sources for mediaeval techniques are few and the same applies to the Renaissance. Our authors, however, as good humanists, and wishing to appear both cultivated and learned – even those who claimed to be unlettered – themselves put us on the right track. It soon appeared that neither Vegetius nor Vitruvius, the latter at least in the most strictly technical section of his work, could, despite the renewed interest shown in them at this period, supply the essential foundations of our own technological research. The hypothesis we present – for it is impossible to speak of absolute fact – may be based on a weak argument. Nevertheless we thought it was worth while drawing attention to the tradition of the early mechanics and to their technological encyclopaedias. The substance of these had mostly been lost. It was divided into a number of simple problems which engaged the attention of those who bore the irksome responsibility for practical achievements of this kind from the thirteenth to the fifteenth century. Military preoccupations certainly existed during this long period of the development of technical thought, but it is possible that they were not always of first importance.

In the fifteenth century new tendencies, which favoured rapid progress but were not essentially of a technical order, began to appear. The importance of the technical problems tended to give technicians a high status, while they themselves were trying to acquire mastery of all their activities. Thus we perceive the outline of our Renaissance engineer: an artist and artisan, a military man, an organizer of festivities, a man of such complexity and genius that it seemed that no effect was beyond his powers.

This was the high point of the development which we have tried to describe and was of very brief duration. It was found necessary almost at once to restore specialization and it continued to gain ground. But this short period, which might be called Archimedean – and, as we shall see, the spirit of Archimedes was indeed probably present to people's minds – put science once and for all on the road to becoming contemporary. No doubt this was one of the most interesting consequences of humanism, to have caused this meeting between science and technology at the end of the fifteenth century. Among enlightened princes there was a fashion for both technical creation and amusing inventions. Little more was required to bend scientific thought in the direction of actual experiment, towards which it had for some time been moving.

The last stage of this work was not the least difficult. There was no need for hypotheses: the sources were available. But it was necessary to struggle against entrenched prejudices, against a whole official history, already accepted and considered incontrovertible. Disavowels of paternity were easy. Much ignorance and excessive imagination were required to establish Leonardo da Vinci in the face of his own admissions as a fertile inventor. But his curiosity and his wisdom place him on a different level and require different explanations. And we must confess that we nearly ended up, almost unawares, in the same position as that of Duhem, who makes of Leonardo a scholar who never left the study or, what is worse, a haunter of libraries.

The inspiration of the artist is difficult to define. The fact that he borrows from others should not be isolated from the artist's aim. Leonardo was an artist but he was also a technician and a scientist. And it would be a mistake to oppose the official thesis too systematically by likening the notebooks to a complete work. They represent only borrowings, imaginatively interpreted, an early and passing phase of his thought. The problem of Leonardo's sources has never been tackled and could not have been, given the position that was taken in regard to him. One of our longest tasks was thus to determine, as Duhem had done in a different field, the respective extents of his imagination and of his borrowing. Too many elements are still missing for us to be able to claim perfect results. We hope, nevertheless, that research may be continued in this direction.

Doubtless these notebooks of Leonardo can never have been the fruits of pure borrowing. The action of borrowing was enriched, at the very moment when it was undertaken, by a new approach and new hopes. It is thus the direction of Leonardo's endeavour which has to be determined. Here again, many doubts stand in the way. It would be difficult to deny that Leonardo was sensitive to certain forms and even the design of machines provided material for this undoubted taste. The element which strikes him in the study of eddies and of the way water falls is undoubtedly the same as that in certain sketches which at first sight appear to have a purely technical inspiration.

The link between technical and scientific problems is always quite clear. Leonardo's mechanics are not revolutionary, but it is clear that he attempted, at least in some fields, to find concrete justifications for the theories he wished to adopt, and even to create a general explanation for specific problems.

Works of pure technique, or of applied science as we would say today, constitute perhaps the most substantial contribution made by Leonardo da Vinci. Without dwelling at length on matters which we shall return to later, it is impossible not to mention the hydraulic studies, which certainly entailed the use of models such as we have today in our laboratories. The drawings of workers' positions, reminiscent of the most recent research, are in the same category. Was Leonardo also an inventor? Perhaps. But there is a great gulf between creative imagination and practical realization and it is here that we see how little Leonardo was a man of action. His inventiveness, if inventiveness there was, is all theoretical, as with several of his predecessors. This is demonstrated by his drawings, which are sketches rather than working diagrams. We shall see the difference in this respect between Leonardo and Francesco di Giorgio. Of greater interest is Leonardo's hope of technical progress and his desire for a more complete domination of nature. The feeling for the development of machinery, which is found not only in Leonardo, that is to say the desire to possess the most powerful means of action and to use less manual labour, is, from this point of view, the highest virtue of the great Florentine.

It is possible that after having read this book the reader will feel somewhat disappointed. The engineers of the Renaissance whose work is here presented were not agents of true technical progress. They often only followed a movement of which they were neither the initiators nor, in many cases, the propagators. In terms of achievement their role emerges as, in the last analysis, a very feeble one. They were military men, artists and architects; their taste for techniques, their search for 'inventions', appear to us as a kind of pastime, sometimes even as a kind of amusement or intellectual game.

The compilations and notebooks which we have tried to study are doubtless more a manifestation of curiosity than of true technical research. They have, for those who wish to regard them as our sole source of knowledge in this field, serious gaps and surprising

Leonardo da Vinci:
study of workers' positions.

omissions. We have not tried to make good these omissions nor to correct them. Our aim has not been to write a history of technology at the time of the Renaissance.

The authors discussed here interest us as providing evidence of certain preoccupations and to this extent only they concern us. It was not so much technology that we wished to present as a certain technical attitude and it was in this sense that our engineers seemed to be representative. This is additionally true since their drawings are all we have to go on.

All the same, our aim was most ambitious given the extent of our knowledge. All we have done is to outline an essay which we are aware is insufficient and imperfect. Our purpose was, more than anything, to encourage research, in which we hope that we may have succeeded.

We do not wish to convey the idea that everything in this study is new, that our approach is completely unpublished and that we have entered virgin territory. A large number of publications, many of them from Germany, are witness to the efforts of our predecessors. Pioneers have opened the way and cleared the approaches to this subject. In the last few years Italian scholars have taken up these matters again and have made certain decisive advances. In many cases it was enough to deepen our knowledge and to complete the documentation; it also appeared desirable to take stock of the whole situation.

If the interested reader is unlikely to follow up a somewhat forbidding bibliography, it was nevertheless our duty to lighten the task of the scientific scholar and at the same time to acknowledge our debts. It is for this reason that we have decided to relegate the whole critical apparatus to the end of the book and have divided it into chapters and sections in order to facilitate the work of those who wish to study it.

Chapter I: The Weight of Tradition

If there is any field in which continuity of effort appears to be the rule, in which this continuity is characterized as strongly by the transmission of knowledge as by inventions and imagination, whose sole basis is a long progression of thought, that field is the technical one. While certain scientific ideas have been lost and rediscovered and certain sources of artistic inspiration have been forgotten and recreated, tools and manufacturing processes, with some exceptions, have remained constantly available. From one generation to another, as from one man to another, there are only imperceptible differences. Moreover, while an advance may be concealed, a mistake is easily discernible. Hence progress in techniques is made by balancing setbacks against some spectacular successes.

This makes good sense, perhaps, but it is nevertheless very difficult, sometimes even impossible, to adduce clear evidence for it. There is no spontaneous generation: there cannot be. But Ariadne's thread escapes us: our documentation is, if not totally silent, at least highly discreet. Even the names cited by our Renaissance engineers do not reveal any provable tradition. These are, for the most part, signs of humanist vanity or perhaps the hope of linking their own activity to an honourable pedigree rather than asking the reader to believe in obscure origins. No one wishes to appear more learned than a man who has the hypocrisy to call himself unlettered.

Historians have gone to great trouble to follow scientific ideas and to unravel continuous lines of artistic development. Will these same historians suddenly discover a unique and spontaneous source of technical inspiration? It would perhaps have been better to look, in both cases, for a slow accumulation of knowledge. Our documentation in this matter, it must be well understood, is neither precise nor continuous. But was this an excuse for denying the existence of what we did not know? Would it not have been best to seize upon the slightest clue in order to retrace the passage of the years and to re-establish the essential links suggested by simple logic? We shall try to do this, without concealing the weakness of our evidence, without hiding the undoubted imperfections of the hypothesis. Perhaps it will lead us to further discoveries.

At the beginning of the sixteenth century, the Count Palatine Otto-Heinrich ordered the copying of a very old manuscript on the art of war. When he learned that the figures had been altered to suit contemporary fashion, this prince asked that another copy should be made exactly reproducing the original. This new copy was then inserted into the manuscript, which thus carried two series of illustrations. Otto-Heinrich, like all German princes of this period, was a warrior; but he had the same ambitions as his Italian contemporaries and neglected neither the arts nor the pleasures of the intellect. His desire to include in his carefully assembled library the copy of an old manuscript certainly arose from this double aspect of his personality.

How did he secure it? The information is lacking: perhaps it would have provided the key to everything we want to know. Perhaps an ancient treatise had been discovered by chance. Vitruvius, indeed, had suddenly appeared in this way at the beginning of the fifteenth century. This would, to some extent, explain the considerable number of manuscripts of this work in existence in the fifteenth and the beginning of the sixteenth century. But the case of Vitruvius has today been closely studied and it has been shown that it was a false discovery: Vitruvius had never been forgotten, he had always been safe from oblivion. It might be supposed that in a period when architects were beginning to look for new ideas, the appearance of an unknown manuscript would have been considered an exceptional event. It would probably be no less inexact to suppose that the military treatises of the high Middle Ages had had an uninterrupted tradition, and that in this particular case, they had only been struck by the beauty of a manuscript that had lain hidden until then. In the same way, Vegetius had enjoyed, throughout the centuries, a success which appears never to have been gainsaid. The growth which we observe in the number of manuscripts, is due only to the better conservation of more recent manuscripts. In the inventory made of these manuscripts in 1885, there were 130: one of the seventh, one of the ninth, seven of the tenth, nineteen of the twelfth and thirteenth, one hundred of the fourteenth and fifteenth and two of the seventeenth century.

The work which the German prince had copied was a compilation, probably of Byzantine origin, which came straight by uninterrupted tradition from the work of the Hellenistic schools of mechanics and military engineers. It would thus be interesting to attempt a brief analysis. The great Archimedes, a fertile inventor of war machines and mechanisms of all kinds, never wrote on these subjects. It is possible, even probable, however, that others kept these ideas alive and transmitted them to those inhabitants of the eastern basin of the Mediterranean who were interested in these problems.

From Ctesibius, the supposed founder of the famous School of Alexandria, we have nothing, except a few rare quotations which have been handed down to us by his pupils or admirers. It is known that he had written on pumps, on the hydraulic organ, which he was said to have invented, and on engines of war. This is attested by Vitruvius. He possessed a great reputation as a skilled mechanic and as an adroit inventor. It is to be regretted that his pupil, Hero, with laudable intellectual honesty, did not copy the work of his master.

Hero of Alexandria had the same curiosity and was equally successful. He claimed to be a pupil of Ctesibius and showed an undoubted knowledge of the work of Archimedes. The connexions here are undeniable. He was of humble origin and began as a shoemaker: in this he resembled his master who was the son of a barber of Ascra. None of these men was literate. Hero probably lived at the earliest towards the end of the second century B.C. His work deals with science as well as techniques.

We have a theoretical treatise by him on mechanics, extracts of which are to be found in Pappus. It included also an applied section on the centre of gravity, the general theory of five simple machines (punch, lever, screw, pulley, and winch), and on the power and theory of toothed wheels. The work known as *Baralcus* deals with the famous problem of Archimedes: how to move a given weight with a given force. The machine in question appears to have functioned with toothed wheels and other reducing mechanisms. This work was translated into Arabic, and a translation of this version into Latin was made later. The Latin versions of the treatise on catapults appeared later. Pappus also mentions a work on automata, a kind of collection of games in physics, entailing some very ingenious applications of mechanics. The treatise on clocks, also mentioned by Pappus, by Proclus and then up to the tenth century, is now lost. The *Pneumatica*, however, is well known and need scarcely be mentioned. This treatise concerns the physics of gases and liquids, with practical aspects concerned with water wheels.

Hero is thus the first writer on these subjects whose actual work, albeit partially, has come down to us. This work already seems to

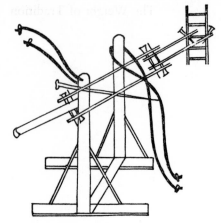

Apollodorus of Damascus: scaling machine.

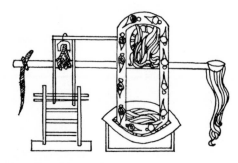

Apollodorus of Damascus: apparatus for pouring boiling liquid over ramparts.

have been the culmination of a long and continuous quest, of which the most celebrated exponents were undoubtedly Archytas and Archimedes. Hero's work contains a double theme, that of mechanics and that of warfare, which, as we shall see, persists. In the mechanical part, theory and practice are equally represented. Some centuries later, Avicenna was to collect under the heading of theoretical geometry a number of sciences which appeared to be the foundation of the investigations of the School of Alexandria:

The science of the measurement of surfaces (geodesy)

The science of moving machines (automata)

The science of the traction of heavy weights (baralcus)

The science of weights and balances

The science of measuring instruments (metrology)

The science of lenses and mirrors

The science of water power (pneumatics)

The science of marvellous instruments (including organs).

These divisions should be borne in mind; we shall find them in our engineers of the fifteenth century.

Military preoccupations were also derived from ancient times. Athenaeus cites among the authors of whom only a few fragments have survived: Pyrrhus of Macedonia, Diades, Agesistratus, and Aeneas. While fortification had its importance, attack and defence of positions demanded apparatus of ever-increasing complexity, in which the aid of mechanics was to be of great utility.

Philo of Byzantium, from the School of Alexandria, was the last link in this military tradition. He had studied in Rhodes before coming to Egypt and was also a pupil of Ctesibius. Like Hero, he composed a great number of treatises concerning an infinity of problems. Many parts of this important work have unfortunately been lost. No trace remains of the treatise on levers. Hero mentions his treatise on automata. Arab manuscripts have transmitted to us fragments of the book of marvellous instruments, and it is by way of the Arabs that the treatise on organs as well as the book on pneumatics have come down to us. There was in addition a treatise on fortification which was widely disseminated, as well as one concerned with engines of war. There are certainly resemblances between the work of Hero and that of Philo of Byzantium. This should probably provide us with clear proof of a tradition which the authors themselves sometimes admit. Book 5 of the treatise on fortification by Philo of Byzantium is no more than a synopsis of the treatise by Philo of Athens. A genealogy of these works, if such were possible, would without doubt produce interesting information on the whole environment of the School of Alexandria, and on the origins of a movement which appears to have undergone far-reaching developments. Partial research has been attempted which deserves to be pursued. Thus at the beginning of the first century B.C. there existed in Alexandria a fairly advanced system of techniques. Not only had practical applications been thoroughly investigated but theoretical problems had also already been outlined. Just as it has been possible, to some extent, to link the scientific activity of this school with men like Strato of Lampsacus, close study of the works of the Alexandrian engineers would doubtless enable us to situate them more exactly in the evolution of Greek thought.

Byzantine sources

It seems logical that the successors of the Greeks of Alexandria should have been the Greeks of Byzantium. Overcome by the Arab invasion, Greek science took refuge in Constantinople. We shall concern ourselves for the moment with the purely Greek aspects of the Byzantine contribution. Athenaeus is interesting less for his original ideas, than because he gives us a compilation of earlier authors whom we know only through him: Diades and Agesistratus in particular, who passed thence into the work of Vitruvius. And thus the fashion of these compilations began, some of which are enhanced by a few innovations, which provide landmarks in the stages of the tradition.

The multiform research of Apollodorus is more original. His engineering work is known. It consists of a bridge across the Danube, a few monuments in Rome, the Odeon, the gymnasium of Trajan. Hadrian, who thought highly of him, commissioned these works. His treatise on fortifications includes a section on engines of war.

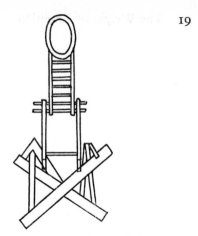

Apollodorus of Damascus: observation platform with protective shield.

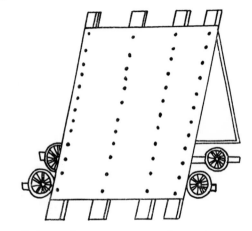

Apollodorus of Damascus: cover of a tortoise.

Apollodorus of Damascus: fire lit in a wall and fanned from a distance by bellows with a long nozzle.

Of Bito, whose work on engines of war has not been republished since the end of the seventeenth century, we do not know a great deal. It would seem here also that we are dealing rather with a compilation than with a truly original work.

The principal merit of all these engineers is that they preserved the work of their predecessors. The tradition of the mechanical and military techniques of the Greeks has thus been perpetuated, copies and compilations being transmitted from generation to generation, each adding to the common stock of work with, to a greater or lesser degree, the contribution of the author's imagination.

Roman sources

The Romans were good imitators and solid builders, but they were not technicians of genius. Two essential texts mark their contribution to the common effort: that of Vitruvius and that of Vegetius. Neither of these two authors possessed much originality.

Vitruvius in his first book and Vegetius in his fourth book give us the elements of the art of fortification followed by information on engines of war. Their common source is undoubtedly Athenaeus as well, perhaps, as the authors drawn upon by the Byzantine engineer. The tortoises, rams, machines fitted with scythes, approach galleries, the shielding devices, the 'muscles' (small machines under which the attackers filled a moat with stones, earth and faggots), are the devices which are to be found in most Greek and Byzantine treatises. There is nothing new here.

The exact origin and development of Roman artillery, based mostly on the principles of cable torsion and rope tension, have not been well elucidated. We know that the Romans were not great innovators and it is probable that most of their machines were borrowed from the Mediterranean east.

Roman sources have therefore only a modest role in the formation of the technical tradition which we are trying to define. The great collective engineering feats are better known and better appreciated. A work such as that of Frontinus on the aqueducts of Rome had a better chance of coming down to us. Vegetius himself was not an expert except in so far as he dealt with the subjects of organization and administration. It is curious to note that the Romans did not translate the Greek works which they needed. There is no trace or record that they used these at all frequently. Although Vegetius was clearly inspired by the Greeks, he does not quote them. It should also be added that Vegetius was not a military man. He was a high official who was more anxious to administer correctly than to promote technical progress.

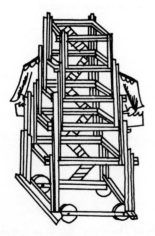

Hero of Byzantium: assault tower.

The works of Greek and Byzantine authors continued to enjoy a considerable reputation which only gradually faded. Thus it is not surprising to see them still being collected, imitated and reproduced more or less freely and more or less completely right up to the high Middle Ages.

The personality of Hero the Younger or Hero of Byzantium has been much discussed. Having often been confused with his Alexandrine predecessor, he has ended by being given an independent, and much later, existence. Certain facts enable us to place him in the first half of the tenth century.

Hero of Byzantium, undoubtedly an anonymous author, whose name is probably fictitious, interests us especially for his treatise on engines of war. The earliest manuscript of his that we possess dates from the eleventh century. We should note – and this links up with our initial hypothesis – that it was translated into Latin in 1458. In his preamble, Hero the Younger regrets that not only the treatises dedicated by Bito to King Attalus and by Athenaeus to Marcellus and the work edited by Apollodorus for Hadrian, but also the scientific method taught in these works, had, with the long passage of time, fallen into deep neglect. He therefore proposes to reinstate the method, presenting it without experiment in a simple manner, intelligible to everyone, basing himself principally on the work of Apollodorus but adding a few inventions of his own. He also borrowed elements, which he acknowledged, from Athenaeus, Bito, Philo of Byzantium and Hero of Alexandria.

The Emperor Constantine Porphyrogenitis had undertaken to have prepared under his direction a sort of vast encyclopaedia, consisting of extracts from ancient authors, divided into a number of collections. A whole section was to be dedicated to the art of war and was to include both historical accounts and extracts from ancient theoreticians. The patrician Basilius had, to fill a gap in this section, composed a treatise on maritime war of which we have only the beginning. It is highly possible that Hero of Byzantium participated in this great work and that he was one of the collaborators chosen by the Emperor. It is from him, at all events, that we have received certain historical compilations and works on military techniques which have survived.

A treatise called *De rebus bellicis* generally accompanies the *Notitia dignitatum* in the manuscripts. This treatise has some very fine illustrations. The manuscripts which we possess, all late in date, have been copies from a very early original, called the Manuscript of Spirus, now lost, which probably goes back to a period between the

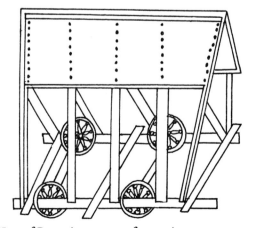

Hero of Byzantium: cover of a tortoise.

ninth and eleventh centuries. It is a compilation, in fairly good Latin, the sources of which once again derive from that ancient fund of knowledge which we have seen being built up from successive contributions. The figures thus date from the Carolingian epoch, but no doubt reproduce older illustrations, perhaps even those that adorned all the treatises which we have already mentioned. It is this manuscript that Otto-Heinrich ordered to be reproduced so carefully.

From the eleventh century we have a whole series of Greek manuscripts, composed of extracts from Greek and Byzantine authors, often illustrated. MS.Grec 2442 of the Bibliothèque Nationale is certainly one of the finest: it possesses a binding carrying the arms of Henri IV and belonged to Cardinal Ridolfi. The main sources of these manuscripts are Athenaeus, Bito, Hero, Philo and Apollodorus. The very fine illustrations that adorn these pages probably also come, with some alterations, from these authors.

Thus in the Middle Ages there existed a tradition that had been preserved since Greek times. We know only the culmination, but we may suppose that alterations were only slight. The comparisons which have been made between the drawings of the eleventh century and ancient illustrations are sufficient proof of this.

There were ancient funds of information available not only to the theoreticians but also to the illustrators, who, in the fifteenth century, especially in Germany, were called upon to execute figures for military treatises. They drew from them an inspiration which was, in its turn, to influence the theoreticians.

The Arab attitude

It is about the Arab attitude that we know least. Greatly concerned to garner the scientific heritage of the Greeks, the Arabs did not neglect the engineers of the Hellenistic period. The treatise of Hero of Alexandria on the traction of heavy bodies was translated into Arabic on the orders of the Babylonian caliph, Achmet ben Mustasin, by Costa ben Louka of Baalbek; the Library at Leyden possesses a version. Philo of Byzantium appears to have enjoyed the same renown. It is in the Arab texts which we possess that we find the most important fragments of the book on marvellous instruments and the treatise on organs. It does not appear, however, that these Arab texts of Greek authors were known in the West. It is possible that one day interesting discoveries in this connexion may be made in Spain. For Alphonse the Wise in the thirteenth century commissioned the translation of a treatise on lifting apparatus which may have been an Arab compilation of Greek works.

The Arabs also undertook some original work, mainly in the field of automata. This tradition had not been lost. We know that in about 835 Leon the Philosopher was occupied with this and had resumed the work of the School of Alexandria. The Arabs were more than pupils in this field; they appear to have been true innovators. From the ninth century onwards an Arab school began to take shape. This was concerned mainly with the clepsydra, with automata, with floats and movements transmitted by chains and cords. The best representatives of this Arab school certainly played an important part in the transmission of the ideas of the School of Alexandria to the Middle Ages. In about 850, the brothers Banou Moussa, who were of Persian origin, composed a work on automata, part of which was copied from Hero of Alexandria.

The best known author is the Mesopotamian Al Jazari, whose treatise is later, dating from the first years of the thirteenth century (1206). He used mainly automata activated by floats. The Bibliothèque Nationale has the manuscript of one of the two parts of the treatise and a translation of this into Persian. Most of Al Jazari's instruments are clepsydra. He regularly uses the camshaft. The treatise of Ridwan of Damascus (1203) is similar in many respects, but is less complete.

The Arab tradition spread to Western Europe through Spain and Sicily. Roger II of Sicily (1130–1154) summoned Arab engineers to his court and the Hohenstaufen kings who succeeded him, especially Frederick II (1194–1254), continued this tradition, welcoming at their courts Christian, Jewish, and Moslem scientists and engineers. All the members of these scientifically minded courts put their best efforts to making clocks with improved mechanisms and automata of which each was more astonishing than the last.

So we have a whole network of traditions. With the passage of time, the texts had become altered and the great encyclopaedias had been broken down into a series of more limited problems. It was these which were in existence at the dawn of the Renaissance and formed the basis of the material which occupied the minds of our engineers. These problems had been stated long since and had also often been resolved. These words by Roger Bacon (1214–1294) from the *Epistola de secretis operibus* are exactly parallel in a different form to the nomenclature of Avicenna given above: 'We can construct for navigation machines without oarsmen, so that the largest ships on rivers and seas will be moved by a single man . . . We can also construct vehicles, which, although without horses, will move with incredible speed. We can also construct flying machines of such a kind that a man sitting in the middle of the machine turns a motor to activate artificial wings that beat the air like a bird in flight. Also a machine of small dimensions to raise and lower enormous weights, of unequalled usefulness in emergency . . . We can also make machines to move through the sea and the watercourses, even to the bottom, without danger . . . These machines were constructed in ancient times and they have certainly been achieved in our time, except, perhaps, the flying machine, which I have not seen and I do not know any person who has seen it, but I know an expert who has perfected the means of making one. And it is possible to build such things almost without limit, for example bridges across rivers without cords or supports and unheard of mechanisms and engines.'

It is important to keep in mind these phrases with their echo of ancient times for they will constantly reappear in the form of drawings.

A mediaeval engineer: Villard de Honnecourt

Indications of mediaeval activity are extremely rare. They may have been numerous but they have disappeared. Nevertheless we possess two excellent pieces of evidence to which an important place must be given.

The notebook of Villard de Honnecourt is typical of those engineer's notebooks such as we shall find from the fifteenth century onwards, that is to say a simple collection of drawings and notes for work in progress. It is probably far from complete. In a kind of preface he dedicates his notes to the men of his profession,

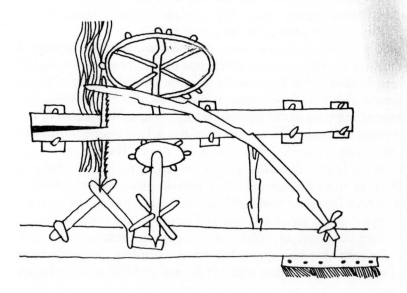

Villard de Honnecourt: hydraulic saw.

hoping that they can use them in building, the construction of machines, and the application of geometry to the plotting of figures.

We shall not dwell much on the author himself, a well known architect who has already been studied at some length, nor shall we concern ourselves with the artistic and architectural parts of his notes. We shall concentrate rather on his machine designs which, it must be said, are not very numerous. These machines are already familiar, so that there is no need to describe them at length. The methods of representing them are the same as those used in the Greek manuscripts of the eleventh century. In this respect, up to about 1270, the date of Villard's notebook, there was no change.

His hydraulic wood saw is the first example which we have of this instrument. It is possible that it was not very old at the time when Villard de Honnecourt drew it. The mechanism is very simple: the saw is moved in one direction by a system of cams and in the other by the release of a spring formed by a long pole. It would appear that there was an additional mechanism to make the piece to be sawn move forward automatically.

The saw for levelling wooden piles is also very curious. 'For with this engine piles in water are sawn off in order to set a platform upon them.' Part of the mechanism is missing, unless the uprights of the saw were moved by hand in the opposite direction to the weight moved by the wheel, without which there could have been no two-way movement. The instrument shown on the right of the drawing appears to be used for setting the level of the action of the saw. This machine is important for any kind of foundations built in water and in particular for the construction of piles for bridges since it was not known how to sink piles except with the help of caissons.

Villard de Honnecourt: pile saw.

The screw-jack also appears here for the first time. 'Thus is made one of the strongest appliances in existence for lifting weights.' A long screw, by its movement, lifts a nut between two guides. A rope passed round the nut and well knotted in front forms the link between the motive force and the resistance.

Two other machines are represented by incomplete descriptions: perhaps the explanations were on pages now missing. A circle, to the surface of which is fixed a gauge with three slots, while a cord wound round the circumference leads off at a tangent, must be part of a design of a turning-lathe for making press screws. Here we have only the system for marking out the screw: the rope describes the spiral movement and the gauge measures the groove.

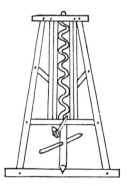

The other design is that of a hub, shaped like a frame held by four cross-pieces, to the ends of which are pegged eight spokes which originate under the frame: 'In this way the slots of a wheel are made

Villard de Honnecourt: screw-jack.

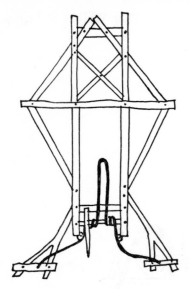

Villard de Honnecourt: trebuchet.

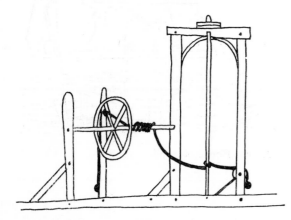

Villard de Honnecourt: mechanism of mobile angel.

without removing the shaft.' Here we certainly have the procedure used to mount wheels on the axles which connect them and carry the carriage or wagon. Too many elements are missing for us to be able to interpret this incomplete sketch correctly.

Villard de Honnecourt was also concerned with siege machines, as is proved by the design of a trebuchet, also incomplete. It is known that the trebuchet consisted of an enormous sling placed at the end of a jib which carried at its other end a counterweight, the jib pivoting on two pins, and the whole being supported by a large stand. When it was wished to lower the jib, that is to say to raise the counterweight, it was often difficult to do this at first, the counterweight being too heavy and the jib too vertical. That is why springs had to be used. It is these that are represented in Villard de Honnecourt. They are pieces of flexible wood, assembled in a T-shape. To stretch them there was a cable which return pulleys and a turning device led to the end of a strong bar fixed to a winch. The author indicates that when these springs were taut, that is to say when the bar was turned back, 1296 cubic feet of earth were required to hold it steady. It can be seen from this figure how powerful this type of apparatus was.

Apart from the design for a crossbow, which shows nothing new, the other illustrations are concerned with automata. Here we rediscover one of the traditions of antiquity.

The first device is an angel which points its finger towards the sun. At one time it was customary to put statues of angels on the roofs of large churches near the apse. Before the fire of 1836 there was one in lead on the cathedral of Chartres, which also turned on itself. It was probably not so much a weather-vane – the lead would have been rather heavy – as an automaton similar to the one drawn by Villard. All that was needed to put this movement into practice was a clock-work mechanism: Villard brings us, therefore, the first sketch of an escapement known in the west. A counterweight suspended at the end of a cord moves a smaller opposing weight at the other end of the cord. The force produced is utilized by means of various re-actions of the movement in the intervening space. Thus, on the side of the counterweight, the cord, guided by a return pulley, winds on to a horizontal axle regulated by a flywheel; from there it passes to a vertical axis which is the pivoting piece on to which it again winds; finally, after having been taken up by a last pulley, it resumes the vertical position due to the effect of the weight.

The system of Villard de Honnecourt is certainly an escapement weight system which depends, in addition, on the friction of cords. The escapement is constituted by the passage of the cord across the spokes of a wheel. Given the friction, the heaviest weight pulls on the cord which rests on the spoke of the wheel. The wheel is set in motion and turns. It is sharply stopped by the cord which arrests the following spoke and this check makes it turn in the opposite direction; it then pulls the weight up, slackens the cord which is again made taut by the counterweight as it goes down and, in the second part of the movement, the axis around which the cord is wound turns, set in motion by friction. The alternating movements of the flywheel thus constitute the escapement. This is as yet only a very primitive mechanism. We know from other sources that at this period mechanical clockwork was being developed and that there is no doubt about its appearance at the end of the thirteenth century.

The second of Villard de Honnecourt's automata is the eagle which turns its head towards the deacon when he begins to read the Gospel. The illustration needs to be completed and slightly corrected. It must be supposed that the neck of the eagle was slotted on to the body like a sliding box lid. The pin on to which the cord was wound and knotted had to remain stationary in the neck of the bird; the two pulleys, also fixed to stationary axes, were in the body. The machine was made to work by pulling the end of the cord which passed through an opening near the tail. This cord shortened, making the neck turn in its groove by pulling on the pin. When this was released an internal counterweight operated and the eagle resumed its former position.

Villard de Honnecourt: articulated eagle.

Other small pieces of apparatus show that Villard de Honnecourt was interested in certain mechanisms the purpose of which was entertainment or which only had slight usefulness. Such is the hand warmer with a kind of universal joint to stop the source of heat from spilling, and the apparatus called a wine funnel which makes use of the properties of the siphon.

Villard's notebook, which, as we have said, is incomplete, appears to be the record of a man who approached technical problems with a view to perfecting them and who at the same time showed a keen interest in these automata which had attracted the attention of the Alexandrian inventors. The marvellous world of automata is for that matter an object of fairly widespread interest. Literary sources record these objects, especially mechanical statuary, statues which move, strike wrong-doers, and dub knights. We would mention the works of Heinrich von Veldeke (c.1165) and Albertus Magnus (born about 1200). Our knowledge in this matter becomes more precise when we reach the fourteenth century and includes the Strasbourg cock, which was imitated everywhere, as well as the Jacks o' the clock, of which the earliest was that of Orvieto (1351).

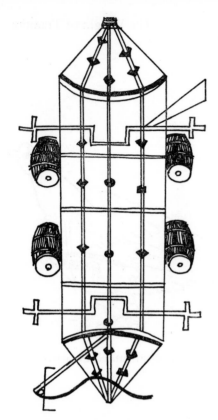

Guido da Vigevano: boat with propellers.

Guido da Vigevano: pivoting assault tower.

The military treatise of Guido da Vigevano

The military treatise of Guido da Vigevano is of an entirely different type. It is all the more interesting for us since it anticipates the works of the engineers of the Renaissance. Of even greater importance, it appears to be the milestone – or one of them, for there may have been others – between the early works whose history we have outlined and the achievements of the fifteenth century. Certain of the illustrations of this treatise show striking analogies with some of the figures of the Greek or Latin manuscripts. We know little about this author except that he was doctor to the queen, Jeanne of Burgundy. He also edited a manual of hygiene and a treatise on medicine which has been the object of detailed study. When, in 1328, Philip V of Valois conceived the idea of going on a crusade, Guido da Vigevano became military adviser and wrote for the King this treatise on engines of war for the purpose of aiding the royal expedition. The Bibliothèque Nationale possesses the only known early illustrated manuscript (MS. Latin 11015). There is a later copy in the Turin library.

The work is divided into thirteen chapters, each devoted to a particular machine of which there is a description and the method of construction. Apart from some defensive instruments and means of crossing rivers and moats, the treatise is concerned mainly with turrets, chariots, and bridges. It is remarkable to note that all these machines, some of which are very bulky, were designed to be dismantled into separate parts to permit of rapid and easy transport. This interest of the author in what we would today call prefabricated objects seems to be quite new, but we shall find it again later on. It is also possible that it was known that there was a lack of wood, especially of large pieces of building wood, in the regions where fighting was to take place. This procedure was probably an ancient one but it was avoided as often as possible in order to reduce the necessity for transport which was always a problem.

We can pass rapidly over certain machines, the illustrations of which will become familiar to us. Thus there are toughened shields, hardened with iron filings, to protect the attackers in a siege. There are also blown-up skins with which soldiers and horsemen could cross rivers and moats. Neither of these are inventions of the period.

The illustration of a ship which is held up by floats formed of casks is also interesting. This ship is fitted with propellers which are moved by handles which can be clearly seen. The lateral rudder is also to be seen protruding from the right of the drawing. The text contains the whole process of construction of this ship of which the different parts can be carried on the back of a horse.

The lightweight bridge, mounted on floating drums very properly arranged and fastened together, also shows great ingenuity in assembling parts to be carried by animals. The different parts of the work appear to be linked by ropes which go through staggered openings.

The assault towers were used to reach the tops of walls. Various systems are utilized for this purpose. The problem was to have a single apparatus, since it had to be transported, that could be adapted to walls of different heights. In the first drawing the assailants are placed in a crow's-nest situated at the top of a mast. This mast is made to pivot round a horizontal axis in order to reach the desired height, either by means of cords or of another pole. The crow's-nest must have had to pivot at the top of the mast. It was also necessary to calculate the distance which was to separate the wall to be reached and the axis of the pivot. Another drawing shows a kind of inclined plane which probably served the same purpose.

The other towers of Guido da Vigevano are all based on the principle of the lift. These are, apparently in the case of the first three drawings and certainly in the case of the last, platforms hoisted by means of ropes and pulleys to the desired height. The platform could be a simple one or a series of platforms one on top of the other.

Guido da Vigevano's chariots are interesting on several scores. There are some relatively simple ones, such as chariots bristling with spikes and drawn by armoured oxen. Later on we shall see similar machines which barely improve upon these, although they are equipped with cannons.

The treatise also shows huge machines which are perhaps not so much chariots as true mobile towers. The first of these machines is moved 'without animals and without wind'. Indeed, two handles for the two axles of the wheels can be seen. Between the handle and

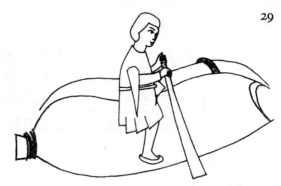

Guido da Vigevano: blown-up skin for crossing rivers.

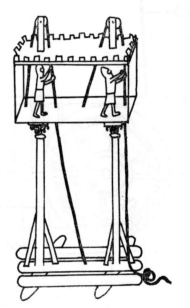

Guido da Vigevano: assault tower with mobile platform.

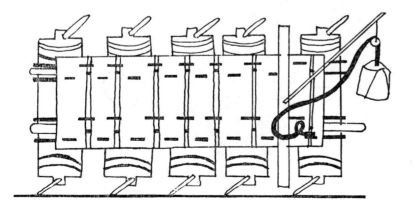

Guido da Vigevano: bridge floating on casks.

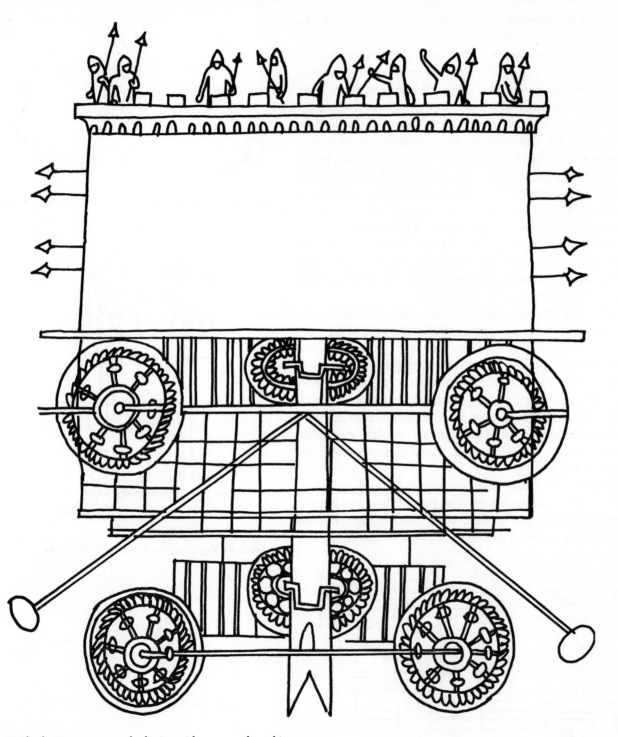

Guido da Vigevano: assault chariot with tower and cranking system.

the driving shaft there is a series of pinions, presumably for the purpose of gearing down. It would seem that one of the two axles is free for the purpose of steering. Such an engine could not have been easy to manoeuvre.

One of the last drawings shows a similar chariot, but this one uses wind power. The wings are geared by means of a pinion to an axle which itself transmits the movement to the two pinions of the wheels. Should occasion arise, in the case of there being no wind or an unfavourable one, the wheels can always be set in motion by means of a handle, as in the previous case. This idea, the effective realization of which appears to be most doubtful, will be taken up repeatedly in later times.

The work of Guido da Vigevano has thus a different slant. It is concerned with problems of a military order. His is more than anything a book about engines of war. We shall see that since this is its bias, it takes up some of the problems raised in Bacon's text: navigation without oarsmen, vehicles that move without animals, machines which traverse the sea-bed, bridges thrown out without ropes or supports. We are thus squarely within the tradition.

The difference between Villard de Honnecourt, the practical man, who tackled problems without ambition and sought only efficient solutions, and the imaginative work of such a man as Guido da Vigevano is very great indeed. Villard had only limited interests and he knew the extent of his own ability. With Guido da Vigevano everything is theoretical, viewed through the intellect, and is, perhaps, a reminiscence of earlier figures and ideas. They had, however, certain points in common, although these may not be very obvious at first glance. The collection of Guido da Vigevano is not entirely lacking in the practical element. We have emphasized the fact that his concern with the question of 'prefabrication' recurs throughout his work. There is more than this. Faced with precise problems, the author tries to give the appropriate responses: this may be seen in the drawing of certain reducing gears and in many other drawings of precise details of execution. The search for mechanisms and the difficulties relating to the transmission of movement already seem to be major questions.

Villard, for his part, also gives himself up to his imagination. The curiosity which he shows about automata is surely a clear proof of this. In this he shares, to some extent, the state of mind of Guido da Vigevano. Machines which move, the marvellous instruments of antiquity, the extraordinary engines of Bacon, may exist equally well within the military order as in the sphere of automata. More than final solutions, the realization of which was more or less doubtful,

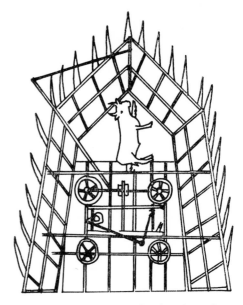

Guido da Vigevano: chariot, fitted with scythes, pulled by oxen.

the movement of pieces, the fitting together of continuous chains, constituted so many problems which it was amusing and interesting to be able to solve. The mechanical approach of the School of Alexandria is present throughout this collection of drawings. And Villard de Honnecourt, in a design to which we shall have occasion to return, also pushed this research to the point of solving the problem of perpetual movement.

The link between technical activity and scientific preoccupations, which in certain periods, notably those of Archimedes and the School of Alexandria, had given birth to new ideas, was never completely lost. And just as Avicenna did not forget the curiosities of our 'engineers', neither did the men of the Middle Ages neglect the interest which technical research could have for pure speculation. In the eleventh century, a period during which it is almost possible to see the tradition handed down from the Greeks hesitating and even petering out, we see the same attitude of mind delineated by the pen of a true mystic. The *Didascalion* set out to teach what it was desirable to read and the order in which it should be done. There are four fundamental sciences which are the source of all the others: theory, practice (theology and morals), mechanics, and logic.

Mechanics includes clothing, armament (engines of war), navigation, agriculture, hunting, medicine, and the organization of games. Already we note certain differences from the lists that we have already examined. Hugh of Saint Victor, the author of this work, died in 1141. At or about the same time Domingo Gundisalvo produced a Latin translation of the *Statistics of the Sciences* of the Arab Al Farabi, which he adapted and transformed following the works of his immediate predecessors. In the classification of Al Farabi, science includes arithmetic, geometry, optics (*scientia de aspectibus*), astrology, music, the science of weights, and finally the science of engines. It has been observed by Beaujouan that the incorporation of the science of engines into doctrinal knowledge was a great innovation: 'The science of engines teaches us the means of imagining and inventing the way of adjusting natural bodies by an *ad hoc* artifice, similar to numerical calculation, of such a kind that we can obtain from them the usage that we require.' This science of engines is applied to masonry, to the construction of lifting machines, musical instruments, bows, weapons, burning mirrors, etc. We are thus certainly within the same tradition, although this assumes new aspects with the succeeding generations.

All these ideas reappear in the thirteenth century in the *Speculum doctrinale* of Vincent de Beauvais. This writer, however, emphasized the exceptional role of the architect whose knowledge must be very extensive. This is the old idea, adopted by the Renaissance, of the single activity which embraces all knowledge.

In 1296, in the *Arbor scientiae*, Raymond Lulle gives his list: it comprises metallurgy, building, clothing, agriculture, commerce, navigation, and military art. Here again, in a slightly different form, are the terms used by Hugh of Saint Victor.

Apart from the theoreticians, those who practised these arts showed that they had scientific interests. The fighting men of the Middle Ages read and discussed the military treatises. There is evidence that they read Vegetius and it is not impossible that, like Count Otto-Heinrich, they studied the ancient Latin or Greek manuscripts of which the illustrations were reproduced. In 1151 Geoffrey le Bel, Comte d'Anjou, laid siege to Montreuil-Bellay, and the monks of Noirmoutiers, who went to see him, found him absorbed in Vegetius. Hugues de Noyers, Bishop of Auxerre (1183–1206), who was a great builder and deeply learned in the liberal and mechanical arts, frequently read this same author. There were, however, a number of timid spirits who thought the propagation of mechanical secrets would have undesirable consequences among evil-thinking men. Roger Bacon suggested the use of cryptographic writing, and we shall see some examples of this at the beginning of the fifteenth century.

When, in 1268, the 'engineer' Assaut asked in writing to be received by Alphonse de Poitiers, who was preparing to set out on a crusade, he presented to the prince a collection of machines, similar to those of Guido da Vigevano. His letter was, perhaps, not so very different from Bacon's text or the letter that Leonardo da Vinci was to send, for the same purpose, to Francesco Sforza. Here again tradition holds.

Beaujouan has also shown that the writings intended to be purely scientific were not free from technical preoccupations. The works of Jordanus, those of Gérard de Bruxelles, of Guillaume de Moerbeke, who in 1276 translated the complete works of Archimedes, and of Pierre de Maricourt, echo the preoccupations of technicians and derive support from their great and wide experience.

It is, perhaps, surprising, and the reader may well wonder, that our thesis of a continuous tradition is upheld by such slender evidence. There are other fields in which the sources are more abundant and more obvious: collections of receipts, principally chemical, are innumerable and it is easy to follow from one generation to the next the successive additions and the weight of accepted ideas.

There is nothing like this in the mechanical arts, but the case is not exceptional: treatises on agriculture were also rare; on the one hand they followed Roman tradition which was very rich in this field, and, on the other, showed numerous innovations. War, with all the problems that it presupposes and all the inventions that it implies, has always been a reality. All the techniques have impressed themselves equally on the human mind; here we come back to the assertion with which we began the chapter: it was impossible for there not to be a certain continuity. Our technical renaissance was thus, perhaps, only a renewal of awareness of these problems. It was necessary, in order to give more breadth to this movement, in order to link together the various elements, that a certain development should be discernible in the general behaviour of men. All human activities are linked one to another: the general direction of western civilization made possible the full flowering of technical progress.

Chapter 2: The Weight of Civilization

Given that the history of technology is one of the elements – and by no means the least significant – in the history of the human intellect, it is surprising that those who have written the history of so prodigious a period of intellectual development as the Renaissance have not paid greater attention to this important mental activity. Having recalled the introduction of printing and having bestowed their praise – which has perhaps been a little exaggerated – on the talent of Leonardo da Vinci, they have felt that they have done what was needful. In connexion with the question 'Is there a Renaissance economy?' Mollat has recently referred to technological problems. Of course he mentions printing and naval techniques, and, identifying the Renaissance with the sixteenth century, declares the latter to be the heir 'of the era of invention of the fourteenth and fifteenth centuries, which the sixteenth century utilizes and perfects'.

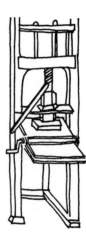

Printing press in 1507.

Any 'revolution' presupposes material changes which are often considerable. There is no intention here of attributing really prime importance to technical progress, nor should we seek in technical inventions (with all the reservations which that other difficult word 'invention' may contain) the source of all upheavals. Yet it is essential to establish the necessary links between a new idea and the possibilities or material necessities that it implies. Certainly, the desire to discover the western route to the Indies did not depend essentially on the appearance of ships that were easier to manoeuvre, and the experience not only of the ninth and tenth centuries but that of our era shows that a given level of technique may not be indispensable. But the exploitation of the discovery, which in the long term is more interesting than the discovery itself, would not have been conceivable without adequate ships. The opposite approach is also logical. No modern machinery, beginning with that of the sixteenth century, would have existed if the rod and crankshaft had not been discovered. Charles VIII would not have had such striking successes in Italy if his artillery had not been crushingly superior to that of his enemies.

It is not so much the relations of cause and effect that need to be determined as the concomitant circumstances. A technical revolution gave the men of the Renaissance all the material facilities which were its essential support. A new mode of thought suggested to the engineers or technicians – it is a little difficult to know how to describe them at this stage – the steps that would lead them to 'invention'. New social structures finally made it possible for the one group to achieve a full flowering of its knowledge and at the same time for the other to learn to use the new techniques.

Let us return to the last half of the fourteenth century. The vicissitudes of this epoch are well known. The Hundred Years War ravaged part of the western world, upset the economy, and blocked the traditional exchange channels. The failure of the Italian banks confirmed this economic decline. The famine of 1315–17 and the Great Plague of 1347–50 caused a considerable reduction of population. This great crisis of the fourteenth century naturally influenced the development of the whole of society. The Flemish revolts, the French peasant risings, and the disturbances of 1381 among the English peasants are also signs of this. At the same time we see a prolonged and progressive decline of feudal society, eroded in its economic foundations, its political organization, and its intellectual and moral justifications.

This set-back to western civilization was naturally far from favourable to technical progress. 'This slump in productivity', writes Hilton, 'results from the incapacity of the feudal economy to create investment for technical improvement.' And he adds: 'It was this same technical collapse that made impossible the continuation of population increase in the twelfth and thirteenth centuries.' The growth of agricultural production was no longer possible without technical changes.

Technology, taken here as both result and determining cause, is at the centre of this great crisis of the fourteenth century which was to sweep away the feudal world. This statement may be both true and untrue. A society which is economically, politically and demographically stable is not prompted to technical progress, which always brings with it some unwanted change. External crises, such as wars, famines and epidemics, also contribute to technical stagnation. Nevertheless some limited but perceptible technical progress is to be noted in the fourteenth century. It was in this period that the paper mill became more widespread, progressively extending to most of Europe during the first half of the fourteenth century. The mechanical clock was perfected in the fourteenth century, a very important achievement for the technical development of certain machines. During this period, to take the textile industry which is so dear to historians, the spinning-wheel which facilitates spinning appeared, together with carding. Finally, and the importance of this fact will not easily be forgotten, the fourteenth century saw the first developments in firearms.

Thus we would note a grave economic and social crisis which gave rise to disturbances of all kinds. Technology was relegated to the background and progress, which rarely comes to a complete halt in this field, was more concerned with accessory techniques than techniques of production properly speaking. Technical ingenuity was largely exercised in perfecting and presenting all that had been conceived in a final spasm of inventiveness at the end of the thirteenth century. But the point of departure, when favourable conditions were restored, was greatly strengthened during the last years of the century.

The decline of the feudal regime had a great many consequences. The change was made to the detriment of those ancient powers, the feudal lords and the Church. The most noticeable phenomenon was the rise of the bourgeoisie which had been developing for centuries. 'In Germany in the fourteenth century', it has been noted, 'the city became one of the dominant elements in everyday life. A realistic and bourgeois order took the place of the universal hierarchy, abstract belief in a superior unity was abandoned: existence was understood in a more direct fashion, and thoughts were turned more and more to the external world; signs of scientific mastery appeared.' 'A new attitude', continues Fierens, 'is propagated during the fourteenth century. Society becomes more and more detached from mediaeval spirituality; people become greatly concerned about the true properties of objects, the nature of things, the spectacle of the universe, and the appearances of bodies and faces. The appearance of civilization changes.' These comments may be transposed to the field of technical activity. They tally perfectly with all the other phenomena: the 'realistic and bourgeois' order is even more sensitive to the details of material life and thus to technical progress. This rich and active middle class, which has new aesthetic requirements, comes into close contact with the circulation of goods and industrial production. The newly rich peasants, whose rise following the decline of agricultural production has been noted, are more active and more 'dynamic' and think only of increasing their yield.

Spinning-wheel (English fourteenth-century MS.).

A remarkable change of attitude can also be seen in the domain of the sciences. Following up the suggestions made by art historians, Beaujouan notes the important role of the middle classes in this development. 'With the development of economic activity in Flanders and in Italy and the influence of the jurists of Philippe le Bel, the science of the fourteenth century is realistic and even utilitarian in its preoccupations. Ockam, Buridan, Albert of Saxony, and Oresme accentuate the empirical, experimental, and mathematical tendency. The monetary ideas of Oresme, the ideas of Pierre Dubois on the education of women, the theories of Sanudo on economic war and the efficacy of blockades, testify, if testimony were needed, to the opening of the mind to an external world which devotes much space to purely practical preoccupations.'

The teaching of mathematics was marginally introduced into the universities, Oxford first and then Paris. A little before 1366 the candidates for bachelor degrees had to swear that they had followed at least 100 mathematics lessons, this formula being, however, interpreted in a very restrictive sense. At the same time mathematics was included in the degree, but in a very imprecise manner. Thus the University of Paris up to a point tolerated private teaching of mathematics which was very rapidly to gain importance.

This intrusion of mathematics into scholastic teaching certainly represented the triumph of technology. Indeed, from halfway through the Middle Ages, and this opinion was still to be sustained by Descartes, mathematics was held to be useful only in relation to the 'mechanical arts'. Geometry was no more than one of the factors required by carpenters, architects, and surveyors. Gundisalvo, as early as the twelfth century, emphasized the interest of mathematics for the science of engines, that is to say engines of war, and for architecture. As for arithmetic, it was the main foundation of the art of commerce. When the new methods of accounting, which had been invented on the shores of the Mediterranean in the fourteenth century, began to spread, the abacus schools, where the rudiments of arithmetic were taught, became more numerous.

Thus the efforts of certain scholars from the thirteenth century onwards, taken up and developed by the University of Oxford, tended to make of mathematics and, through mathematics, all techniques, a branch of knowledge analogous to all those which had traditionally been taught. Commercial arithmetic, derived from the *Liber abaci* of Fibonacci, was associated in the abacus schools with the diffusion of double-entry book-keeping. The manufacture of astrolabes used the weight movement and escapement envisaged by Villard de Honnecourt for the construction of astrological clocks. The interest shown by the Oxford teachers in the optics of Alhazen embraced both the invention of spectacles and the introduction of geometric perspective into the painting of the Renaissance. Buridan, the theoretician of impetus, marked out the field of study of ballistics. Anatomy also developed, with the first dissection of bodies at the dawn of the fourteenth century. This return to reality in every sphere of civilization was exactly parallel to that insistence upon efficacity in all domains, in politics as in economics, which is one of the main characteristics of the end of the fourteenth century and the beginning of the fifteenth. Return to reality implies also the union of disciplines: the work of the geometricians on perspective and anatomical dissections were to provide new material for painters; drawing, in a different form, became of use to engineers. Doctors, artists, engineers, and technicians found themselves concerned with the same problems and going back to the same sources. This was a unique moment in the history of human thought and of human activity.

We quote André Chastel: 'There is no reason to give up the idea of the artistic originality of the Renaissance or to see in it a problem without implications, since the most recent work tends to underline the importance of certain articulations of social life, of scientific development, and of the scientific and religious thought of the fifteenth and sixteenth centuries.' We might emphasize the influence of neo-Platonism which 'introduced those elements of ancient Greek speculation which upset the system of knowledge, raised poetry and art to an unprecedented level, favoured the contemplation of the harmonic cosmos and in short created a background favourable to a more vigorous and more speculative interest in art'. The same, surely, applied to technology.

In former times, the totality of human activities was exercised within a divine absolute, which also favoured the partitioning of knowledge. But now this search for reality could be conducted only with human means (experimentation and inductive or deductive procedures), that is to say that man, whatever his make-up and whatever his profession, always had the chance of attaining universal truth. This passionate search, since there was no comprehensive and perfect knowledge, required an effort of the imagination which took the place of the scholastic spirit.

Francastel considers that 'this substitution of an experimental universe for the universe of essences is fundamental. The idea that the world is simply an attribute of God is abandoned. This conception of nature, of man as an actor in the theatre of the world, is accompanied by the extraordinary exploration of the universe which constitutes the great achievement of the men of the Renaissance. They thus had a highly specific notion of invention. It implies the idea of a logical cohesion of the universe. And it thus explains also that these inventors had as their major objective the aim of working as much towards the comprehension of generalities, of the organizational schemes of the universe, as of continuing indefinitely to add to the collection of particular cases. It was in a kind of selection, of segregation of the possibilities of action and of thought offered by the techniques, that their main effort lay.'

From this the interpenetration of disciplines stems naturally, disciplines which were no longer isolated and individual stones of an edifice, but separate, converging paths leading to the truth. During the course of the fifteenth century, especially in Italy, although, as we have seen, this has occurred at other times, we may note the claim of certain artistic circles to rise to the level of the liberal arts, as was expressed in the testament of Ghiberti; and, conversely, the interest of certain scientific circles in applications of knowledge and experimental research unknown to university teaching. All this leads to a 'decompartmentalization' of knowledge for the benefit of art. There results a close association between scientists and artists (perspective and anatomy) and between scholars (archaeologists) and artists. Art and technique were at this time unusually intermingled. With certain inevitable shifts, and certain differences of form or of spirit, this change of direction of civilization is manifest in all fields. Political structures and economic development feel the effect of it equally.

The history of economic development is too well known for us to insist on it at great length. Crisis conditions had long been felt when, at the beginning of the fifteenth century, a certain recovery became apparent. During the whole of this century, progress was constant although varying in speed according to country or decade. Towards the end of the century, before the great discoveries, a kind of respite brought some benefit. In about 1470 a return to monetary stability confirmed this kind of economic peace and the Renaissance could begin its true advance.

Thanks to men of exceptional ability, some countries, despite severe struggles, rediscovered an equilibrium favourable to centralization and to the formation of a strong government. These governments organized economic recovery and practised, according to circumstances, technological policies that were the basis of future mercantilism. The reign of Louis XI, in France, is symptomatic in this connexion and its policy of importing new techniques and of perfecting equipment that no longer met its increased needs is now

Opposite: The mills at Corbeil under Louis XI.

L'ancienne figure des moulins du temps passé.

La nouvelle figure des moulins du temps présent

well known. Charles VII had already attracted foreign military engineers to his court, among them Klaus Smerment, a German who was placed at the head of the confiscated mines of Jacques Coeur. He tried to discover the secrets of a Spanish manufacturer of crossbows. He pressed forward with inventions, especially those that were concerned with the art of war; engines for excavating earth from moats and for digging trenches. The King of France took in workers who had been expelled from their own country: copper-beaters from Dinant, glass-makers and printers from Germany, silk-workers from Italy installed in Lyon or in Tours, and who also went to Cologne in 1470, to Marseille in 1474 and to Brittany in 1483.

Henry VI of England, in 1452, gave safe passage to Hungarians or Bohemians in order to perfect the art of mining in his kingdom. Other countries also became involved in this technological fervour. The Italian architect Fioravanti, we shall see, arrived in Russia in 1472 and renewed the art of building according to the standard of the Renaissance, erecting Florentine palaces in Moscow and teaching the art of minting money and casting cannons and bells. The Tzars also looked for miners in Hungary in 1484 and in Germany in 1488. From the confusion which had reigned at the end of the Middle Ages, Italy passed to an order founded both on the prosperity of certain cities and on the rise of certain tyrants whose careers had begun in the profession of arms. During the first half of the fifteenth century the Sforza family succeeded to the Visconti in Milan, while other families, such as the Malatesta in Rimini and the Montefeltre in Urbino, consolidated their positions. And it should be noted that it is not in the old states, like Naples and Rome, or in the city republics, such as Venice, Siena or Florence, that the technological movement developed, but in these brilliant and bellicose courts. Although many of our engineers were born and trained in Bologna, Florence, or Siena, it was in the service of these princes that they did their best work. It was their courts which generally widened their outlook and from them that they learnt the beginnings of scientific meditation.

These Italian princes created the first centres of research where science and technology were to preoccupy the humanist engineers. These were centres of varying importance and interest, depending on the dynamism of their leaders, the activity of the cities and the richness of the libraries. We know a number of examples.

Francesco Sforza, who became duke in 1450 and died in 1466, was one of the enlightened princes in Milan who hoped to find in the company of scientists and engineers both intellectual profit and the

Opposite: glass-making in Bohemia – fifteenth century.

possibility of increasing the power of his house. This was, of course, an ancient activity in which, however, in the fifteenth century, a number of currents converged.

The first was concerned with irrigation and navigation canals which for some centuries had been in course of development. The first great canal (Naviglio Grande) connected the waters of the Ticino and Lake Maggiore with Milan: along this route, from the thirteenth century onwards, was sent the marble that was used in the construction of the Duomo. The canal linking Lake Como to Milan (1457–60), the Martesana canal, was constructed by Bertola da Navate. Finally a canal from Milan to Pavia and the Po was conceived; 97 kilometres of works and the necessity of building locks enabled the engineers to perfect their craft. Filippo degli Organi and Fioravanti of Bologna were attached to this undertaking. Bartolomeo della Valle continued this tradition and probably had Leonardo da Vinci under him.

Two other works are also of importance. The Duomo had already been begun for some time and its completion, in the second half of the fifteenth century, was to set in opposition, in so characteristic a fashion, the upholders of ancient procedures, transmitted from lodge to lodge, and the architects of modern outlook using modern methods. Architects, engineers, and experts came to Milan to discuss, in the construction yard of the Duomo, technical problems formulated in a new way.

Francastel has clearly shown how the debate was organized round a scheme of construction proposed by one of the architects, Stornalco, towards the end of the fourteenth century. It was concerned with the manner of interpreting and utilizing geometry for the construction of buildings. Perhaps the masons of the lodges were more willing to use geometrical figures than their successors of the Renaissance. They used the flat representation of diagrams to calculate relationships and to explain how the passage from plan to elevation was effected by purely visual means, by evaluating the surface of relationships between these figures. In the fifteenth century we are at a period when numbers are beginning to be attached to these geometrical figures, in order to establish a link between abstract mathematical speculation and the figures without being restricted to empirical ratios of displacement. We pass, therefore, according to Francastel, from a fragmentary and concrete empirical rationalism to universal speculation, from a certain conception of stereotomy by means of the quadrature and triangulation of space and materials to an entirely different conception that will lead one day to an idea concerning the irrational. With the age of

Palladio the development reached its culmination. Everybody came to this building yard and took part in these discussions. The great Sienese engineer Francesco di Giorgio came to give his opinion, to the wonderment of the young Florentine, Leonardo da Vinci.

There was, finally, the Sforza castle; curiously conservative in its outlines, it played the double role of guardian of an out-of-date tradition and foil to the work of the innovators. It constitutes the type in Italy of those mediaeval and feudal semi-fortresses which were not yet adapted to modern technology. We are aware of the desire to meet changing needs and at the same time to employ ancient formulae. Leonardo – it is impossible to escape from him – was to serve his apprenticeship there.

Thus there was at Milan, from the middle of the fifteenth century, a technological centre the importance of which must not be under-estimated. Succeeding generations continued this work, attempting to codify and translate into simple terms all the traditions and innovations. Il Filarete drafted his treatise there. Milan seems to have been a centre of applied rather than of pure research. The Sforza library is a striking example of this. It contained, however, a certain number of technical books, though mainly those of the ancients, such as Frontinus, all the agriculturists, Vegetius naturally, and some mediaeval writers, such as Petrus de Crescentiis. It is, nevertheless, curious to note that apart from the *Divina proportione* by Pacioli we do not find in this library – of which, admittedly, we possess only an inventory of 1469 – any contemporary author.

Without being as brilliant, the court of Rimini also played an important role. The Malatesta family which ruled there were, no doubt, *condottieri* rather than humanists. Sigismondo Malatesta was a fervent devotee of the art of war, both in the matter of fortification and of engines of war. He probably designed the fortifications of Ragusa and of Rhodes and perhaps invented the bomb, which was made of wood held together with iron bands. Between 1438 and 1446 he built the Rocca Malatestina, a masterpiece of the period, still very mediaeval in conception.

Although Alberti worked for him in 1449 to 1450, it was his secretary, Roberto Valturio, who was asked to write a treatise, which was very quickly printed, on military technique. This work had a deep and lasting influence right up to the time of Leonardo da Vinci.

It is incontestably Urbino which holds first place among these centres of humanism. The overriding influence was exerted by the Montefeltre dukes, Federigo III (1422–1482) and Guidobaldo (1472–1508). They also, it is true, were *condottieri* but their minds were full of humanism and they were curious and active, now fighting, now searching for rare manuscripts, and now discoursing with the scholars and artists whom they had brought to their court. The Montefeltre family certainly made Urbino the most learned city in Italy and the best provided with libraries. In Milan, Leonardo vainly searched for the manuscripts of Archimedes: he found them in Urbino in 1502, in the train of Caesar Borgia, who looted the library.

The library at Urbino was, indeed, one of the most famous of the century. Not only were the best known works of classical antiquity collected there, but also the best examples of what the moderns had produced. The works which remained after the looting of the city were reassembled in the Vatican.

Federigo III had been brought up at Mantua by Vittorino di Feltre, a humanist grammarian who was one of the few lettered soldiers of this period. In order to fortify and decorate his little capital, Federigo called in five celebrated and talented engineers, Luciano, Pipo the Florentine, Fra Carnevale, Baccio Pontelli, and the famous Francesco di Giorgio Martini. Others, such as Giacomo di Bartolomeo and Marco Cuzarelli, came to learn there. All were architects, artists, engineers, theoreticians, and practitioners, town planners as well as artillery men.

It was also at Urbino that two other people worked whose influence was to be recognized as considerable. Piero della Francesca was a great painter, but also an important mathematician and the true creator of descriptive geometry. Between 1470 and 1486 he wrote, in Italian, his *De perspectiva pigendi* in which he carried forward the research of Brunelleschi, Ghiberti, and Alberti on perspective and optics. His work had great repercussions and its development can be followed in the succeeding years.

Like Piero della Francesca, Luca Pacioli came from Burgo San Sepulcro. After having served as a tutor in a rich family of Venetian merchants he came to Urbino where he consorted with artists and technicians. In 1481, at Zara, he wrote a work on algebra, now lost, and in 1494 his *Summa aritmetica*, followed in 1498 by the *Divina proportione*, illustrated by Leonardo da Vinci. His work appears to have been partly original and partly a compilation from other writers. The chapter of this *Summa di mathematica, geometrica, proportioni et proportionalità* devoted to accounting was only, according to some scholars, a copy of a manuscript used as a scholastic manual in the abacus schools in Venice. His work, which was soon printed, contributed, however, to the spread of new accounting methods. Thus, under the patronage of the Montefeltre at Urbino, a very important centre of science and technology was set up. A multiple system of knowledge, composed of the most diverse elements, was built up there. Exchanges between disciplines were frequent and led to the birth of a new outlook. Certainly we see here the ever-increasing importance of mathematics and the art of calculation.

Some princes, who had neither the opportunity nor, perhaps, the means of uniting at their court similar constellations of famous men, still took pains to keep up to date with the latest discoveries of a movement, the scope of which was continually widening. Their means of arriving at this knowledge varied.

Some set to work to collect in their libraries the most celebrated writings and the most modern treatises. The popes were undoubtedly among these. In 1481 Sixtus IV engaged an active librarian, Bartolomeo Manfredi, who was entrusted with different missions to copy the best-known manuscripts. In July 1484 he was sent to the Duke of Urbino to have copied, among other things, the military treatise of Valturio, although it had already been printed. The King of Hungary, Matthias Corvinus (1458–1490), also had some of these technical works copied and many of these splendid manuscripts are still in existence.

It was thus the end, final and complete, of the so-called disdain for technology. More than that, technology had become one of the dominating activities of modern society. No satisfying political economy could exist which did not give attention to these problems. On all sides people began to pay their respects to the 'engineer' in all his aspects, not only to the man of war, able to construct an impregnable fortification, to carry out a successful siege, to create an astonishing machine, but also to those who could improve a building, construct a seaport, or open up a canal. A future full of brilliant promise was in sight for all those whose knowledge went beyond the stage of mediocre specialization. But it was no longer enough that minds were becoming more open: all the ancient traditions transmitted through books had to be there, as well as the new hopes which could only be the fruit of a fertile imagination.

Technical progress was not only limited to these learned spheres. There were also all kinds of obscure and anonymous efforts. Often genius lay only in the knowledge of how to turn these to account, to make up some kind of coherent system. Research in this field is not a question of famous names, marvellous engines, fascinating courts, or learned discourses; there are difficult stages and long roads to traverse. Our means of investigation are limited and our knowledge is fragmentary; we have to find the connecting links which lie behind the admirable illustrations of our manuscripts and the pencil lines of our artists' drawings.

Towards the end of the fourteenth century, which had seen such remarkable works as the treatise of Vigevano and the exceptional work of Dondi on clocks, there appeared certain new techniques which were to have great repercussions. It is essential to note them well.

Up to this date two-wheeled vehicles had mostly been used, for the simple reason that movable front wheels, which make practicable a four-wheeled chariot, did not exist. Long-distance transport was often made on pack animals. The use of maritime routes from Bruges to Genoa or Venice certainly made it possible to avoid difficult routes and the vicissitudes of land travel; they were also technically more suitable. We know little about the first appearance of steerable front wheels. It is possible that the seal of Francesco di Carrara, dating from the end of the fourteenth century (1396) may give us the first illustration of it. The drawing is not a very good one and is therefore difficult to interpret. It would seem, however, that it shows two mobile pieces for the wheels of a cart. It is probable that these carts were used to transport marble, the main product of this region and a very heavy and often large piece of merchandise. The true appearance of mobile front wheels in their final form is provided by an illustration in a mediaeval record book, the technical information of which we shall have occasion to study in detail.

The discovery of mobile front wheels, apart from the facility thus offered to certain kinds of transport, was to have a great influence on the development of artillery, the moving of which, at least for pieces of a certain calibre, had hitherto presented some very delicate problems.

We have no information about the second great technical innovation. This was the step from direct to indirect procedures in the manufacture of iron. In early times only the former, that is to say the low hearth, was known; it produced only a bar of spongy iron, which was then hammered until the metal acquired the necessary texture. It is probable that the desire to produce more metal led to the progressive enlargement of furnaces. Very soon the lack of air had to be supplemented by bellows activated by water power. Stage by stage the blast furnace was brought to perfection. And it must have been a great surprise to find at the end of the operation, instead of iron, liquid melt. At first it was probably thought that this melt was something to be scrapped. Soon, however, it came to be used for casting, since the point of fusion is noticeably lower than that of iron. It may be guessed that it was during the course of a smelting operation that the melt was accidentally 'burned' and iron thus recovered.

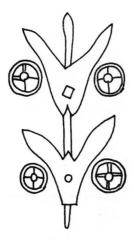

Chariot with movable front wheels (Carrara seal, 1396).

Two-pedal treadle lathe (stained glass at Chartres).

Refining had thus been discovered. These processes had definite advantages: we would mention in particular more abundant output (the operation of a blast furnace is continuous), probably at a lower cost than the ancient techniques.

All this of course is only supposition, and is not founded on any precise text. We shall find in our engineers' notebooks the exact first representations of these hydraulic bellows. A tradition, recorded by Agricola, attributes the invention of the blowing-machine to the region of Göllnitz, in about 1435. The only early examples of casting are not well dated: for instance, the baptismal fonts of the church of Saint Père below Vézelay, which are said to be of the fourteenth century. It may reasonably be thought, however, that the discovery of casting took place at the end of the fourteenth or in the first decades of the fifteenth century. It is possible that this discovery occurred in the region of Liège, which was to give rise at the end of the fifteenth century to a whole metallurgical complex, of which some of our engineers, Leonardo da Vinci in particular, gave us an echo. But if the blast furnace goes back to this time, at the beginning of our period, it spread only very slowly: at the end of the fifteenth century there were still wide areas where it was not known, especially the whole of the south and east of Europe. The spread of the blast furnace, throughout the sixteenth century, certainly contributed to the further development of all the technical progress which had been achieved in the fifteenth century. The development of a machine technology could not be conceived without the possession of certain essential mechanisms. Continuous chain drives were undoubtedly the most important. Five of these, the screw, the wheel, the cam, the ratchet, and the pulley, had been handed down from antiquity. With their derivatives, in particular all the gearings derived from the wheel (toothed wheels, pinions, lantern wheels, etc.), it was possible to transmit movement, to modify its speed and power, but not its nature. The last continuous chain drive, the crank, made its appearance in the Middle Ages, and an offshoot of the crank, the rod and crank system, was to make possible the conversion of circular movement into reciprocal rectilinear movement and vice versa.

Thus it is to be observed that, up to a relatively recent period, the lathes used in many industries were either moved by hand (numerous examples are still to be seen in Diderot's *Encyclopédie*), or by reciprocal movement. A set of pedals and devices allowed the lathe to go alternately in one direction then in the other. Our two illustrations show perfectly that it was possible even to have several types of these machines. Spinning-wheels were moved by hand or with the arms as they were to continue to for some time to come.

Blast furnace (English drawing of sixteenth century).

Pole lathe (French fourteenth-century MS).

Only the connecting-rod and crank enables a continuous movement to be obtained. Such is the treadle lathe which today is universally known. The treadle spinning-wheel is the most widespread example. This new mechanism seems to have appeared at the end of the fourteenth century. Our engineers give us the first illustrations known to us, but of course not all problems were resolved by these simple solutions. Important machines, and we are thinking in particular of suction and pressure pumps, presented serious difficulties, especially when certain materials were used. It was necessary to wait for a more widespread use of metal before this invention could be exploited in all its possibilities. Nevertheless, discovery of the rod and crank system at the dawn of the Renaissance remains one of the essential elements, we think, in the technical progress of this whole period.

It would be easy to name other fields in which progress of similar importance was made. As a matter of fact, our knowledge of the manifestations of this technical renaissance of the end of the fourteenth century and the first years of the fifteenth century is still incomplete. This is the case, for example, with fortification, one of the major preoccupations of our engineers, which has been so widely studied but remains so little known. It was undoubtedly the use of the cannon which upset mediaeval fortification. It became necessary to have greater thickness than height, with openings for the different levels of artillery, the lowest of which could be at ground level. The historian often comes up against difficulties in the dating of ruins or parts of ruins and of rebuildings which make studies in this field highly problematical.

Again, one should not be mistaken over this. It was very probable that the first use of the cannon in a siege of a position or of a castle was to the benefit of the defenders, not to that of the besiegers. The cannon had to be placed on the fortification, which only risked, if not an escalade, at least an attempt at mining. According to certain writers, the keep of Coucy, built after 1450 and before 1475, was one of the first fortifications conceived for the cannon, but still, with its tremendous height, of a very mediaeval appearance. The same was probably true of the castle of Rambures, in Picardy, or of that of Ham, now destroyed, which had even abandoned machicolation and crenellation. The question of the date of construction of the north tower of Mont St-Michel has been much discussed; it is a sort of square prolonged by a triangular spur, the appearance of which is extremely 'modern'. If it dates in fact from the second quarter of the fifteenth century, as some scholars maintain, it would appear to be very advanced in comparison with many other works. The texts are

Metallurgical workshops by H. Blès – sixteenth century.

not at all explicit. The construction of the castle of Langeais, the last example, a magnificent one, of feudal architecture of the old type, with some concessions to modern techniques, was begun in about 1460 and stopped in 1465. It was seen that this military architecture was no longer useful and that it had had its day. A text of François de Surienne has recently been found; he was a specialist in sieges and escalades, and was an engineer like those we are studying who may, perhaps, also have left notebooks; it is possible they have only been mislaid. Surienne's text, dated 1461, concerns the fortifications of Dijon and shows this art in full development. The ramparts, the glacis, and the disposition of low artillery show clearly that the time had come to change the nature of military works. Throughout western France this new type rapidly became very common. We would mention the towers of Surienne himself, of Raoul, in the Château de Fougères, and the sunken, or apparently sunken, towers of the châteaux of Nantes and of Saint-Malo. The period of transition is now in full sway.

These few rapid notes enable us to assess more accurately the considerable backwardness of German and Italian military architecture and the sudden leap forward made by certain engineers of the Peninsula. The classical approach long remained the rule, combined with an imperceptible movement towards new forms, as in France. The exterior aspect of the castle of Milan gives this impression. Begun in 1450, it is a large quadrilateral flanked by round towers. Leonardo may have done some work there, though probably less than Bramante.

We thus see the outline of different aspects of a movement which originated at the end of the fourteenth century and which became during the following century more and more important. A new society and a new spirit among the leaders combined and, although their aims were certainly different, their means were strangely similar. This shared sense of the interest, importance, and necessity of a new technique became apparent after the beginning of printing. The new machine for the diffusion of ideas undoubtedly had to begin its work with the most urgent and uncontroversial item: this, of course, meant, first, the Bible, and then all the devotional books, but also technical treatises, some of which appeared before the great works of classical literature. Here was a true technical humanism which made its needs felt and forced itself, increasingly widely, on the civilized world.

The good Latin authors, the study of whom had probably been resumed a few years previously, were not neglected. Pliny, whose works are so full of numerous and varied details, was printed as early as 1469 and went through many editions up to the end of the century. Vegetius was also published early, but the dates here are less certain. The first edition was perhaps that printed in Utrecht in 1471; it was probably followed by two other editions, in 1475 and 1478. The first edition of certain date is that printed in Rome in 1487. In all, we can count eight editions of Vegetius before the end of the fifteenth century. Nor were the four great Latin agriculturists, Cato, Varo, Columellus, and Palladius, slow to appear: the first, collective edition of these works was printed in 1472 in Venice. By the end of the century there were already four editions. Columellus was printed separately in Paris in 1495. Frontinus's work on the aqueducts of Rome was first printed in Venice in 1480 and went through five editions before the end of the fifteenth century. Finally Vitruvius appeared in Rome in 1487.

Perhaps the most remarkable fact about this enterprise is that it was not limited to Latin authors. Contemporaries and even certain mediaeval writers profited by this movement and sometimes anticipated it. This is the case with the agriculturist Petrus de Crescentiis, who had written his work in the fourteenth century: his treatise was published in Augsburg in 1471. And there were twelve editions of his works before the beginning of the sixteenth century, which beats all records. The first printed abacus manuals appeared in 1478 in Treviso and also had great success. And finally we would mention two of our engineers who had the honour of being printed: the first, Valturio, who appeared in 1472 and went through four editions before 1500; the second, Alberti, whose treatise on architecture was published in Florence in 1485.

During the last quarter of the fifteenth century technology thus had a relatively important volume of printed literature, at least if this is compared with the other titles printed during the same period. There is no better proof of the interest in these technical problems than the number of editions which appeared. The notebooks of Leonardo da Vinci show that this literature was at any rate used. The increasingly important role of engineers in the life of this period perhaps led to the publication of all these books. It was both a matter of providing them with texts that were usable and of showing that their research did not neglect the old authors. Practical utility was probably combined, at least in the minds of the publishers, with a concern for humanism. It would be possible to extend this study, which has never been undertaken in its entirety, and to name also books on pure science that were published before the end of the fifteenth century. We would mention, as one example, that a Latin edition of Euclid was issued in Venice in 1482, a fairly early date.

No doubt, if one wished to explain such a movement in all its aspects some mention would have to be made of philosophical agreements and disagreements. We will limit ourselves to these few preliminary remarks. It is possible that our engineers, in a world that was probably very Platonist and upheld both religious aspirations and scientific desires, were divorced from the intellectual élites. Ucello, Piero della Francesca, Alberti, and Pacioli to some extent were Platonists: the true technicians did not follow this path and belonged to another tradition.

We have now reached the threshold of our study, sustained by a long tradition that had not been forgotten, but only submerged, and of which there remained a kind of skeleton, at the threshold of an age of dreams, of ambition that was sometimes unbounded, and of profound contact with nature. New powers had emerged in all fields, entirely changing the face of politics, society, art, thought, and of technology. Our drawings may be examined, both those which appear naïve and those which appear precise. It is the whole body of thought which these represent that we must now tackle.

Chapter 3: The German School

There is no doubt that it is in Germany toward the end of the fourteenth century that we may discern a kind of awakening of technological thought. This movement is shown by a number of very different works. The first and earliest follow on from the authors we have rapidly studied: these are collections of machines, especially of war machines to be used in the siege of strongholds. The influence of tradition is evident, both in the design of these machines and in the idea itself. Artillery occupied as yet only a modest place. A considerable number of these manuscripts associate these machine designs with the treatise on fire of Marcus Graecus.

A slightly earlier first group may be distinguished together with a treatise, the effect of which was to be considerable, the *Bellifortis* of Konrad Kyeser. The success of this work during the whole of the fifteenth century gave it a dominating influence which certainly extended beyond the frontiers of Germany.

There were many imitators of Kyeser. We may see how numerous these manuscript collections of machine-designs were throughout the century. This interest diminishes as artillery techniques increase. The anonymous designer of the Hussite War represents an important turning-point in the development of military techniques. This work belongs to a different idea of things. We are dealing here not with a didactic work, with a treatise or even with a collection: it is one of the first notebooks of a man moved by the spirit of curiosity. It is, therefore, linked rather to the line of Villard de Honnecourt than to the military works that we may call classical.

The Germans took a long time to come out of the impasse constituted by designs that were repeated indefinitely. Then followed manuscripts dealing mainly with artillery problems, the founding of cannons and the manufacture of powder. It is interesting to emphasize the efforts at research in this direction undertaken in about the last third of the century.

Such, in broadest outline, is the picture of the German school. In the first half of the fifteenth century in southern Germany, which is essentially the region where these developments took place, a kind of resurgence of technical progress occurred. The German school was less rich and less systematic than the Italian but, nevertheless, it made itself felt in a lasting fashion. It also participated in a certain artistic renaissance. Drawing clearly becomes more refined and aesthetic concerns more precise. Certain works which do not come within our field, such as books on fencing or treatises on human combat, constitute excellent studies of movement. The development culminates in the type of composite manuscript, probably by many authors, known as the *Livre de raison mediéval*, in which genre scenes are juxtaposed with drawings of machines. But this is only an isolated case. Already Italy had succeeded in supplanting the southern Germans. The only path then left to the latter was to mix, in sumptuously presented collections, the images of traditional thought with the imagination of the Mediterranean. Moreover, the memory of works which had been widely disseminated shows even more clearly how much out of step the Germans were with the much more highly developed technological thought of the Italians.

The primitives

Every school has had its primitives and they are not the least interesting to study. We have a certain number of manuscripts, fairly close to one another, to which some library catalogues have a tendency to give dates later than the true ones. The drawings, all within red borders, are generally very unpolished; and their interest is unequal. They constitute a curious mixture of military preoccupations and concerns that lie outside technical problems.

The dating of these works is difficult. In some cases we certainly only possess later copies: the manuscript of the National Library of Vienna, is, for example, dated 1415. The analogy of the drawings, their primitive character in relation to works of the second third of the fifteenth century, enables us to attribute them all to the end of the fourteenth century, without much risk of error. The similarity of the illustrations, the subjects dealt with, the red borders and the resemblance of the figures certainly appear to prove that we are dealing, if not with a single work, at least with works that stem from a common source.

The designs are often not so much simple drawings of machines as veritable miniature scenes, a procedure that we shall find, although in less systematic form, in Kyeser.

Engines of war occupy the most important place. Arms of ancient types are the best represented: trebuchets, *ballistae*, slings, and crossbows. Artillery has already made its appearance in the form of cannon, some of which are supplied with hoists. Doubtless these were more like mortars than cannon proper.

A few siege engines are to be seen, especially ladders. The shields for the manipulators of projectile weapons do not differ from those familiar to us from the earliest Greek manuscripts. To be noted are a few more highly perfected machines, lifting apparatus, boring machines, handmills with a connecting-rod and crank, rope-making machines, and pole lathes. Different kinds of bridges must also be mentioned, especially wooden bridges with prefabricated elements, such as are shown in Guido da Vigevano, and ships equipped with artillery.

It is impossible not to recognize that these manuscripts, apart from their undoubted relationship, show traces of the tradition that we have tried to outline. Similarities with certain images of the eleventh century and with some of the ideas of Guido da Vigevano come immediately to mind. But differences are also to be seen, which derive partly from the appearance of artillery and the utilization – certainly recent and thus all the more highly appreciated – of new mechanisms, such as the connecting-rod and crank. The sector studied is also narrower than it was; we do not find here the breadth of ideas of Villard de Honnecourt.

The Vienna manuscript, which we have just mentioned, may also

German primitive: cannon with screw lift.

German primitive: trebuchet.

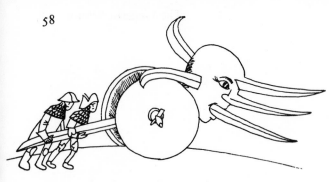

Kyeser: *ribeaudequin* with human face.

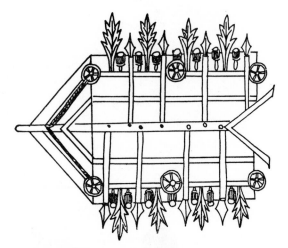

Kyeser: artillery-carrying chariot.

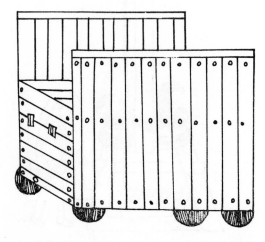

Kyeser: shelter on wheels for miners and soldiers (*mus*).

have a more precise value. Some of the drawings which it contains are repeated in the manuscripts of Kyeser and are among the most characteristic: we would mention in particular the *ribeaudequins* with human faces, the lance on the blade of which is written a magic word, and the diver, and there are many others.

It would be quite justifiable to ask ourselves whether this is not an early work of Kyeser. Another possibility is that the latter is the direct heir and perhaps, to some degree, the plagiarist of this whole group of primitives. Unless new discoveries are made, this problem, which would go some of the way towards explaining the origins of Kyeser's treatise, will probably never be resolved.

Konrad Kyeser

Kyeser is the first great engineer who has left us a well-established technological *œuvre*. The importance of this, the astonishing success that it had, made us regret that we do not know the author better, despite a series of excellent studies of him which were made at the end of the nineteenth century. The catalogue of the manuscripts of this work is now more accurate and should permit some of the points in the research on this subject to be followed up, or so, at least, we hope.

We do not know much about the life of Kyeser: the only points mentioned by him in his text are that he was born on 25 August 1366 at Eichstätt, a small city in Franconia in Bavaria, situated halfway between Munich and Nuremburg. He claims to be of noble family. From 1396 political and military circumstances obliged him to go into exile and he took refuge in the mountains of Bohemia. He was still living in 1405, the date on which he dedicated his treatise to the Emperor. We do not know the date of his death. This personality is therefore difficult to place.

Kyeser was certainly a soldier. Had he had any formal education? It is probable, though it is impossible to confirm, that the fragment of Latin verse with which some of his manuscripts open is not by him. It would also appear that the drawings were the work of a local artist which some German historians have thought to identify with the illustrator of certain missals of the Bohemian region. He quotes some of his predecessors, especially Vegetius. The work is dedicated to the Emperor Ruprecht of the Palatinate (1400–10). In his epitaph, Kyeser declares that he has been connected with the principal sovereigns and princes of Germany, of Bohemia, Austria, Bavaria, and even the north of Italy. He expresses some sympathy with Wenceslas of Bohemia, deplores the defeat of Sigismund of Hungary against the Turks, mentions Francesco di Carrara, who was one of the great warriors of his time. The battle of Nicopolis (1396) is the only event mentioned in the text of the work.

This is, according to Duhem, not so much the work of one man as the fruit of many centuries of thought. According to this historian, Kyeser was a blunt, unlearned man who claimed the invention of the most terrifying firearms. From this came his reputation as an emissary of the devil. Nevertheless he remained the most alert of the German authors of the fifteenth century who dealt with mechanical inventions generally appropriate to the science of fortifications, of fighting and of sieges. The authority of Kyeser as engineer was so great that his treatise remained the foundation of the science of machines, as is expressed in the drawings of numerous manuscripts during more than a century. It seems also that a work-shop producing copies acquired this work and made several copies of it: a certain number of manuscripts, indeed, are identically bound and, what is more, used papers which the water-marks show to have come from the same source. There was thus what might almost be called a true edition of Kyeser's work.

Kyeser was above all a military engineer: the machines that would appear to be in current use, such as cranes, mills, scoops, or Archimedean screws, could be used by armies in the field and it is without doubt for this reason that they appear in the treatise of which the title, *Bellifortis*, indicates the character.

The most complete manuscripts divide the material of this work into ten books as follows:

Chariots
Siege engines
Hydraulic machines
Firearms
Defensive weapons
Marvellous secrets
Military fireworks
Fireworks for festivities
Tools and working instruments.

In this list we find some of the traditional themes that we have already recorded. Some of the manuscripts begin with a series of astrological images, heraldic drawing and symbols. The twelve signs of the zodiac and the seven planets are shown by mounted knights each having his characteristic colour. Then comes the war standard, called the *Almerio*, attributed to Alexander the Great, who is supposed to have obtained it from Aristotle. The tip of the standard, represented separately, carried the inscription *Meufaton*, the meaning of which had been lost at that period. This standard had marvellous

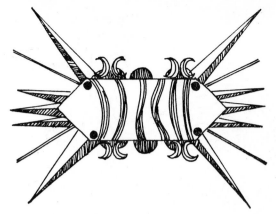

Kyeser: fantastic chariot.

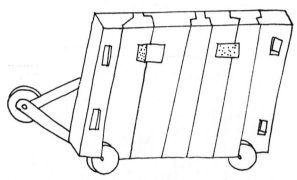

Kyeser: shelter.

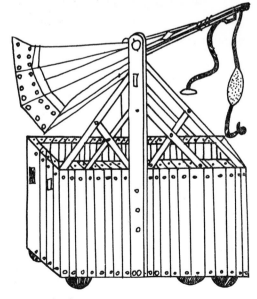

Kyeser: trebuchet.

Kyeser: fantastic ram (*cattus*).

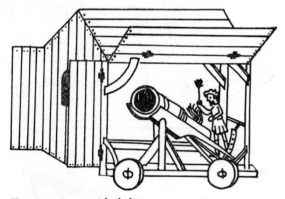

Kyeser: cannon with shelter.

virtues. All this symbolism appears to link this work with some kind of distant tradition, the clues of which we have lost.

Most of Kyeser's chariots are similar to those of Guido da Vigevano. Except for two of them equipped with cannons, they are all armed with pikes and scythes, lances and hooks. Mounted on wheels, they provided protection for the soldiers. Some of them were perhaps covered with sheets of metal intended to stop enemy projectiles and to protect them from fire.

Two of these chariots carry rudimentary artillery, in the form of a sort of small mortar. Kyeser claims that one of these chariots was invented by Alexander.

The *ribeaudequins* are also engines mounted on wheels and armed with cutting and piercing instruments. Unlike chariots, they are drawn by men. One of the curiosities of these drawings is the fantastic appearance of some of the figures. Anthropomorphism, figures of terrifying animals, everything is utilized by a designer whose imagination seems to have been very much alive.

All this apparatus was undoubtedly much used in the armies of the period. In 1387 three large chariots each carrying 144 small mortars, placed in three tiers, were made for a member of the Scaliger family. Each tier was divided into four compartments of twelve mortars each which fired simultaneously. These instruments were called organs. These were engines of war which were completely eliminated when field artillery, with a longer range, made its appearance.

Kyeser's artillery is still very primitive. An important place is always reserved for the trebuchets, which we know were still used in the siege of Rennes, in 1370. Fire artillery remains essentially mortar artillery throwing heavy material with a short range and very

Kyeser: trebuchet.

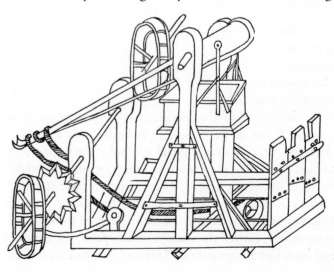

little efficiency. The men who worked these machines had to protect themselves with wooden shields against the arrows of their adversaries. The transport of this material presented some difficult problems. Culverins made their first appearance at this time: these are the first portable firearms which are known from other evidence of this period. They were much lighter arms, though still extremely cumbersome, and were placed on stands, as shown in Kyeser's drawing, since their length, which served to give them some counterweight in the absence of sufficient mass, made them difficult to handle. Also to be mentioned are the weapons which have been incorrectly called machine-guns; these are triple or sextuple, and rotate like a revolver. They consist, in fact, of a number of tubes, mounted on a wooden turntable which moves horizontally, an idea which was to inspire Leonardo da Vinci. For anything concerning gunpowder and its manufacture, copyists simply reproduced the treatise of Marcus Graecus known as *Liber ignium*.

Kyeser: long-barrelled cannon (culverin).

Siege machines occupied a large place in Kyeser's treatise. The rams, the attack towers, the scaling ladders are not noticeably different, at least in their general conception, from the machines of Guido da Vigevano. A great many terms are used to designate these machines; the 'rat' (*mus* or *musculus*), a fairly small breaching or sheltering machine with a pointed head, the 'mouse' (*sorex*), a similar machine, placed on three wheels, the *chape*, the ram or breaching hammer (*raptorium*); there are also catapults, rolling shelters covered with skins, mantelets, and palisades. There is no doubt that we are dealing here with ancient devices and using a terminology that dates from the high Middle Ages. This is true, to take only one example, of those devices using a screw and a tourniquet, more particularly tipping apparatus which raises to the level of the walls of the fortress a kind of bucket, in which the soldiers stand. This is exactly the same instrument that we find in Guido da Vigevano: Kyeser calls it the snail (*cochlea*), a term used in this sense by Isidore of Seville at the end of the sixth century.

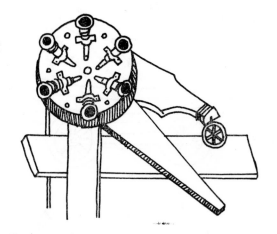

Kyeser: rotating cannon.

Our work also carries a number of illustrations of crossbows, shooting either one or two arrows forwards or backwards. The arrows are sometimes fitted with incendiary projectiles, similar to the *sagitta plumbata*, *tribulata*, and *mamillata* in manuscripts of the early Middle Ages. There are also devices to be used for drawing crossbows, *ballistae*, mangonels, and engines with pulleys which also recall Greek or Latin manuscripts.

The scaling-ladders have not changed since the first illustrated military manuscripts: there are ladders of various kinds: grapnels, articulated ladders (*serpens*), a vertical mast carried on wheels,

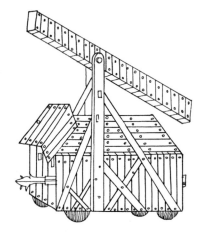

Kyeser: escalading machine and ram (*cochlea*).

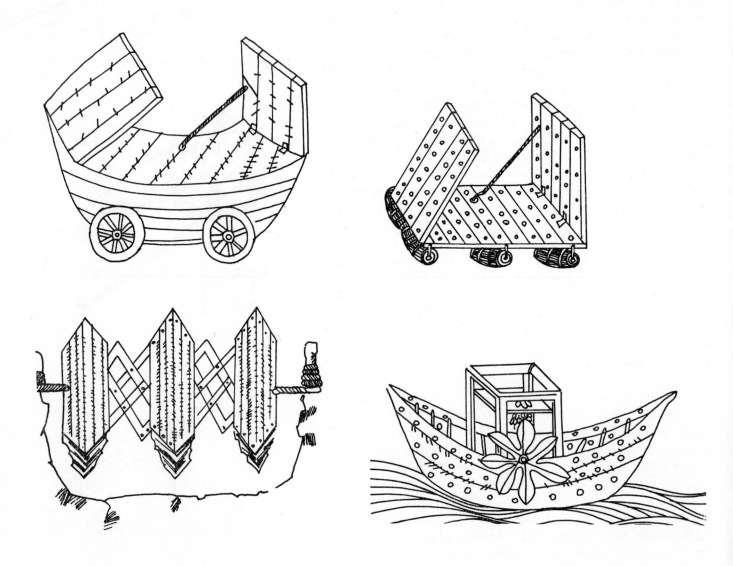

Kyeser: mobile bridges and a wheel-propelled ship.

wooden ladders, rope ladders, with all kinds of provisions for protecting the users. They are supplied with hooks and often associated with a long lateral fork (*phalanga*), which was used to place the top part in position. Kyeser has not forgotten mobile towers, with an open or closed framework, towers with platforms, raised by a central pivot on a rotating screw, somewhat like certain drawings by Guido da Vigevano, ladders carried on a frame or on a chassis, so that they could be raised or pulled down by means of hinges, always according to the usual technique.

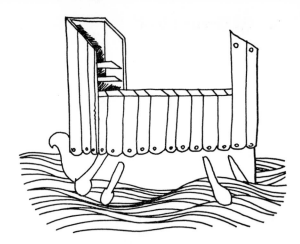

Kyeser: part of a floating bridge.

Certain machines, although used by armies, have an interest which is not strictly a military one. Perhaps it is here that Kyeser shows the most originality: he goes, as it were, beyond the narrow problems that concern the counsellor to the King of France. His bridges, however, are directly derived from him and include bridges to rivers or dykes, constructed in advance, mobile bridges, floating bridges, and folding bridges. This problem remained in the minds of all our engineers, up to Leonardo da Vinci. The drawings of Kyeser are rougher, but the ideas are the same.

The same applies to ships on wheels, moved by an internal crank, sometimes by a horse-driven wheel, a design which persists, in innumerable variants, up to the middle of the sixteenth century.

We may mention, since illustrations of it are not so frequent, a water mill, of the most classical type, equipped with an overshot wheel. Against this we have no windmill, although it is true that these are rare in this region of Germany. Handmills are provided with a rod and crank, although only, it would appear, on the later copies. A pole lathe is shown, however. It is thus rather difficult to determine whether, in fact, Kyeser knew the connecting-rod and crank system.

Kyeser: mill with overshot wheel.

The hydraulic section is relatively well developed. Drainage machines are represented by an Archimedean screw and by two chain pumps, all instruments of the most everyday type. Siphons are shown also in a number of manuscripts: one is being used in a valley, the other one in the hills. These are not novelties, nor are the blown-up skins for crossing rivers. Also to be noted are the life-buoys and life-belts. More original is the drawing of two divers under water, facing each other, one with a hood over his head, breathing by means of a tube inserted into a bladder, the other wearing a great helmet, with glass eye-holes and an inside sponge, covered by a closed surtout which is fixed to his belt by a metal brace. This is the first example of the divers who occupied a position of importance in the notebooks of Kyeser's successors.

Kyeser: fight between divers.

The drawings showing fire in its most diverse applications show the attraction, still alive at this period, of all products used in the composition of Greek fire. Lighting apparatus is whimsical and is represented by some very attractive, more or less fantastic drawings, in which phosphorescence is often associated with lighting proper. We would also mention the man blowing a fire, by means of a wick, according to an artifice known by trick performers, showing inextinguishable candles. There is undoubtedly a good deal of sport and magic in all this. Incendiary weapons are abundantly represented: the fire-carrying horse, bundles of straw and incendiary panniers, flying trays, and arrows and petards. We are still very close to Marcus Graecus and to many of the similar treatises of the Middle Ages.

A whole chapter is dedicated to the uses of fire in kitchens, furnaces, and baths. The drawings of bathing establishments are among the most amusing if not the most interesting. A number of figures set out to illustrate the effects, beneficial or otherwise, of smoke: palaces infested with foetid smoke, produced by throwing sulphur, resin, pitch, and horses' hooves into the fire, and other palaces perfumed by the vapours emitted by crucibles set on low fires and on charcoal and containing amber, musk, alloes, sandalwood, incense, camphor, oliban, and saffron.

One of these drawings has been thought to represent what has been called one of the 'first aerostats'. It is a dragon which appears to be fixed to the end of a lance carried by a knight. According to Berthelot, it is an incendiary device of a more or less fantastic nature. According to Duhem, this 'aerostat' was made of paper stretched over a wooden frame. The liquid fuel was composed of one part of oil, four of sulphur, and one of bitumen. A cotton wick was plunged into this mixture and thrust by means of a bottle into the throat of the monster. There was also some gunpowder, the combustion of which counteracted the effects of the wind. The vapour from the bottle was pushed into the inside of the dragon and caused it to rise. So, in effect, we have a kind of oil lamp which was to warm the air which went into the animal and lift it into the air. This apparatus must have been rather difficult to control.

The book ends with tools, arms, and various instruments which do not show any great originality, including net traps, iron flails, hooks, iron maces, and buckles. We would mention only the baskets activated by cables and what appear to be some small windmills. Kyeser seems not to have been much interested in the problem of fortification. The castles shown in great numbers in the manuscript are only there to demonstrate the usage of some of the

Kyeser: Archimedean screw.

Hussite MS: horse carrying fire.

Handmill in the castle at Sion in Switzerland: fifteenth century.

machines. In one of the drawings a man may be seen coming out of a mine-gallery laid out under a castle.

On the whole the work of Kyeser appears to be very close to that of his immediate predecessor and even closer to those engineers we have called the German primitives. The drawings are, perhaps, better conceived and better executed. The material is also richer and more abundant. Although Kyeser is, above all, a military engineer, his curiosity often goes beyond the simple aim of his profession: he has noted the ideas which to him appear to be interesting and the machines which have seemed to him to be the most ingenious. Those curious examples of anthropomorphism, machines in the form of human figures, and strange apparatus with eyes and mouth like fantastic dragons, still belong to the Middle Ages. Equally remarkable is the fact of the persistence of a tradition which we have been following since antiquity. Nevertheless, Kyeser is perhaps its last true representative. Some traces will remain in his successors but not this abundance of ideas and images derived from the same source.

By the Middle Ages this tradition, as we have already stated, had broken up into a certain number of problems. Kyeser's work is thus not a treatise, but an anthology, a collection of machines, such as was, in the sixteenth century, to be called a 'Theatre of Machines'.

There are some innovations, which form the link with the succeeding generation. The transformation of artillery, the search for arms that were easier to handle, the appearance and notes of certain more advanced mechanisms, like, perhaps, the connecting-rod and crank system, machines for lifting, screw-jacks, winches, and pivoting cranes, show that there was an attempt to advance beyond the previous technical level.

This work appears to have been very widely disseminated. A large number of manuscripts have survived: it was still being copied deep into the sixteenth century. It is difficult to say, however, whether its success went beyond the region of Germany where it was written. The manuscripts are now in the districts of origin, in the Rhine region, in eastern France and in Vienna; there do not appear to be any in Italy. This raises the problem of the influence of Kyeser on the other schools which we will be studying. Nevertheless, we would observe that when Vegetius was printed for the first time, in the region of Ulm in about 1471, the illustrations were mere copies of a manuscript of Kyeser, the costumes being barely brought up to date. The Paris editions of 1532 to 1534 repeat the same illustrations. By this date the author himself had no doubt been completely forgotten, but his memory was kept alive in this manner.

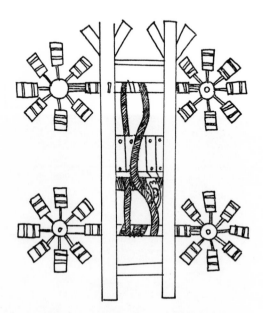

Kyeser: raising apparatus with windmills.

The Lüneburg crane. Fifteenth century.

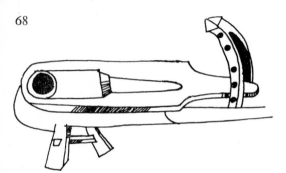

Hussite MS: cannon with lift.

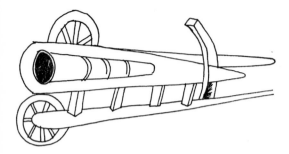

Hussite MS: cannon with lift.

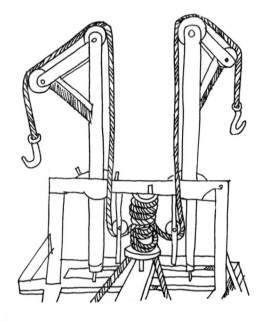

Hussite MS: double lifting machine.

The Manuscript of the Hussite War

The next stage of German technological thought is represented by a single manuscript which German scholars have called 'The Manuscript of the Hussite War'. As it is now preserved, this manuscript embraces two different works. The first part comprises a German manuscript of the first half of the fifteenth century; the second is a notebook of a Sienese engineer to which we shall return later.

The first notebook, the only one which interests us here, is not very large. The numerous written notes are in old German. The names of Munich and Nuremburg are mentioned and chariots used during the Hussite War are cited. We are dealing, therefore, with an author who comes from roughly the same region as Kyeser, that is to say the country between Bavaria and Bohemia. It dates from after 1421, a year mentioned in the notebook. All these facts have enabled German scholars to give this manuscript its name and to fix its date at about 1430. The manuscript has already been very carefully studied and has been partially reproduced a number of times.

The drawings are apparently arranged without order. Nevertheless, they have a style that is polished enough to enable us to say that this document is not a simple collection of notes made on the spot. Perhaps the author jotted down drawings and notes taken during a course of lectures or journeys in a notebook which, later on, was to be a 'Collection of Machines'. It is, perhaps, a combination of lecture notes and direct observations. In the drawings themselves we find if not the actual drawings in all their detail, at least the types of drawings that we have noted in Kyeser, including articulated ladders, combat chariots, bridges, and boats with propellers. But other machines are attributed to foreigners, to Hussites, Venetians, and Catalans. Military preoccupations are still dominant. The author, and here it appears that we cannot distinguish between author and draughtsman, must have been, like Kyeser, who, however, is never mentioned, a military engineer. His curiosity is, nevertheless, noticeably wider than that of his predecessor: what may be called civil machines are more numerous.

The artillery shown is certainly no more highly developed than that of Kyeser. The small bombards, supplied with their own lifting gear, show no marked progress. We would, however, report the first drawing of a 'cannon', that is to say, one of these bombards mounted on a carriage with two wheels with the classic lifting gear and, it would appear, two handles behind. This is certainly the first indication of a transformation, the consequences of which were to be important. This artillery is also found on chariots which are less numerous than in the previous collection. A bombard is also mounted on a ship. Side by side with these are arms of the old type, not only crossbows which could not yet be replaced by firearms, but also the inevitable trebuchets.

It is suggested that the reinforced gun screens and the mobile protective screens were very large: 'This screen was used by M. Arcking before Staz (?). One hundred men could easily hide under it: the winch may be moved and, on reaching the required place, the screen is removed and the guns are fired. After which it is again lowered. After which the winch is moved, the men sheltering behind the screen, which moves while they are behind it.'

The presence of numerous hook and articulated ladders and attack towers shows that artillery had not yet altered the technique of sieges. As in Kyeser, we find bridges for crossing moats and rivers, bridges formed from prefabricated pieces, assembled when wanted, and articulated bridges.

Lifting apparatus takes pride of place in this notebook. Many drawings lead one to suppose that these were mainly intended to lift guns and bombards on to chariots. They are nearly all made in the same manner, stepping-down being achieved by pulleys or by winches moved by horses. We show here the 'double-acting lift of Nuremburg', which was operated by two horses. One drawing appears to show a method for pulling mine wagons on wooden rails to the surface. Unfortunately this drawing is incomplete and carries no explanation.

The less strictly military drawings are no doubt more interesting. In their diversity, they reveal a mind drawn to solving technical problems, concerned less to resolve its own difficulties than to appreciate another person's machine or imaginative faculty. This broadening of outlook is symptomatic of a new era and its scope should be emphasized.

The drawing of the diver is the most significant. It shows the progress accomplished since Kyeser. We have here a true piece of apparatus which strikes us by its modern appearance. We can make out the waterproof – or supposedly waterproof – tunic, the lead-soled shoes and the helmet, details of which are given separately. Leonardo's drawing is much less precise. But there is no annotation as to how it was used.

The manuscript shows us a number of boring machines. The first is a machine for hollowing wooden pipes: 'This is a machine for boring pipes; the people of Nuremburg have built one that bores fifteen pipes a day, each 18 feet long; fountains are constructed with these pipes.' It is known that water pipes were frequently made of wood in the Middle Ages. The bark of the tree-trunk was often left

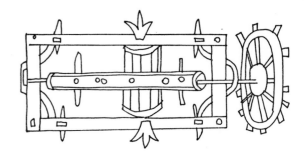

Hussite MS: machine for hollowing wooden pipes.

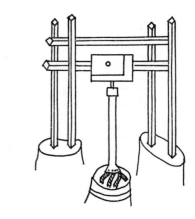

Hussite MS: machine for boring cannon.

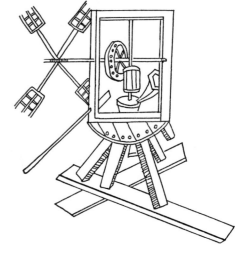

Hussite MS: windmill.

Hussite MS: diving suit.

on for protection. Oak, elm and alder were used. Pipes were generally bored by drills of larger and larger calibre, the last one carrying a kind of semi-circular spoon, the diameter of the pipe to be hollowed. The length of the drills was limited and boring was started from the two ends of the tree trunk. This machine thus probably constituted a double advance, in regard to the length of the pieces used and the speed of operation. We cannot easily see what the second machine was used for. The tool-carrying axis, operated by two crossed bars, appears to move into a frame, just like a jack. We should note, however, the highly developed form of the cutting tool.

The Hussite War manuscript shows numerous examples of windmills. They are all of the same type which was apparently the only one known at this period. They consist of a windmill perched on a huge wooden tripod, the whole apparatus being able to turn. This method of construction avoids the delicate problem of gearing. There is not much to be said on the internal mechanisms of these mills. The vanes appear to be quite ordinary.

Below the famous Hussite chariot, next to a windmill, there is a drawing of a machine for polishing stones. Above it there is an explicit note: 'This is a wheel for polishing precious stones, such as the great masters of Venice possess; it is used for polishing all kinds of stones: it requires three discs, the first of lead, the second of tin and the third of copper.' The drawing is certainly not complete: it shows only the driving mechanism, with an endless cord. The method of holding the stone is not shown. This drawing has a certain importance in the history of this particular technique. Until recently it was considered that stone polishing was done on a flat surface, by friction. A miniature in *Ars memorativa*, published in 1480, provides an excellent illustration of this. The first mention of the modern disc method was given in 1568 by the celebrated Italian goldsmith Benvenuto Cellini and the first drawing of this machine was that of the Frenchman Félibien, published in 1676. It would appear that our manuscript shows an early version of this machine. We shall see that there is a very exact drawing of this method in a manuscript of the third quarter of the fifteenth century.

We come now to those drawings that acquaint us with what was undoubtedly the most important innovation of the beginning of the fifteenth century, namely the rod and crank system. The drawings of handmills in the manuscript provide the first certain illustrated representation of this mechanism. The drawing is also repeated many times, as if it were a novelty. The driving rods, operated by hand, can be clearly seen, as can the cranks. There are other features. It was probably very soon understood that there existed two dead points

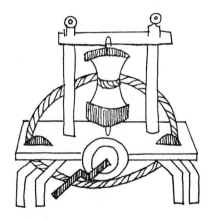

Hussite MS: stone polishing machine.

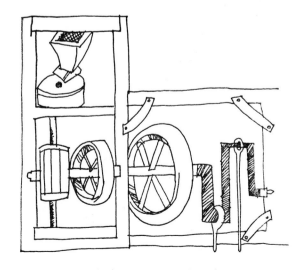

Hussite MS: handmill with rod and crank system.

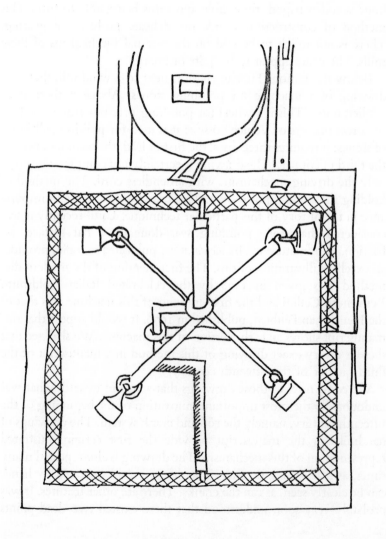

Hussite MS: different types of flywheels.

capable of blocking the system. The problem was resolved by using a flywheel, which can easily be seen on the first drawing which we reproduce. This was, indeed, an application – though quite clearly an unconscious one – of the principle of inertia. In one of the sketches this flywheel is even supplied with hanging weights which fly out and regulate the movement. This idea was to be taken up a little later, in a more accomplished manner. Although the flywheel is the most frequently used, we should also mention bars set at right angles with a kind of mallet on the end; these were to remain in use for a long time.

Thus the Hussite manuscript is not devoid of interest. Its intellectual craftsmanship is better than that of Kyeser. It is more varied and has a wider approach. Its great value lies in its written comments that show that it has gone beyond the stage of pure imagination. These are machines that really existed. We see here a practical man, a craftsman who has begun to collect evidence about his craft and whose curiosity is always on the alert. He is careful to state where he has seen each machine and even notes what it can produce.

This compilation is the last original work of the German school. Throughout the last years of the fifteenth century, illustrators continued to reproduce the drawings we know already, interspersing them with those of the Italians. Concern for artistic quality increased, with the result that small pictures were produced of which some are veritable masterpieces. A number of groups may be distinguished in these manuscripts which often differ considerably from one another.

Later works

The first group is composed of works of the second half of the fifteenth century and, possibly in the case of some manuscripts, the beginning of the sixteenth century. These are more or less close imitations of the work of Kyeser. People's costumes have been modernized, brought into line with the taste of the day. The artillery is different: all guns are mounted on carriages and are easier to handle. But the inevitable trebuchet is still in evidence, although it had certainly been abandoned at this date.

The finest manuscript is indoubtedly that in Erlangen University Library. It was executed for the knight Ludwig von Eyb zum Hartenstein, who lived from 1450 to 1521. This nobleman had commissioned a 'battle book', such as had become the fashion of the day. The artist was strongly inspired by Kyeser, which was not very surprising since the owner lived at Eichstätt, Kyeser's birthplace, where his memory had perhaps remained alive. The Heidelberg

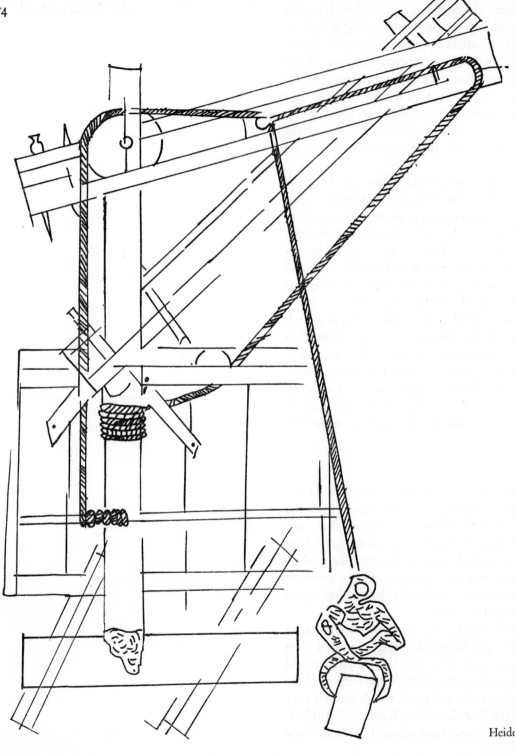

Heidelberg compilation: mobile crane.

manuscript is incomplete, many designs having been traced only in dry point. We may note a drawing of a mobile crane, which, from the point of view of a machine-design, looks very modern.

There is finally a third group comprising two manuscripts in Munich and one in Weimar. They still contain many designs by Kyeser, brought up to date. A second source is represented by the reproduction of the illustrations from the *De re militari* of Valturio, which we shall examine later. Then there is an original section which does not come from any previous work. It is especially concerned with artillery. There is a sudden jump to the most modern arms, without any earlier stages having been noted.

Gun-making was discussed in more detail by a certain Martin Mercz. His work is closely related to the German manuscripts of the end of the fifteenth century. A first section contains what amounts to a collection of engines of war: guns, ladders, hooks, hoists, cutters and protective shields. The following part deals with bronze smelting, standardization of pieces, calibration and the manufacture of gunpowder. These are descriptions rather than techniques in the strict sense.

Ulrich Bessnitzer and the monk Philibs appear to have been the authors of two manuscripts preserved in Heidelberg University Library; they date from the end of the fifteenth century. They are also collections of machines and well executed little pictures, generally without written explanations. Artillery is well represented, in a very modern form. The second author resembles Kyeser with his hoisting machines, hand rammers, bridges, norias, ladders, cranes, pivoting guns, trebuchets, views of castles and camps, all of which closely recall Kyeser's subject matter if not his exact style. There is, however, a curious attempt to design a perpetual motion machine: a pump that lets the water it has raised fall back on the wheel that operates it. Artillery is still lifted by pulleys on to heavy chariots.

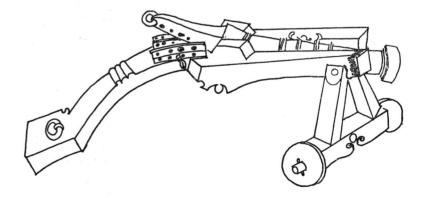

Munich MS: cannon.

The guns, now made of bronze, have to be bored and drilled to get an exact calibre. In the early days of this process this was done vertically. The picture we show of one of these great machines proves that they were operated by a team of horses.

The last manuscript we have to deal with is one that has been called a mediaeval record book. It has given rise to numerous controversies regarding its origin and attribution. The author has recently been identified as a painter, draughtsman and engraver, working in the region of the middle Rhine during the last decade of the fifteenth century. In fact it would appear that we have a number of notebooks, arbitrarily put together, compiled by a number of authors. The first part is undoubtedly the work of an artist. It represents German life at the end of the fifteenth century. It also contains some features of interest to the historian of technology: two ploughs, a mill with an overshot wheel and one with an undershot wheel, a windmill which is barely comprehensible, some turret crossbows, the manufacture of organs and of a pendulum. A different hand has added a hydraulic ram with a rod and crank system. A drawing of a spinning-wheel, which stands on its own, is no less interesting: it is the first spinning-wheel with a pedal and vane, that is, the first modern spinning-wheel as we know it. This drawing is certainly earlier than those of Leonardo da Vinci which show analogous machines, less clearly represented.

A second group of drawings concerns mining. A general view of the mine shows galleries running flush with the hillside with miners of traditional appearance. Similar views are to be found in the reredos of Annaberg, executed by Hans Hesse in 1521 and in the manuscript of Heinrich Gross concerning Sainte-Marie-aux-Mines. The other drawings show the foundries. In a general view of the workshop, a group of visitors is to be seen, the oven made of bricks or stones and the bellows controlled by a hand-operated beam. The three sketches that follow are concerned with bellows, an important problem that drew the attention of all our engineers. One is operated by cams and counterweights, using either weights or levers. Another is like a squirrel cage and seems to be a piston-operated bellows. The last one in this series is a machine for minting coins prior to the invention of the screw press. This entire series is thus concerned with silver mining. Work in mines, and particularly in silver mines, seems to have attracted artists: we possess numerous works of art up to the the middle of the sixteenth century that have been inspired by this activity and the historian of these techniques thus has at his disposal precise and valuable documentation.

The last pages of this manuscript form a collection of engines of

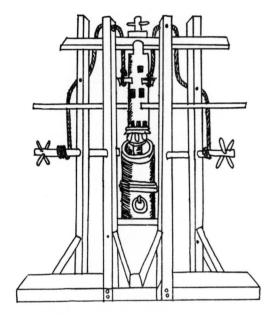

Munich MS: machine for boring cannon.

war, very similar to other German manuscripts of the period. The first two drawings show us handmills, using a crank or a rod and crank system with a large ball as the flywheel. Then there are classical engines of war: an artillery dray, multiple guns with lifts, hoisting apparatus, chariots and shields for cannons, escalading ladders, trebuchets and two views of military camps very much like those in the previous manuscripts.

It is quite clear that this is a tripartite composition that arbitrarily groups together different works. First of all there is the work of an artists, perhaps in preparation for a series of engravings of the life of a nobleman at the end of the Middle Ages. Then follows a book on mining, like others we know. Finally, the manuscript ends with a collection. Even if there were only one artist, we still have before us three very different compositions.

Thus ends our brief study of the German School. After a promising beginning, the Germans appear to have ceased, to some extent, to move forwards. The very real influence of Kyeser, in both the artistic and technical spheres, may have somewhat limited the development of their imagination. What we possess, indeed, is a basic work repeated innumerable times with a few minor amendments. The Germans seem to have remained too strictly military. They lacked the universal curiosity and style that are so characteristic of the Italian engineers of the Renaissance. By confining themselves too exclusively to one technique, the German engineers to some extent sterilized their own imaginations.

This is not to say, however, that this school had a mediocre and limited influence. At the end of the fourteenth century we find the military engineer resuscitating a very long tradition that was more or less disappearing from memory. He restarted the fashion for collections of machines, he captivated the imagination of his contemporaries, both of those whose technique was their craft and of those to whom it represented a source of power. The gesture of Count Otto-Heinrich in having an old manuscript recopied would not perhaps have been possible without the *Bellifortis* of Kyeser. This rebirth of technique in southern Germany could not have widespread repercussions: the intellectual climate and political requirements became favourable only after Italy had seriously taken the lead. In the second half of the century we see the copyists interspersing passages from the archaic Kyeser with the modern Valturio, combining the German with the Italian.

Chapter 4: The First Italian Generation

The technological preoccupations of the Germans appear, in the last analysis, to have been somewhat limited. Technical progress, in so far as it was able to free itself from an extremely slow evolution, seemed to depend on military men who were seeking to improve their weapons. From the beginning, the technological approach of the Italians was fundamentally different. Even in the early fifteenth century the difference is clear to see between northern Europe, freeing itself with difficulty from the mediaeval period, and Italy, where what is usually called the Renaissance had already begun to operate. The first technicians whom we shall mention are from a completely different environment and had completely different aspirations. They were true humanists, artists or scholars, who, beyond their particular problems, which were in any case greater than those of the Germans, looked for general solutions, valid explanations, and also the means for completely dominating the new world which was opening out. It was almost by accident that, as they proceeded, they encountered the military problems which were simultaneously engaging the attention – but in their case almost to the exclusion of everything else – of their contemporaries north of the Alps.

From the beginning, also, Italian thinkers seemed to be to a greater extent divorced from tradition. Tradition was not, however, unknown to them and they also tried to deal with identical problems, but the scope of their curiosity suddenly broadened. The striking thing about their research is the fertility of their imagination. The early steps, which were slight enough in Germany, are here completely missing. There are no early manuscripts, none of the mediaeval compilations which are to be found in Germany, in Italian libraries of the late fourteenth century. We might almost believe in a kind of spontaneous generation which would, to some extent, explain the environment from which technicians were recruited and the enlargement of their knowledge.

Brunellesco (1377–1446) is almost a contemporary of Kyeser. From the first he represents the type of Renaissance artist-technician and is thus completely different from Kyeser. His education is a good indication of the new tendencies that we have mentioned. Born in Florence, he began, as later did Francesco di Giorgio and Leonardo da Vinci, as a goldsmith and sculptor. After a journey to Rome, he became an architect passionately devoted to the antique. Even if he has not filled small notebooks with revealing drawings, Brunellesco was no less a technician concerned with all the problems of his profession. At the church of Santa Maria dei Fiori, in Florence, it was not that he rediscovered the dome which, indeed, had never been entirely forgotten, but that he found new methods of building domes.

It should be noted, writes Francastel, that at the beginning of the fifteenth century there appears in Brunellesco a third original inventive element: Brunellesco, the inventor of machines. Brunellesco had invented a small optical instrument. It consisted of a kind of box containing a panel on which was painted a view of Florence and which, by means of mirrors, gave an impression of relief. Here again is that great quest for perspective which was to assume such great importance in the Renaissance. Brunellesco also had other interests, in particular the construction of all kinds of machines, described in forgotten texts of Vasari, some of which were used in entertainments. In this liking for festivities, which was another of the elements of the Renaissance spirit, we rediscover the tradition of Hero of Alexandria.

Another current of thought is represented by Giacomo Fontana, the first of the Italians whose writings, in particular a notebook of machine drawings, have been preserved. Unhappily we are ignorant of numerous biographical details which would have enabled us to ascertain his position in this Italian school. He was probably born in about 1393 and died in about 1455. He was thus slightly younger than Brunellesco and Kyeser and would be roughly contemporary with the anonymous artist of the Hussite War. In 1418 he was studying arts and medicine in Padua. He was appointed physician to the Republic of Venice and in this capacity was, from 1420 to 1432, with the armies stationed at Brescia. His scientific work is important and fairly well known. He was concerned with natural history and physics and thus seems to have been more a scholar than a practitioner. A collection of machine designs entitled *Bellicorum instrumentorum liber*, of which only one copy, preserved in the Munich Library, is known, has been attributed to him. A special characteristic of this manuscript is that it carries explanations written in cipher. This writing is the same as that in a treatise on physics and alchemy in the Bibliothèque Nationale attributed to Fontana. It is possible that the Venetian doctor wished to protect his mechanical and alchemical secrets from indiscreet scrutiny.

His collection is only remotely concerned with military art. It is a 'theatre of machines', similar to those works that became more numerous in the sixteenth century. The only machines in which we can perceive military preoccupations are a few for destroying walls and a warship provided with paddle-wheels. There is nothing on projectile weapons or on artillery. The notebook is mainly concerned with hydraulic matters, fountains and water channels, and with automata, the various parts of which are drawn with great care. Fontana's work is undoubtedly more interesting for its thought than for the drawings themselves. These, although they indicate great familiarity with the subject, are merely illustrations that can be found elsewhere.

The drawing of one of these automata is superior to anything that has been seen in this field. The precision and the details of the mechanism are very striking. Here we are on the threshold of that world of fantasy, which was so common in the Middle Ages and which is to be rediscovered in festivities and theatrical scenes. Many automata are thus represented, which work by all kinds of mechanisms which were certainly known and used cord transmission.

A whole series of drawings is concerned with fountains and water channels. The principle of the siphon is utilized many times: it was to constitute one of the commonplaces of these Italian notebooks of the fifteenth century. We find in Fontana a reproduction of the famous drawing of the aeolipile of Hero, which used the properties of steam. It is possible that Fontana recognized that water cannot be raised above a certain level, and that a column of water could not exceed a certain height. But his drawings are not detailed enough and in this instance, unfortunately, there are no written indications, even in cipher. It would be going too far to regard this Italian of the early fifteenth century as a precursor of Galileo.

With Marianus Jacobus, called Taccola, we come to another group of engineers, which is closer to the German school. If Brunellesco and Fontana made an undoubted contribution to the technical construction of the Renaissance, it is equally certain that men like Taccola were the central figures. These were men of more modest origins, with a less widely based culture, on their own admission

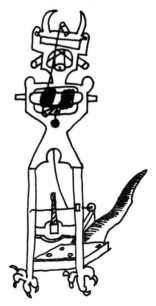

Fontana: mechanism for automaton.

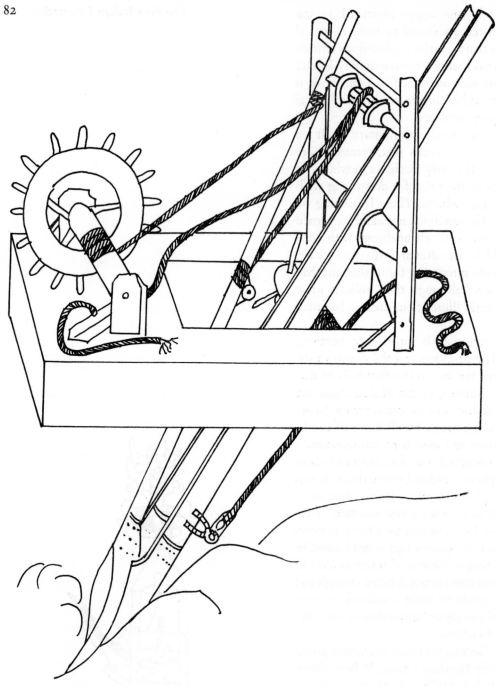

Fontana: rock-clearing machine.

unlettered men; but they were, perhaps, more specialized, as we should say today, and therefore able to play a more decisive part in the advancement of technology.

Were we willing to make broad comparisons, which, by their nature, would be exaggerated; were we anxious to link these engineers with some of the traditions which we have described, we could say that, whereas Fontana emerged, to some extent, as the disciple of the Alexandrian school, Taccola could be regarded as the heir of Archimedes.

The biography of Taccola is very uncertain although many historians have attempted to establish it. Born at Siena, in Tuscany, the region of Italy which was to become almost the centre of technological progress, Taccola was the son of a humble vine grower. He died before 1458. His career appears to have been solely that of a military engineer. His reputation was very great. All this seems to amount to the fact that he was the Italian Kyeser. Although his name was barely mentioned in the decades that followed his death, his influence may easily be followed during the succeeding generations. It has already been shown that Leonardo da Vinci knew Taccola and certainly borrowed from him. The manuscript tradition of Taccola is very much slighter than that of his German counterpart, Kyeser. Five manuscripts, of which one has probably recently disappeared, are all that remain. The most important are two collections of notes that were used for elaborating his definitive work.

This work, a collection of machines, *De machinis libri X* appears to be represented today by only two manuscripts. The most magnificent is that preserved in Paris. It was bought for the library of the King of France in Constantinople at the end of the seventeenth century by a scholar who thought that the manuscript might have some interest from a military point of view. It may have been preserved in the Seraglio library since the time of a military expedition to Hungary.

Taccola preserves many links with the Middle Ages. Some of his machines and some of his ideas clearly show that a tradition is being perpetuated and traces of this will still be found in the succeeding generation. We still find in Taccola counterweight artillery and the solution of the perpetual movement that was already to be found in Villard de Honnecourt. Certain of his military protective devices are strangely similar to those of Kyeser. Even his drawing technique is closer to that of the German than to that of Fontana and perspective is not always correctly represented.

Taccola's curiosity is markedly wider. His research is also some-

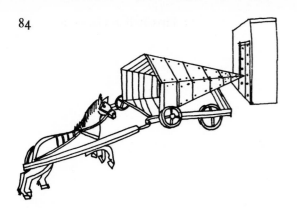

Taccola: ram.

Taccola: trebuchet.

Taccola: scaling machine.

times carried further. In regard to the various types of usable power, the Italian was no innovator and, for that matter, could not have been. Although he frequently uses human energy, especially in treadmills, and animal power in devices of all sorts, as well as hydraulic power, there is only one illustration of the use of wind-power and that is only harnessed to a modest machine for raising water out of wells.

In regard to water power, Taccola's research did not go very far. The various types of hydraulic wheels, overshot, undershot, and horizontal, are used, but nothing more. The inclination of the vanes on the wheels appears to be an old device which cannot be attributed to Taccola.

In the field of transmission and the transformation of movement, the Italian work seems to be very traditional. It contains no revolutionary mechanism. There is nothing remarkable on gears, which are of the most ordinary type. The use of pulleys for stepping down had been known for a long time. Further on we shall mention suction pumps actuated by a connecting-rod and crank: these are the first examples to have come down to us. This connecting-rod and crank system reappears in handmills identical in all points to those of the earliest German manuscripts. Finally we would note the first representation of a chain transmission system, a rather clumsy realization of an idea which was to make good progress in less than fifty years.

Although Taccola made no great revelations where the principles of mechanics and energy were concerned, it may be said that he knew all the existing systems and he applied them with good sense. This exhaustive knowledge of the technical possibilities of his period is undoubtedly one of the best elements of his work.

To go into greater detail, the enquiries of the Sienese engineer appear on the whole to be the same as those of his German predecessors. Taccola is certainly above all else a military engineer. But an attentive examination of his work in this connexion is a little disappointing. It is surprising to see how little space artillery occupies in his drawings. There are few designs of bombards, of rudimentary type, which show that at this date the German engineers were more advanced than those in the Peninsula. Only one light firearm, carried by a horseman, is shown.

The remainder of the military machinery is only a repetition of what has been known since the end of the fourteenth century: folding ladders, rams, shelters covered in wood, fire carriers, and trebuchets. There are some prefabricated and articulated bridges which are very similar to those of Kyeser. It may be said that there is a striking resemblance between the two treatises: it pervades the whole work, from beginning to end.

The same applies to the lifting apparatus. The use of pulleys, of pivoting cranes, and more or less complex apparatus, is singularly similar to that which we have already seen. The screwjack is also there. Only one more curious drawing may be mentioned: that of the lifting, by means of a crane placed in a boat, of a column from the bottom of the sea or of a lake. This may be associated with similar attempts made in Italy at about the same time and of which records remain.

What we may call the 'marine' section is strongly developed. There is certainly nothing remarkable about the form of ships – indeed, the drawings were presumably not made primarily for the sake of the vessels – but they carry all the apparatus that we have already seen for land armies. We again find mobile ladders, trebuchets, and grappling irons for boarding. Here again there are ships moved by propellers, worked either by a crank, or by a rope coiled round a shaft and attached to a fixed point on shore. These mechanisms show no great originality. Nor are the purely hydraulic problems treated with any great depth. There are many drawings of siphons and the machines for draining are the same as have been known for centuries and include Archimedean screws, shadoofs, and chain pumps. We would note as a novelty the double suction pump with its rod and crank method.

Other machines, however, such as the machine for boring wooden tubes, show a classical traditionalism, exactly similar to those depicted in the manuscript of the Hussite War.

We may ask ourselves whether we should subscribe to the praise

Taccola: machine for hollowing wooden pipes.

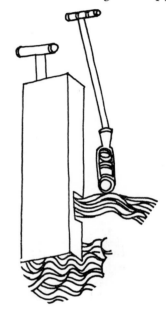

Taccola: water-pump.

Taccola: suction and pressure pump.

that from an early date has been accorded to Taccola. If we look at the positive side of this work, we certainly cannot fail to note that it contains practically everything. There is a certain technological erudition which is worth emphasizing. The truly interesting machines, however, are not very numerous. Apart from the suction pumps we would note one of the first representations of a pair of hydraulic bellows, probably used in some kind of metal fusion furnace. The bellows are moved by cams and must have had a counterweight which is not shown in the drawing. The cams are arranged so that the bellows act alternately and so that the current of air is constant. It is the first time that this apparatus is to be seen, at the very moment when the blast furnace made its appearance in Europe.

The drawings of measurements, especially measurement of height, are also all very instructive. This was to be one of the preoccupations of all our Italian engineers of the fifteenth century. It is possible that one of the drawings may represent a theodolite.

More interesting are the wooden couplings. Here we have the beginning of research into a difficult question which was to be taken up by all Taccola's successors.

Taccola's fame, according to the historians of a period only slightly later than his, appears to have been so great that he was called the Sienese Archimedes. We may ask ourselves whether he was aware of his worth, whether he had that kind of self-satisfaction so often experienced by the technicians of this period. Some phrases from his notebooks may lead us to think so. 'I keep to myself what I know how to do, do not believe that I do anything without receiving the price.' Some modern authors have attributed to Taccola a number of inventions, especially in the field of military technique, for which there is no real proof. In particular it is quite impossible to discover in his notes confirmation of the fact that he was the inventor of modern ramparts, a means of fortification that is quite different from that of the Middle Ages. The castles that he designed, or which were designed to his instructions, are of the classical type. He has also been credited with having been the first to have used powder in mines dug under fortifications. One drawing would, indeed, appear to show this. But was Taccola the first to attempt this? Historically, the powder mine is formally recorded in 1495 at the Castel Nuovo in Naples, and in 1501 during the siege of Cephalonia, and therefore later than Taccola.

If, by a close and precise study of some of the drawings it is possible to determine the influence of Kyeser on Taccola, the influence of the latter on all the Italian engineers is quite obvious. We

Taccola: hydraulic bellows.

shall rediscover Taccola's ideas in Francesco di Giorgio. But, before that, we shall find certain elements in Valturio.

Roberto Valturio lived at the court of the Malatesta at Rimini, the importance of which as a centre of technological progress we have already mentioned. Born in 1413, he belonged to an old family from Macerata, a small town to the south of Ancona. His family had settled at Rimini. His ancestors had worked in the Chancellery at the Vatican and his father had been Apostolic Secretary. He himself began his career in Rome and did not go to Rimini until 1446. At the request of Sigismondo Malatesta he drew up the treatise of military technique dedicated to the lord of Rimini. In this work Valturio appears not so much as a technician and practical man as a man of letters. Some people have thought that he was nothing but a secretary who did no more than give literary form to the ideas and inventions of his master. The illustrations were executed by the engraver and medallist, Matteo dei Pasti, who borrowed a great deal from the drawings of Taccola, a copy of whose work must certainly have existed in the Rimini library. The work was finished in 1455 and was printed in 1472 and both the manuscript and the printed version had considerable success. Today there remain twenty-two manuscripts of the work of Valturio: two of these bear the arms of Matthias Corvinus, a great collector of technical works.

The originality of Valturio's work is purely relative. He mentions the authors he used and Taccola is there, together with the masters of antiquity. Although Kyeser is not mentioned, it would certainly seem that the illustrator knew the German manuscript, since there are cases where it is difficult not to see a close relationship.

Valturio's offensive weapons are of fairly archaic type. The missile launching apparatus, using either rope torsion or springs, comprises the whole range of mediaeval apparatus, added to which – and this is certainly more up to date – there are reminiscences of antiquity. Chariots, armed with scythes or cannon, and mobile shields are a legacy both of Taccola and of Kyeser. Noteworthy is a chariot propelled by small windmills, which figures with certain variations in all military treatises since Guido da Vigevano.

Assault apparatus still utilizes the same kind of mechanism: multiple ladders, towers that are raised to the height of walls by means of winches and jacks. The instruments for forcing the protective bars of a window are the same as those of Kyeser. The same may be said of all the prefabricated machinery which has been noted from the beginning of the fifteenth century, including folding bridges, section bridges, boats with side propellers worked by winches. The same goes for the divers and water-skins.

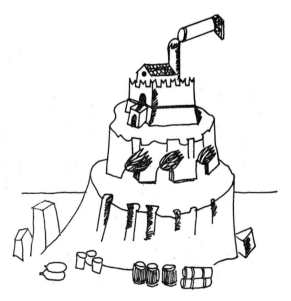

Taccola: destruction of a castle with mines and powder.

Evolution of chariot driven by windmills: Guido da Vigevano.

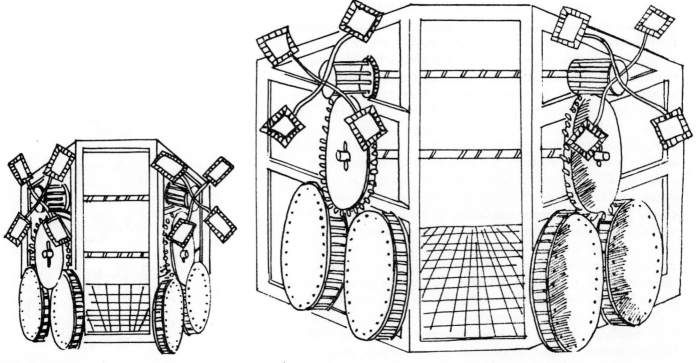

Valturio.   Taccola.

The hydraulic section is in the same vein and includes the now familiar pumps, siphons, Archimedian screws, and chain pumps.

A study of Valturio's artillery leads to similar conclusions. The trebuchet, a mediaeval siege-engine, still appears in this work of the mid-fifteenth century, although it would seem that it was no longer used at this period. Gunpowder artillery is still rudimentary. The mobile multi-gun is the same as Kyeser's. Only the fantastic machine, which we reproduce and which was to meet with justifiable success, lends a certain note of originality to this work of Valturio's.

Valturio: trebuchet.

Valturio falls into the same error as the Germans: he was unable to rid himself of certain ideas, which, as we have seen, originated at the beginning of the fifteenth century and he made no advance upon the models that inspired him. If we did not know the work done by the Malatesta, principally in the field of fortification, we might be justified in asking ourselves whether this centre at Rimini was not becoming more a kind of repository of old formulae. It may also well be that, despite their castles, and despite their wish to appear in the vanguard of progress – a wish which caused them to send for Alberti – the Malatestas had not fully understood the true direction of technical development. Although research in this field is not easy, it might well be interesting to try to acquire more accurate information about these illustrations, all these drawings which were copied one from the other during the middle years of the fifteenth century. The drawings of Vegetius, of Valturio, the Venice manuscript and the German manuscripts of the second half of the fifteenth century, which we mention in our catalogue, are very closely related to one another. It is no less true that we find in Valturio, in the clearest possible form, the influence of the manuscript of Kyeser, who is nowhere quoted as one of the sources of the treatise.

The Germans, Taccola, and Valturio appear to be so many stages in the same tradition. All these authors must have known each other's work, and must have been copied, re-copied, and plagiarized in step with the slow progress dominated by the use of artillery, which disrupted, though only gradually, the ancient techniques. At the end of this first generation of Italians we arrive at the moment when the cannon was about to acquire its true importance and value. Delbrück has convincingly shown that firearms did not have any serious influence on the outcomes of battles before the last quarter of the fifteenth century.

While this awareness of a profound change in techniques was gradually coming about a kind of renewal of the problems was taking shape. Not only did the cannon modify the army, but it also influenced the whole of metallurgy, developed ballistic concepts, and completely transformed fortifications. This considerable widening of scope was to be matched, though far from brilliantly at first, by more advanced intellectual means. The more complex technique becomes, the more vast and advanced knowledge does it require. Various activities are interconnected. Artists, sculptors, and architects meet each other in common undertakings. Brunellesco and Fontana had been precursors and the military technicians had remained isolated. Others were to come who would try to tackle all problems at once.

There is, perhaps, no better example of this than Leon Battista Alberti (1404–1472). The history of his life, well known today, reveals a man who was more a seeker than a practitioner, somewhat like Leonardo da Vinci. He was born of a noble Florentine family, members of which, before entering upon the great adventure of commerce and banking, had occupied the position of notary. Alberti was the true son of these newly rich bourgeois, intimately concerned with material realities before passing on to intellectual interests. Political disputes had driven the family into exile and Alberti was born in Genoa. He lived part of his youth in Venice where he was given a wide culture which he followed up in Padua. In 1421, he went to Bologna and began to study law, which he soon abandoned, for reasons of health, in favour of mathematics and natural sciences. Papal protection enabled him to go back to Tuscany for some time. Between 1430 and 1432 he travelled to France, Belgium, and Germany, probably in the train of a legate. He settled in 1432 in Rome, where he discovered the ancient world. He was an intellectual in the complete sense of the word: he studied literature, was interested in scientific matters, and later gave himself up to artistic investigations. He was a painter and sculptor as well as an architect and there are monuments to testify to his ability. He was also given engineering work such as the attempt to recover Roman ships from Lake Nemi, which he did in about 1447 at the request of Cardinal Colonna.

This taste for science and technology, as well as for general technical problems, thus fitted naturally into the cast of Alberti's thought. All his life he showed himself to be curious, greedy for knowledge, endeavouring to understand, to explain, and to generalize. There are inventions of his, of fairly limited significance, it is true, but interesting for the state of mind which they denote: experiments with the camera obscura, like those made by Brunellesco, with topographical instruments, hygrometry, methods of sounding in deep water. He also took pleasure in problems which were absorbing the scholarly or literary world. His *Ludi mathematici*,

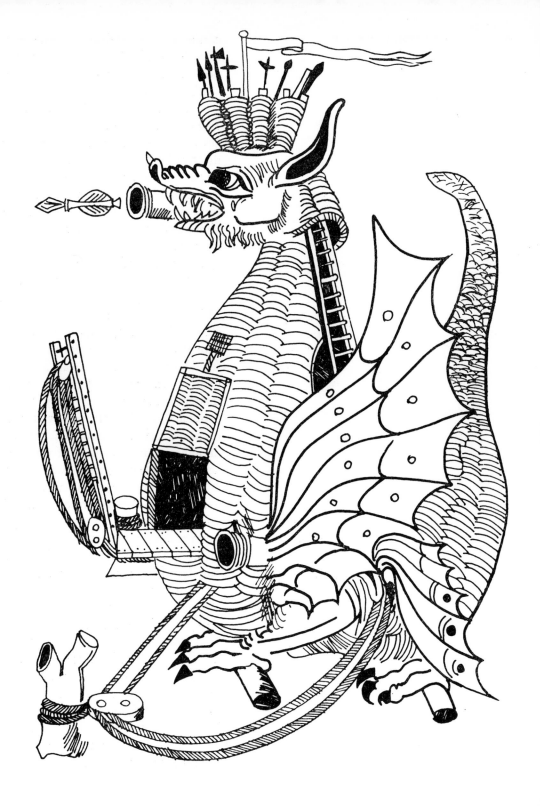

Valturio: espringal.

composed for Meliadus d'Este in about 1450, show a certain knowledge of calculation and an attachment to some of the traditional problems that had excited the imagination of his predecessors.

The volume of Alberti's written work is considerable. Much of it is unhappily lost, especially in the field of science and technology. The *De motibus ponderis*, which contained his theory of physics, has never been found. In the sphere of technology we would mention the treatise on perspective, which has also been lost. Alberti also wrote on the attempt at Nemi in 1447. This work should have formed an appendix to the treatise on architecture, but it has not come down to us. It is possible that it would have contained notes on diving and on lifting columns, of which we have already mentioned examples.

The great work of Alberti, at least in the line of our interest, is the *De re aedificatoria*, the treatise on architecture. Its existence was disclosed in 1452, when it was nearly finished. It was printed in 1485. This work was intended as a complete treatise on the 'science of the engineer'. Perhaps, like the work of Francesco di Giorgio at a later date, it was not finished and Alberti indeed mentions subjects that he would have wished to explain and which are missing from his book, such as 'engines for carrying, mills, grain reservoirs, and other matters which although they are held in little esteem are still profitable'. He also mentions water channels, the manner of cutting rock and piercing mountains, sea dykes and river embankments, draining swamps, engines of war, and fortresses. In short, we have here the whole programme which was to be the concern of engineers.

In fact, the work deals not so much with architecture in the narrow sense of the word or with architectural techniques as with a whole programme of town planning. Alberti's treatise is a treatise on town planning. He was an innovator though no revolutionary and insists on the proper choice of site, the suitability of the plan, without, however, hiding his inclination for geometrical plans, which were generally radioconcentric and difficult to apply. He shows himself to be both practical and a follower of Pythagoras. His ideas are often still mediaeval in their conception of the city: he preaches the localization of crafts, functionalism, and curving roads. Against this, he demands respect for urban aesthetics, for perspective, and for a certain order, which are fruits of the Renaissance. A large part of the treatise is devoted to the disposition of dwellings and to the decoration of façades. This concern with indoor practical life, this logic of private life inside the house, is undoubtedly a new preoccupation, at least in its general conception.

This does not, however, lead Alberti to neglect the more purely technical problems, where we find the same preoccupations that we have already glimpsed. He mentions the important questions of materials, and gives some advice on the ageing of wood for cooperage and on the art of cutting and making up barrels. Some pages in particular are devoted to methods to be used for lengthening joists; similar designs will be found in Francesco di Giorgio and Leonardo da Vinci. A whole section is also dedicated to building stone. In short, it is the engineering section which is the least developed, either because Alberti did not complete his work or because he felt that he had too little practical knowledge to deal with it. Nevertheless he mentions the art of building bridges, temporary wooden bridges on pontoons or on boats, and the prefabricated bridges that we have already seen. Certain notes are also concerned with ports, dykes, and sewers. The problem of water channels, so completely treated in certain other works, is here very summarily touched upon. One drawing shows a chain pump, another an Archimedean screw, and a few lines deal with water channels. There is a reference to the question of levelling.

The military section is not very well represented. There is some discussion of the plan of fortresses and Alberti shows himself to be very traditional. A whole chapter deals with ships, but without great detail. Drawings here are almost non-existent.

Alberti is the true contemporary of the other engineers we have studied: the same things excite his curiosity and he is subject to the same influences; he has the same preoccupations and he encounters the same difficulties. But on reading his work we feel that he is less close than the others to reality. He tries to be more didactic than precise and more philosophical than technical. In this respect he resembles Leonardo da Vinci.

Alberti's influence was very great. His treatise was taken up and modified, no doubt, according to temperament, and inspired most of the Italians of the second generation. He was the founder of a school and his pupils contributed to this enduring success, especially Bernardo Rossellino (1409–1464), only a few years younger than himself, who worked at Pienza and built the first modern square, the centre of the cities of the future.

Antonio Francesco Averlino, called Il Filarete (1416–1470), had neither the importance nor the range of Alberti. Although not a great thinker and leaving little written work, Filarete was no doubt much closer to technical realities. He also came from Florence and worked in Rome and especially in Milan at the court of the Sforza, where Alberti had also spent some time. The treatise on architecture which he wrote has never been printed but was widely circulated in manuscript, which signifies that it was successful. Less cultivated than his predecessor, Filarete composed his work in the vernacular and dedicated it to Sforza for whom it was written. The King of Hungary, Matthias Corvinus, had it translated into Latin.

There is no doubt that Il Filarete owed much to Alberti. Most of the general ideas, the quotations, and part of the aesthetics come from the latter. Il Filarete was an architect and a sculptor and had certain preoccupations which are unique to him; he took good care to emphasize the fact that he was neither Vitruvius nor Alberti.

His ideal city, Sforzinda, however, has many points in common with that of Alberti. But Il Filarete did not have the pragmatism of his predecessor. His city is purely an ideal one and takes into account neither the site nor the mediaeval forerunners. It is a polygon where everything is disposed according to a rigorous logic, and here we are in the pure Pythagorean tradition.

Since Il Filarete was more of an engineer than a theoretician and was more at ease with practical problems, he gave much space to machines and other techniques. Indeed, he considered everything that was required for a well-organized city. The sections concerning building materials are inspired by Alberti, whose drawings are repeated. There follow notes of a military nature, on walls and towers, fortifications in general and on citadels. He then considers some of the important buildings such as the cathedral, the palace, and the bishop's residence. Then follow planning ideas on the squares and market places. He also gives attention to utilitarian buildings, such as hospitals, houses for patricians, merchants and craftsmen, and does not omit the theatre, which is a new consideration, as well as the parish church and the monastery. He also includes groups of buildings, such as bridges and ports. At the end of his work he even mentions a museum, a naval seaport, water channels, houses for fishermen, and water reservoirs. His work also includes a description of a metallurgical factory and he deals with an architect's house, schools, public baths, salt warehouses, and even with the administration of the city. He did not neglect the art of drawing and devotes part of his work to familiar buildings, mostly those that had been constructed by the Medicis.

Much of all this literature is still very formal. Alberti was certainly the founder of a school. But the rejection of accepted solutions gathered momentum as the century advanced. Technical preoccupations became more perceptible but still had the appearance rather of scholarly concerns, of historical research extending back to antiquity, than of an attempt to re-state the problems inherent in what was later to be called civil engineering.

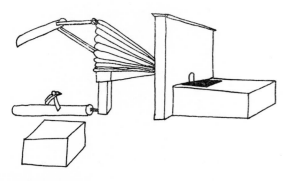

Filarete: refining oven.

The Fioravanti family came from Bologna. The father had worked on the canals in the district of Milan, an admirable engineering school at which successive generations had been trained. He had worked under Filippo degli Organi. It is said that he was the inventor of the mobile sluice-gates, first mentioned by Alberti in his treatise on architecture. In fact, we do not know much about the first Fioravanti.

His son, Ridolfo Fioravanti, called 'Aristotle', bridges the two generations. He appears to have been a talented engineer and his work and ability were praised. He was, at the beginning of his career, a 'specialist' in difficult cases. In Bologna, he straightened the tower of the Palazzo del Podestà. In Magione, in 1455, he shifted the church tower, which weighed 87 tons, about 20 feet. The recollection persisted of this delicate operation, which brought into use machines that had been subjects of interest since classical times.

Aristotle was employed by Francesco Sforza on his canals and fortifications. He thus formed part of the group to which his father, Alberti and Filarete had probably belonged and which was joined, some years later, by Leonardo da Vinci. Fioravanti later entered the service of the Duke of Mantua, then of Pope Paul III, before going to Hungary in about 1470, to Matthias Corvinus, the king, who was interested in all techniques. Finally, in 1475, he arrived in Russia. In that distant country he was an architect as well as a gun-maker, bell-founder, and head of the mint. He died there in 1479. Both Corvinus and the tzars of Russia imitated the Italian princes and, a little later, the kings of France by attracting to their courts men whose genius lay in the fact that they knew how to do everything. Simultaneously with the emergence of this type of universal engineer, there arose, among those in power, a desire for efficiency which of course led to technical progress. Other talented engineers, such as Pietro Antonio Salario of Milan, who arrived in 1480 and whose father and grandfather had worked on the Duomo of Milan and the Monastery of Pavia, went to Russia with Fioravanti. Alevisio of Milan, 'maestro di muro', left for those distant lands in 1493.

We know very little about these men of the end of the first generation of Italians. We can sense that a modern outlook was developing, which would give rise, in the sixteenth century, to a new science very closely related to all these engineering works. Aristotle of Bologna was considered to have an encyclopaedic mind; he was an architect, engineer, founder, medallist, and an expert in hydraulics as well as in fortification and pyrotechnics. His reputation was immense. He was the bridge between his own and the following generation.

Such technical progress arose out of all the contacts with practitioners and, no doubt, out of a more general view of all problems. Unhappily we know little of this slow beginning of the practical approach; these 'specialists' are largely strangers to us. Some were also artists, attracted by certain technical details of their craft. They did not leave to posterity works comparable with those of more ambitious but sometimes less well-informed contemporaries. Lorenzo Ghiberti (1378–1455) was mainly a worker in bronze, celebrated for the doors of the Baptistry in Florence. The *Commentaries* that he wrote towards the end of his life marked a new attitude: that of the Renaissance. In this work we can see how great was his interest in technical and scientific matters. His research into optics and perspective, the great topic of reflection of the period, undoubtedly shows his culture and his taste for working in depth. A small manuscript preserved in the Biblioteca Nazionale in Florence (BR 228, cl. XVII, 2) is most curious from this point of view. Its attribution is difficult; it was long thought to be a notebook of Lorenzo Ghiberti, but it would now appear that it was compiled by a nephew of the celebrated Florentine sculptor, Bonaccorso Ghiberti, who was much younger than his uncle. The *Zibaldone* is a collection of notes and drawings, very similar to our engineers' notebooks. It is about architecture, metallurgy, artillery, and, especially, foundry work. It would appear that the owner of the notes was a founder first and foremost and that either he or some successive owners noted everything of interest. The architectural part is only of slight interest.

Ghiberti's nephew has left us some drawings of his founder's craft. His external view of the foundry only shows the water wheel that activates the bellows and a half-timbered house of the most classical type. Apparatus is represented mainly by bellows, a problem which seems to have been of paramount interest to all these technicians; they are actuated by cams working by counterweights.

These workshops supplied two essential products, at least according to the indications of this notebook. These were bells and guns. A certain desire for rationalization may be discerned. In regard to bells, for example, it is not only a question of examining processes of manufacture; in addition to the making of moulds, a difficult phase of the operation, there is a kind of diagram which indicates the main characteristics of bells of a given shape. These 'tables' may be said to express an attempt to give the work precise rules; the complete technique can no doubt be found in these simple rules, transmitted from generation to generation; but it is the first manifestation of this knowledge, of which, as regards other activities, we shall learn

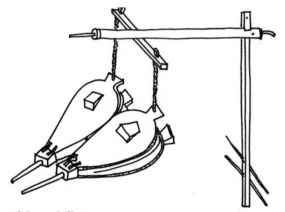

Ghiberti: bellows.

Ghiberti: model for bell-making.

Neroni: cannons –
a. screw lift.
b. quadrant lift.
c. rack lift.

nothing until much later – in the case of shipbuilding, for example, not until the sixteenth and seventeenth centuries.

The same is done for guns; the measurement of the different calibres is specified with great care. Empiricism is replaced by measurement established and observed with precision. It then became possible to search for the reasons for these rules and to try to improve them. Simple onslaughts on a problem were replaced by logical deduction. The transition from one state of mind to another represents an effort that is worth emphasizing.

Other difficult problems attracted the attention of the author of this notebook. We have, for example, at a time when precision of aim was clearly improving, the problem of gun elevation. Until then, only rack and pinion elevation had been used. Two pieces of curved wood carried a number of holes through which was inserted a small billet of iron which supported one end of the gun; we show a number of illustrations. Movement was therefore limited to a certain number of positions, which did not matter in a siege, but was a handicap in a battle. A system of notches, also shown here, was no more practical. Finally, elevation by means of a screw was adopted and this was to be the future development.

The remainder of the manuscript is of less interest. Some drawings would appear to have been done much later; some are copied from the notebooks of Francesco di Giorgio. There are also borrowings from previous works, a clear proof of the persistence of tradition. This is true of the engines of war and especially of siege apparatus, ladders, apparatus for breaking barriers, ships constructed from several sections, paddle-wheel boats, armed chariots, and trebuchets. The most immediate inspiration came from Taccola and Valturio.

The manuscript thus seems to be composed of a number of elements: architectural notes, observations on bronze founding (bells, statues, and guns), and copies of old and well-known images. Before the traditional last section on war machines there is a section on geometry and theoretical arithmetic. It is symptomatic to find problems of pure mathematics in this work written for technicians. This is an additional sign of the change to be observed in this period.

A manuscript in the Siena Library (S IV 6), which was long attributed to Francesco di Giorgio, has recently been restored to a certain Bartolomeo Neroni, called the Rich. About half this note-book consists of architectural drawings, mostly capitals and columns, and the rest is devoted to machines, none of which related to the art of war, except for some cannon.

In fact only a small number of problems are dealt with. The lifting apparatus is of the contemporary type and some of the illustrations are to be found in Taccola. We should note, however, the rotating cranes mounted on rollers.

There are numerous pumps and machines for raising water. Besides siphons and fountains a very simple noria is shown. Pumps are abundantly represented. There are suction and force pumps, actuated either by a rod and crank (in a drawing that curiously recalls Taccola) or by cams. There is also a horse-driven machine, supplied with an endless chain passing along suitable piping.

Grain mills, possessing a system of simple gears, are driven either by horses or by treadmills. A number of pile drivers are shown with an arrangement of cams.

The mechanisms used by Neroni are thus not revolutionary; their use was, at this period, already known if it was not widespread. The influence of Taccola, moreover, is certain. The drawing, however, is more highly developed and the details are better represented. The only curious point is the total absence of engines of war. The manuscript ends with a series of problems in simple geometry; thus it belongs to a tradition similar to that of the previous manuscript.

We have now reached the beginning of the great period, the threshold of a new era. Although the works which we have tried to analyse reveal a fairly clear development and show incontestable marks of progress, the hold of tradition is still very strong and persists from one notebook to the next.

Assuredly it is no longer the ancient tradition, which seems to stop at the beginning of the fifteenth century. Kyeser already contributed certain new elements and these were to reappear in the middle of the century in the works both of the Germans and the Italians. Artillery, the invention of a rod and crank system, and the more widespread use of metal are probably the causes of this development. In a way, this represents the first step in technical progress; it was a reasonably well-defined and homogeneous advance which in the sequel gained only in greater subtlety of design.

But the Italians of the first half of the fifteenth century introduced a fresh outlook. They deal, however, with the same problems, first and foremost the military ones of artillery and the besieging of strongholds; and with various mechanical problems – though these are not very numerous; with lifting apparatus, hydraulic pumping plant and windmills – the list is again quite short. Seen as a whole, the Italian machines seem to be better conceived, although perhaps they are only better drawn, in a period and place where problems of perspective have become singularly important. As early as the middle of the fifteenth century a pitch of ability in this respect was reached which is, at times, surprising. But although the drawing of Francesco

Neroni: bellows.

di Giorgio is more diligent, more precise, as well as being stripped of unessential detail, he is nevertheless in the line of his immediate predecessors.

Thus this new outlook is not yet concerned with the overall and direct problems of this technology. It is more an extension of curiosity to embrace new and wider possibilities. The most important fact is certainly the attention which is beginning to be given to certain mathematical aspects. The connexion between technique and the scientific approach is still very loose, but many of our authors, such as Brunellesco, Fontana, and Alberti, were preoccupied with mathematical or physical science; the two whom we examined last were concerned with problems of pure geometry. This is a tendency that existed in the universities themselves. Arithmetic and geometry are no longer restricted to a narrow circle of initiates. The relationships between scientific ideas and the daily work of the technician became established only very slowly and with great difficulty and Leonardo himself was to see only the humble beginnings of this.

The most noticeable change is the appearance of a new type of man, still only incompletely sketched out at the end of the second third of the fifteenth century. He did not appear in all his complexity until artillery became the dominant theme in military life. Francesco di Giorgio, in this sense, marks the turning point. Taccola was still what the middle ages called an 'engine master', an important and esteemed army auxiliary, but still occupying only a subsidiary position. On the other hand, Alberti, an architect and theoretician, is not properly speaking a technician and Bonaccorso Ghiberti is perhaps too exclusively a technician, concerned with precise and limited problems.

All the elements of the 'engineer' of the future existed but the conjunction had not yet occurred. Between 1465 and 1475 the world was to swing towards modernity. This is thoroughly implicit in the work of Francesco di Giorgio Martini, who stands exactly at the turning point.

Chapter 5: Francesco di Giorgio Martini

All that were needed to co-ordinate these various tendencies were men of more powerful personality, of more universal mind, and of yet more wider-ranging curiosity. The last quarter of the fifteenth century saw these men emerge, at the very moment when western Europe was finding some kind of new balance. Nothing, however, would have been possible without the immense labour of preceding generations. Long relegated to the background, where if not quite forgotten he was at least neglected, Francesco di Giorgio Martini has recently come into his own. His artistic ability has been honoured, important works marking essential moments in the art of this epoch restored to him. He has recently been so highly praised as an architect that things are now attributed to him which he could never, perhaps, have done. As an engineer he has not been neglected to the same extent: works in this sphere have emphasized his role in the development of fortification and artillery and there are also his achievements in the field of water supply. As a machine-maker he has been more neglected, overshadowed as he no doubt was by the great figure of Leonardo who borrowed so much from him; in order to rehabilitate the Sienese it has been necessary to some degree to belittle the reputation of the Florentine. Despite these new contributions to our knowledge of Francesco di Giorgio, his written work is still insufficiently known: his treatise was published towards the middle of the nineteenth century in an incomplete and faulty version, so that we have only an unauthoritative and partial text. We have attempted a new classification of the manuscripts, an essential prelude to serious study and eventual publication.

The role of Siena in technical progress had been important. If its old rivalry with its more powerful neighbour, Florence, had contributed to the development of military art, it is certain that other techniques had not been neglected. It would be surprising if Taccola had not left pupils; the reputation he enjoyed, during the entire period at the end of the fifteenth century, shows, if demonstration be necessary, the influence that he must have exercised. But once again the connexions are difficult to establish. Francesco di Giorgio knew the work of Taccola, but it is possible that he was not his immediate successor.

A few names have come down to us of interesting engineers who have unfortunately not left any written work and whose achievement has not yet attracted the curiosity of historians. As a typical example we would mention Lorenzo di Pietro, called Il Vecchietto (1412–1480), who began as a sculptor and perhaps a founder. He met Donatello in Siena in 1457. Towards the end of his life, between 1467 and 1470, he became an architect and builder of fortresses. He built some of the most remarkable fortresses of this period, at Sartaneo, Orbetello, Monte Argentoli, Talamone, and Montacuto. Lorenzo di Pietro was undoubtedly one of the masters of Francesco di Giorgio.

Francesco, son of Giorgio, grandson of Martini, was baptized at Siena on 23 September 1439. We know practically nothing about his origins except that he must have come of a modest family, but perhaps not of such humble parentage as Taccola. His apprenticeship must have been similar to that of all artists of the period, and, by more or less subtle comparisons, art historians have discovered his masters. Thus he may have studied painting and sculpture at Orvieto with Angelino da Fiesole. He certainly collaborated with Lorenzo di Pietro, who was in a position to give him wider knowledge, greater curiosity, and more varied abilities.

From 1458 to 1464 Francesco di Giorgio worked in Turin and made his first journey to Rome. Some historians have believed that the first draft of the treatise, or at of least some of its sections, probably those that deal with architecture proper, may date from this period. Francesco di Giorgio thus appears to have been an architect. In order to live more comfortably he always practised sculpture. A payment of 1464, which has been preserved, shows that he carried out such work, especially for religious communities or for the cathedral of Siena. He married twice, in 1467 and in 1469.

On 28 April 1469 he was entrusted, jointly with a certain Paolo d'Andrea, with maintaining the water-supply, fountains, and aqueducts of the city of Siena. To have been given a task of such importance he must already have acquired a certain reputation as an engineer. It was under his direction that the fountain of the main square, which still exists, was erected. Unfortunately we possess no information about the activity of Francesco di Giorgio in this field; we shall see that numerous notes in his manuscripts relate to this aspect of engineering science, but do not provide any very precise indications.

In November 1477 the city of Siena authorized its engineer to accept an invitation from Federigo Montefeltre, Duke of Urbino, its traditional ally. This summons to Francesco di Giorgio was an indication of the reputation he had already acquired. It was certainly a piece of good fortune for him to be introduced into an environment where scientific, technical, and intellectual preoccupations were given first place. It is inconceivable that Francesco di Giorgio did not profit from the richly stocked library and the brilliant conversation at Urbino.

He had been invited to Urbino as an architect and military engineer. It is not our purpose to discuss here the attribution of certain monuments on which historians are not yet agreed. But we may well believe that before 1477 Francesco di Giorgio had already worked as an architect, perhaps in the cathedral of Siena, in those prodigious workshops in which generations of technicians were trained. The reputation of his master, Lorenzo di Pietro, was no doubt partly responsible for the Duke of Urbino's invitation.

A military architect at this period was not only a builder of fortresses, he also was expected to capture those of the enemy and was often in command of the trenches. Taccola had certainly been a fighting man and so was Francesco. That is why no military problem was new to them; and why they clung to those ancient traditions that we have tried to define. We also see the contemporary technician beginning to emerge. He began as a sculptor. When bronze statuary resumed its importance it was to his advantage to be a founder as well, at a moment when bronze artillery was being substituted for forged iron. So, being a maker of statues, he also became a maker of cannons. This last activity led him into the fighting forces, where he took part in sieges that required a number of other machines. Being both artist and military man, he thus naturally became an architect and builder of fortresses. Everything was now open to him, including organization of water-supplies and the arrangement of festivities. This man of the late fifteenth century had thus achieved the union of all traditions and his technique was universal.

The discovery of Roman antiquities, which had also been traditional for about fifty years, contact with scholars fond of experience and reality, the rubbing of shoulders with merchants busy perfecting their methods of calculation, an astonishing thirst for knowledge, interminable discussions, love of generalization, a taste for abstract concepts – these were the elements which were all to fuse in the same crucible.

When he arrived at Urbino, Francesco di Giorgio was undoubtedly more of a technician than a thinker, more of an artist than a scholar, and although he joined a highly intellectual circle it was mainly in the field of practical work that he began to develop. As early as 1478 he took part in his first military campaign, with Federigo Montefeltre. It was also as a military expert that he accompanied the Duke of Calabria from 1479 to 1480. On this occasion he went again to Rome.

His most fertile period falls between 1480 and 1486, when he lived in Urbino. He carried out, in the form of palaces and fortresses, a whole series of undertakings for which he is famous today, working for the successive dukes of Urbino: Federigo and his son Guidobaldo. If he did not build the whole of the palace of Urbino, recent research has shown that he must, at least, be credited with the Renaissance parts, which are so highly regarded, and which had hitherto been attributed to Luciano Laurana. We may still see, in the decoration of some of the rooms, bas-reliefs traditionally accepted as the work of Francesco di Giorgio, which represent engines of war, many of which are borrowed from the work of Valturio. Francesco di Giorgio also made some alterations to the ducal palace of Gubbio.

His military work, although it is less familiar and, no doubt, pleasing, is, all the same, of great importance. The attributions in this instance may be accepted with less caution. Francesco di Giorgio was, in fact, instructed to surround the city of Urbino with a series of fortresses intended to protect the approaches. A certain number of hill-tops are thus crowned with fortresses, now ruined, which were built to the plan and under the direction of the Sienese engineer. The finest are those of Mondavio, Mondolfo, Cagli, Sasso di Montefetto, Tavoletto, and Serra Sant'Abbondio. We shall return to these later.

In 1486 Francesco di Giorgio returned to his own country as an engineer with an incontestable reputation. He nevertheless continued to work for the Montefeltre, whose buildings he supervised. He also resumed his old artistic activity and painted and sculpted to order.

He had become an expert, and received summonses from all over Italy to give advice, plans, or consultations. Casole d'Elsa in 1487 and Lucignano in 1490 asked him for plans for their fortifications. In 1490 he participated in a kind of congress of architects and engineers meeting in order to complete the Duomo of Milan. He made the acquaintance there of a young engineer attached to the Sforza, whom he took to Parma where he had also been asked for consultation about the building of the cathedral. His name was Leonardo da Vinci. At the end of the same year Francesco di Giorgio gave Orsini drawings for the fortress of Campagnano. In 1491 he was at the court of Naples. In the same period he carried out the detailed plans for the façade of the cathedral of Siena. We know little about the end of his life as we know little about his work, despite the intensive research that has been carried out. He died in 1502, presumably in Siena. We only have one great work written by Francesco di Giorgio, the treatise on civil and military architecture which he composed in imitation of many of his predecessors. Although the architectural and military section has been known since it was published by Promis in the middle of the nineteenth century, the highly important mechanical part has always been neglected.

We have little information about the origin of the treatise. It is possible, and certain texts appear to show this, that it was begun before Francesco went to Urbino. It was certainly finished in this city, between 1470 and 1480. It was dedicated to the Duke Federigo di Montefeltre. According to one tradition, a manuscript in the Siena Library (S IV 4) is a draft of the treatise. A careful study of the manuscript, which has never been published, is required before this can be established with certainty. There exists in the Vatican a working notebook (Cod. Urban. 1557), similar to many engineers' notebooks, which appears to be by Francesco di Giorgio; it contains mainly designs of machines and artillery. Another collection, preserved in Florence in the Biblioteca Nazionale (Cod. Palat. 767), has many drawings of machines which are undoubtedly the work of Francesco di Giorgio, together with other unpublished drawings: it is possible that this work is no more than a compilation. Francesco di Giorgio's notebook preserved in the Uffizi (Architectural Designs, 318 to 337) in Florence is mainly concerned with architecture.

There are a number of manuscripts of the treatise itself, some of which are incomplete. A classification of these will be found in the Appendix. Three of them appear to be contemporary, four others later. One of these is of exceptional interest: it is the Ashburnham manuscript in the Laurenziana at Florence (Ashburnham 361), an incomplete manuscript of the treatise, comprising essentially the mechanical part of the work; this manuscript has marginal annotations by Leonardo da Vinci, which led to the belief, long held, that he was the author.

Many of the manuscripts contain only the drawings of the treatise without any text. This shows, or appears to show, that the interest lay in the drawings rather than in the text, which was not, perhaps, of any great originality. Nevertheless it would be most desirable to have a text that is properly and fully edited. Now that the manuscripts are known, work on them should be relatively easy.

The treatise of Francesco di Giorgio has three very different sections. There is, first of all, a treatise on architecture, similar in broad outline to the works we have already noted. It is followed by a treatise on fortification, much more highly developed than the few notes that we find in Alberti or in Il Filarete: it is the first work on the art of fortification that has come down to us. Finally, there is a treatise on machines, which is more a theatre of machines than a true treatise, and which deserves much more consideration than the oblivion in which it has been left.

Drawn up in the pattern of previous works, the resemblance between each of which we have already emphasized, the treatise on architecture and town planning is within this tradition, with a few innovations. It has already been noted that the ideas of Francesco di Giorgio were closely related to those of Vitruvius and to spontaneous mediaeval practice. Not one but two cities are examined in the treatise. After having surveyed the siting of the city with regard to water, wind, and terrain, Francesco admits that the plan of a city has to be adapted to the site and that the main preoccupation of the architect must be to make the best of the terrain which is given to him. Parallel with this empiricism, there is the ideal city, situated on even ground. Francesco now pleads for a concentric plan, a city in the form of an octagon, with a central square, also octagonal, from which there radiate eight roads leading to the gates of the city. The choice of terrain is essential: the author insists upon this, he requires that it should neither be ore-bearing nor bituminous but close to sources of drinking water, avoiding low-lying and unhealthy sites. He follows the prescriptions of Vitruvius who advised the choice of land on which sheep prospered, a sure sign of its healthiness.

Like Alberti, Francesco devotes a few pages to building materials. These pages provide precise information since they offer an appreciation of the stone of a large number of quarries, of which many are situated in the environs of Urbino. Francesco, like Alberti, is also interested in timber and in wooden buildings and he gives illustrations which are very similar to those of his illustrious predecessor.

The Sienese architect then deals with two different types of building. His remarks about private dwellings and how they should be fitted up, the position of staircases, chimneys, store-rooms or cellars (the wine cellar to the north, the oil cellar to the south), are not, perhaps, very original but they are very complete. These plans deal especially with the *palazzo*, with interior courts, covered

Francesco di Giorgio: mine showing powder and various instruments.

galleries, and all the luxury that the aristocratic classes or the richest merchants could afford. There is no space, either here or elsewhere, devoted to the more humble dwellings about which we would like to know. The proportions of the rooms are borrowed from Vitruvius. The stables are a description of those at Urbino. The gardens are symmetrical and geometric, with fountains, arbours, and hedges: it is quite the garden *à la française*, which later flourished and became popular in the manner that we all know.

The *palazzo pubblico* must be situated in the main square. Its approaches must be free and unencumbered and it must have only one doorway, in the interests of security. And Francesco adds: 'I am of the opinion that *palazzo pubblico* should be constructed like a fortress, in anticipation of popular risings and of the inconstancy of events.' The interior courtyard has porticos like the palace of Urbino.

Although the military architecture of Francesco di Giorgio marks a certain development, and although he offers certain new ideas, his style is nevertheless not very revolutionary. The treatise gives us the plan and sometimes a drawing of about sixty citadels of triangular, heptagonal, hexagonal, pentagonal shape: some are even rhomboid, which appears to be the author's favourite form. But he adds that the security of the fortress depends more on artifice than on its shape or the thickness of its walls. Although the fortresses of Francesco di Giorgio no longer look like mediaeval fortresses, they are not yet like modern ones. They were to influence strongly those who, like Leonardo da Vinci or the San Gallo, were entrusted with building similar ones. Crenellated towers, machicolated walls, the existence of a keep, the entire general disposition, except the height of the walls, appears mediaeval in spirit. There were, nevertheless, certain new elements.

It is obvious that the walls have been made lower; this does not yet, however, lead to a new conception of fortification. Towers and walls are still machicolated, a relic of mediaeval techniques. Although in Francesco's drawings the outlines of the surrounding walls betray more imagination than sense of reality, it should be mentioned, since this is his main innovation, that he produced a design for a tenaille bastion. This idea, as we shall see, was to be followed up in the first half of the sixteenth century.

We know the castles built by Francesco di Giorgio. They follow a tradition which was already ancient when they were built, which is represented at the beginning of the fifteenth century by such edifices as the Rocca di Forlì and the Rocca di Lugo. We recognize in these ruins the very appearance of Francesco di Giorgio's drawings; and we shall do so right up to the castle of Ostia. The transformation is very slow, despite the imagination of the engineers. Other countries may have developed differently, sometimes more rapidly and sometimes not at all. We shall return to this topic.

In the same way, and it would be surprising if it were otherwise, Francesco di Giorgio's artillery always remains highly traditional. The shift from iron artillery to bronze artillery is barely noted. Nevertheless, it is known, if only from drawings of Pisanello (1377–1455), that the latter had made its appearance with all its rich Renaissance decoration. Florence, at about the same period, employed the services of renowned artists to cast its cannons: these included Simone dal Colle, Maso di Bartolomeo, and Michelozzo Michelozzi: the latter was an architect, sculptor and goldsmith and worked with Ghiberti and Donatello. The drawings of Francesco di Giorgio are still closely related to those of Taccola. From certain sketches, however, it may be guessed that a transformation is taking place. Leonardo da Vinci himself does not mark much progress. It seems that in this respect the Italians were somewhat backward; this explains to some extent the rapid successes of the French armies which descended upon Italy in the last years of the fifteenth century. Francesco di Giorgio fits perfectly into a military tradition, one stage of which had been marked in his time by Taccola. We shall find again in this great Sienese engineer the trebuchets and all the defensive and escalading equipment, the ladders, the assault towers, the engines for forcing barriers, the chariots, and mobile shelters, which are, perhaps, the last manifestations of the tradition which we outlined at the beginning of this study.

Francesco di Giorgio was incontestably more original as a designer of machines. This field probably offers more scope to the imagination. Perhaps also the designs are rather an expression of hopes than actual achievements. The richness and the diversity of mechanical combinations caught the attention of all the engineers of the period. They take on, with Francesco di Giorgio, an importance that is not found in his immediate predecessors and which will not cease to develop from that point onwards.

The sources of power are always the same: it could not possibly have been otherwise. Hand machines and the utilization of human and animal energy still exist in the work of Francesco di Giorgio, but less frequently, perhaps, than previously. Windmills are rare and of little mechanical interest. We would mention, however, the windmill machines, mounted on rollers, which are the earliest records of windmills with revolving roofs, placed in a brickwork foundation. We do not find here the enormous wooden tripod mills,

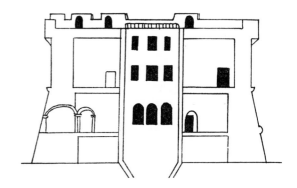

Section of the San Michele tower at Ostia by Michelangelo.

which were common with the Germans. The main source of energy must have been running water.

We should note Francesco's desire to make the best use of it. His attempts are still clumsy, his solutions incomplete, but his research is interesting. It was not, however, systematic. It was rather a matter of chance if a new form appeared or a new idea emerged. His interest at first was concentrated on the shape of the vanes of the mill wheels. Francesco di Giorgio usually used overshot wheels, which is natural in a country where the water supply is irregular and may cease altogether. The vanes were curved so as to form receptacles, which added to the force of the current, which was probably feeble, and the weight of the water was thus retained on the vanes.

The other interesting idea is to lead the water on to the wheel in a conduit and not in a free fall. It is the first indication that we have of this technique, which appears to be new. Francesco di Giorgio goes even further, since he appears to understand that there exists a relationship between the section of the conduit and the motive force. The end of his conduits appear always to be formed of a tapering section. Unfortunately we possess no accurate text which would enable us to comment correctly on these drawings. It appears, however, to be impossible, since the drawing is repeated, to deny that this is the effect intended. There is, however, nothing to prove that this technique was in fact employed.

This latter innovation probably led Francesco di Giorgio to imagine another position for his wheel. No doubt discussions will continue for a long time to come as to whether primitive mills had horizontal or vertical wheels. The former eliminate transmission gears, since it is possible to fit the millstone directly on to the axle of the motor wheel. The latter appear to be more logical. Although all early drawings of mills, from the tenth to the fifteenth century, show vertical wheels and Vitruvius himself mentions only these, it is known that in certain regions, at a date very difficult to establish precisely, there were horizontal wheels; this is true of the region occupied by present-day Yugoslavia, the south of France, and Scandinavian countries. These were perhaps not so much proper wheels but simple blades fixed directly on to the motor axle. The yield of these wheels is less than that of vertical wheels.

The difficulties of horizontal wheels can be resolved in part by devising suitable means for forcing the water through. And we see in the notebooks of Francesco di Giorgio, perfectly conceived and shown, the hydraulic turbine which has been attributed to Leonardo da Vinci, who made some very imprecise drawings of it. However, we have no example of the employment of the process at this time.

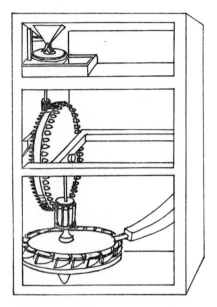

Francesco di Giorgio: hydraulic turbine.

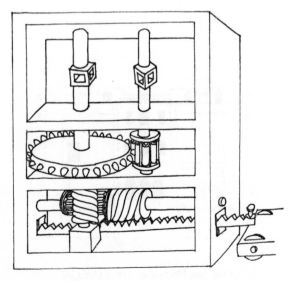

Francesco di Giorgio: types of gears.

The problem of the transmission and the transformation of motion must inevitably have interested the Sienese engineer. It is, indeed, the essential question in any advanced mechanism. The demultiplication of forces, much used in all the apparatus required by architects and engineers, was already widely known and Francesco di Giorgio only adopted the old solutions to this problem.

Gearing constituted another, by no means trifling, difficulty in this survey of generalized machinery. A large part of the difficulty probably was the problem of materials, to which Francesco di Giorgio appears to have been less sensitive than Leonardo. He gives, however, unremitting attention to the transmission of motion in different planes, already realized in the system of toothed-wheels and lantern-wheels. His designs in this respect are a little lacking in precision. He is clearly looking for the present solution of pinions that together form a right angle. He fails to find it because he does not think of making them, as they are made today, of metal.

It is the same preoccupation that leads to the search for a mechanism that will permit variations of speed. Lantern-wheels and truncated cones, cleverly arranged, provide a solution, a poor one it is true, but practicable. Francesco di Giorgio made much use of screw and rack systems. By combining these various types of transmission, he undoubtedly achieved very surprising results.

He was too good a mechanic not to profit from the connecting-rod and crank idea, which was undoubtedly already widely used in his time. It was too badly needed to be neglected. The designs that he gives us of suction and pressure pumps, of a hydraulic saw, show that he came up against the same difficulties as his predecessors, that is to say, the impossibility of correctly putting his designs into practice. Only the development of metallurgy, the turning of metal, and the use of lubricants would have permitted him to achieve a proper application of these ideas.

While he was using this idea, with all its inevitable inadequacies, particularly in the link between rod and crank, Francesco di Giorgio could not ignore the problems it presented. That of the two dead centres had already been resolved by using a flywheel which we find here once again. But the flywheel, since it must not be too heavy and thus brake the movement, was insufficient to regularize the motion, this being especially desirable in hand-operated machines. And there is no doubt that here we have the most astonishing idea of the Sienese inventor: the ball governor, which at its final stage of development, was one of the achievements of Watt, three centuries later. The design, which we reproduce, proves in any case that Francesco di Giorgio was perfectly aware of the goal that he wished

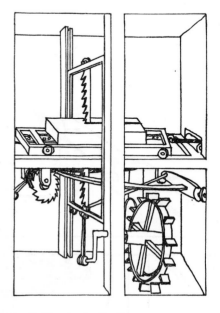

Francesco di Giorgio: hydraulic saw.

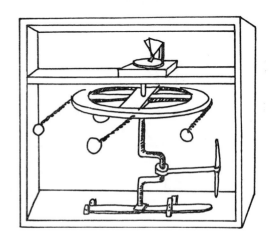

Francesco di Giorgio: handmill with ball governor.

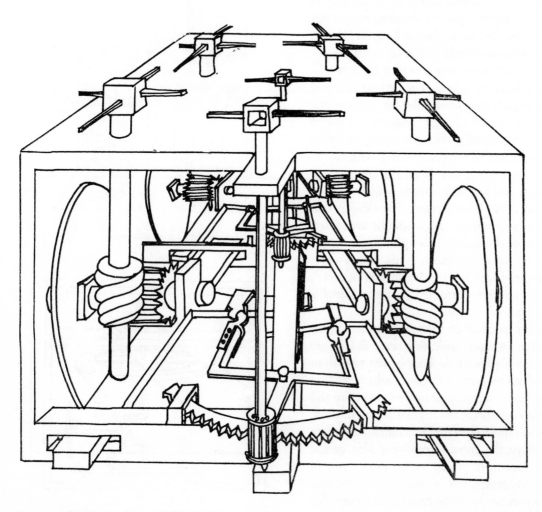

Francesco di Giorgio: 'automobile' vehicle.

to reach and of the means to be employed. This represents an intellectual effort which gives us the measure of the mechanical imagination of its author.

Francesco di Giorgio was certainly an inventor of talent. This is shown quite clearly in some of his achievements, such as the one which might be called the 'automobile'. These designs are surprisingly precise and were subsequently taken up by others. It appears to be the mechanism for a festival chariot, the motor of which is constituted by gears moved by hand by means of a kind of capstan. The engine was presumably very heavy and it was therefore necessary to transmit the drive to a number of the wheels. We have several variants of this project: machines with three wheels, the front wheel being the one for steering, machines with four wheels, with four-wheel drive. The steering element is formed by a lantern-wheel which engages with a ratchet; this works two rods fixed to the axles of the wheels. Francesco di Giorgio's final idea was to give the wheels the properties both of steering and drive: this is a kind of distant ancestor of our front-wheel drive. One glance at this drawing is enough to show not only its extreme clarity, far superior to Leonardo's drawings of machines which are always more or less led astray by his sense of form, but also the mechanical subtleties which are brought into play. It is true that this apparatus is reminiscent of some of the *jeux d'esprit* of the School of Alexandria, but we cannot fail to acknowledge the draughtsman's skill and the ingenuity of the designer.

Although a mechanic of talent and a valued builder of fortresses, Francesco di Giorgio was not, perhaps, a great engineer. We have seen his military weaknesses. We are not, of course, very well acquainted with his civil work. None of the drawings which deal with the channelling of water contains any novelties. His pumps are classic, scoop or ball pumps, suction and pressure pumps, using the rod and crank, the Archimedean screw, chain-pumps – all these were already known and used, as we have seen. There is nothing further on conduits themselves: the connected wooden pipes and the innumerable examples of siphons are always of the same type.

We would mention a few preoccupations which already figure in Alberti, although they lack the corresponding drawings and are not developed by him to the same extent as by Francesco di Giorgio. The problems of dykes, locks, and ports occupy a few pages of Francesco's treatise on architecture.

Some theoretical questions are also put to the engineer, who needed to find the answers. There is first the classic problem of the measurement of the height of a tower from the ground, a traditional problem, which recurs here, after Fontana, Taccola, Alberti, and his imitators. This practical geometry is also used by Francesco di Giorgio for wells, for the direction of underground work, tunnels, and galleries, both in mines and elsewhere. It is true that certain of his levelling techniques were ancient: the Greeks themselves had used them for some of their work. This is knowledge transmitted from generation to generation.

Francesco di Giorgio's 'machinery' is undoubtedly his greatest innovation: at all events, it is the most systematic. It can be clearly seen that in the case of some of these machines he wished to exhaust all possible solutions and combine all the mechanisms known to him. This is, perhaps, a little childish; we shall find a similar attitude in the 'Theatres of Machines' of the sixteenth century, in Ramelli for example. The example of grain mills is the most striking. About fifty drawings in his treatise are concerned with mills. The mill is obviously only a pretext to show slightly differing mechanisms, but the differences are sometimes very slight. He was certainly concerned rather to show that he knew all the possible solutions, the use of the different sources of power, the different positions of the water-wheel, gears, and transmission systems.

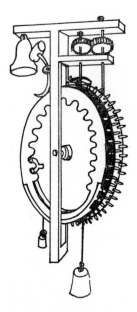

Francesco di Giorgio: striking mechanism for clock.

Hydraulic power is used to activate bellows, probably belonging to a metallurgical furnace, to pump water with suction and pressure pumps, and to drive a wood saw, which is clearly drawn. Water pumping is also carried out with chains of pots or by means of weights. There also exists a windmill which draws water which is then poured over the water-wheel of a grain mill. This simple fact shows that scientific reflection is not yet highly developed with Francesco di Giorgio.

Machines which an architect might need are fairly numerous. We would mention here that many of them were adopted by Leonardo da Vinci, to whom they were later credited. The problem of the transportation of heavy weights was, as we have seen, one of those that had already preoccupied the Greeks of the School of Alexandria. In the fifteenth century, as we have already remarked, success had been obtained in moving complete buildings. In Francesco di Giorgio's work machines are included for this purpose. They are generally winch or screw machines, with various systems for stepping down the power. Also to be found, as in his predecessors, are numerous examples of cranes, jacks, various kinds of lifting apparatus, all of which appear to have been in fairly common use at this period. There are also articulated systems, worked by screws, repeated in a number of examples.

Francesco di Giorgio: multiple position lifting apparatus.

The wider use of columns, which was one of the results of the return to antiquity, gave rise, as far as monoliths were concerned, to a somewhat delicate problem of how to put them into place. Francesco di Giorgio presents an apparatus for raising columns and a whole series of machines, all somewhat similar, in which the technical detail varies from one to the other. We see his desire to show off his ability and to prove that he has full knowledge of mechanisms. We show the drawing of one of these machines, which will enable us to dispense with describing the techniques in detail. Leonardo da Vinci made a number of copies of these machines.

The question of pile-driving is also an architectural one. The mechanism was simple and had no doubt been known for a long time. But Francesco di Giorgio added an ingenious system which enabled the work to be speeded up. The weight is pulled up by a hook so placed that when it comes to the top of the drive it automatically lets go the weight. With a double hook system the movement is continuous.

Public works are, perhaps, less well represented than in Leonardo. Francesco di Giorgio does not appear to have participated, at least not for any length of time, in the great works that have been mentioned earlier on. A dredger of quite simple design, and probably not very efficient, reminds us that ports hold an honourable place in his treatise. There are a fair number of notes on the sinking of wells, the digging of tunnels and of subterranean galleries. These are regarded more as problems of levelling or of direction than as the purely technical ones of the execution of the work itself. There is also the inevitable drawing of a diver which shows no great advance on the designs of his predecessors. Further examples of machines could be given since these are very numerous in the treatise, in the collections of drawings, and in the notebooks. The same desire to exhaust as it were all the mechanical possibilities of the same machine is everywhere obvious. To take only one example, this is the case with numerous paddle-wheels, or with the boats armed with hooks, points, or piercing devices for attacking enemy ships below the water line. Leonardo da Vinci was obviously to draw largely upon this arsenal.

To sum up his work, we might, perhaps, say that Francesco shows more artfulness than true mechanical genius.

There is no doubt that the San Gallo family belongs to the same school as Francesco di Giorgio: the links are evident, the influences are striking, and the preoccupations are identical. The father, Francesco Giamberti, worked in wood: he had been a cabinet-maker and a carpenter. He was probably also a mason and finished up by being an architect of repute, although not widely known. He worked

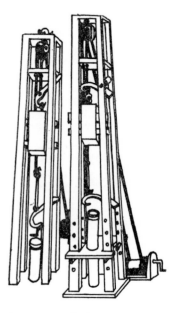

Francesco di Giorgio: pile drivers.

on the fortifications of Sarzana, Pietra Santa, and Sarzanello.

His eldest son, Giuliano di Francesco Giamberti, called Giuliano da San Gallo, appears to have been trained as an architect. He also was a sculptor in wood. In his early years he worked in the Roman workshops. In Venice in 1464 he cut the travertine blocks for the Doge's Palace and made the window-frames, fire-places, and cornices. At the Vatican, in 1470, he took part in the building of three tiers of loggias. He left Rome in 1471.

From this time onwards he must also have taken part in works of fortification and perhaps even in military campaigns. At all events, he entered Florentine service and soon that of Lorenzo de'Medici, to whom his family remained attached. In 1478 Giuliano della Rovere, on behalf of Pope Sixtus IV, laid siege to the town of Castellina. He was accompanied by Francesco di Giorgio and the Duke of Urbino. The Florentines entrusted the defence of the place to Giuliano da San Gallo, who was forced to consent to an honourable capitulation. This was no doubt the first meeting between the two engineers.

Giuliano da San Gallo's great military achievement is the fortress of Ostia, which commanded the entrance to the Tiber and the building of which had been ordered by Cardinal della Rovere, titular head of the episcopal see of Ostia. The plan is preserved in the Municipal Library of Siena among the architect's papers. It belongs to a period of transition between the ancient forms and the new techniques that were to see the light of day some decades later. At all events it accurately represents the type of fortress which Francesco di Giorgio described in his treatise on architecture. It is a wide triangle with circular bastions at the extremities. The old mediaeval tower has been preserved; placed at the most acute angle of the triangle it serves as a keep to the fortress, and is protected by a bastion at an angle and slightly bevelled (tenaille bastion). There are only very slight differences between the designs of Francesco di Giorgio and the citadel of Ostia.

Giuliano da San Gallo returned to Florence in 1485 and seems to have devoted himself exclusively to military affairs. In 1486 he took part in the siege of Poggio Imperiale and restored the fortress of Poggibonzi. In 1487 he directed the attack on Sarzana and restored it after the assault. In the same year he also worked on the fortifications of Perugia. In 1496 he journeyed to the south of France and brought back a number of interesting drawings. The remainder of his life was taken up with works of religious or civil architecture, interrupted by sieges, and repairs to various fortresses. He is to be found at the siege of Pisa in 1509 and at Mirandola in 1511.

It is curious to note that Francesco di Giorgio, who, in his treatise,

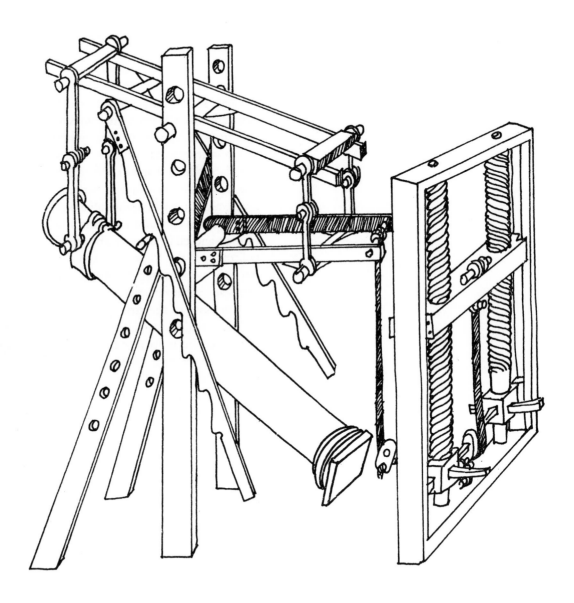

Francesco di Giorgio: column raising machine.

had initiated the development of fortifications, was much more timid in his practical achievements, which continue to bear the marks of an almost mediaeval tradition. It is without doubt at Ostia that we find the most perfect application of the rules which appear in Francesco's treatise. This was the starting point for the transformations that were to lead to the modern systems of fortification.

Giuliano da San Gallo was also, of necessity, a mechanic. His notebooks prove that he had borrowed nearly all his machinery from Francesco di Giorgio. The collection of machines in the Vatican, or at least those pages which are devoted to this aspect of the engineer's art, consists almost exclusively of copies of machines by Francesco di Giorgio: machines for carrying heavy weights, including whole buildings, ships with paddle-wheels, etc. As we know, in the year 1504 Florence decided to erect Michelangelo's *David* in the place where it stands today. It was therefore necessary to transport from the workshop of Santa Maria del Fiore, no mean distance away, a marble of considerable weight. The work was entrusted to the brothers Giuliano and Antonio da San Gallo who devised the capstan and endless screw apparatuses such as are to be found in the collection at the Vatican and in the works of Francesco di Giorgio. An enormous crowd assembled to witness this work. On 14 May 1504 at midnight, the moving of the statue began amidst the acclamations of the crowd. It arrived at its final site four days later.

Giuliano da San Gallo had also participated in certain hydraulic operations, in particular in the region of Cortona. But there is not much information on this work, which shows, nevertheless, that Giuliano da San Gallo was one of those versatile engineers such as appeared during the Renaissance.

The direct pupils of Francesco di Giorgio have perhaps left fewer records than the San Gallo who, although not his pupils, were strongly influenced by him. Giacomo di Bartolomeo di Marco Cuzarelli (1453–1515) worked with his master at Urbino. Baccio Pontelli (born at Florence in 1450) also began as a joiner before becoming an architect. He also worked at Urbino under the direction of Francesco di Giorgio and then went to the citadel of Ostia, the building of which has even been attributed to him. He was also at the fortresses or the fortifications of Osimo, Jesi and at the port of Civitavecchia.

Antonio da San Gallo (1455–1534) worked a great deal with his brother Giuliano to whom he acted, as it were, as understudy. Very often the elder began operations which the younger continued and completed. He lived longer than his brother, so that he was able to mark the passage from ancient methods to new techniques. He worked at Castel Sant'Angelo in Rome, where he apparently began raising the walls and enlarging the moats at the approach of the French armies in 1493. He then altered the fortresses of Civita-castellana, the castle of Nepi, and the fortifications of Leghorn (1499–1504).

By 1515 he had almost completed the restoration of the citadel of Civitavecchia begun in 1508. This is a pentagon with bastions and projecting towers. The citadel of Caprarola, which dates from 1515, certainly marks the turning point which is usually held to date from the bastions of Verona, executed in 1527 by San Michele. Caprarola was still in the shape of a pentagon, like nearly all the fortresses of the San Gallo, with triangular projections at each angle. We have here the tenaille profile of modern fortifications.

Between 1519 and 1532 Antonio da San Gallo is to be found at Montefiascone, at Parma, where he worked with San Michele, at Piacenza, at Ancona, at Nepi, at Ascoli, and finally at Rome. In 1527 he added the triangular bastions to Castel Sant'Angelo, which still exist and which give it a very modern appearance. The citadel of Del Basso, constructed at Florence in 1534 just before Antonio's death, shows the full transition to modern fortification.

The nephew of the two San Gallo, Antonio the younger, continued this tradition, and took part in numerous works of fortification and in hydraulic operations. We are now, however, no longer at the turning point but already squarely within the modern period.

We have seen Antonio da San Gallo the elder taking part with his brother in the moving of the statue of *David* in Florence. But, unlike his brother, he left no collection in which these machines are shown. Architects have ceased to be mechanical engineers. It would appear that a certain specialization has taken place.

Thus is demonstrated the undoubted influence of Francesco di Giorgio. It is necessary to establish his position in the development that we are attempting to reconstitute. A direct successor of Taccola, Francesco di Giorgio represents the typical engineer of the Renaissance. An artist, who began as a sculptor, he soon became a caster, a gun-maker, and consequently a military engineer. All these activities led him to the mechanical problems that so much interested or amused the people of this period.

Although he was a member of the circles fostered by the brilliant court of Urbino, he may not have profited from this to the full. He remained too much the engineer, too good a mechanic to be able to deal with problems other than in purely practical terms. He was not cut out as a scholar and nothing in his treatise or in his notes appears

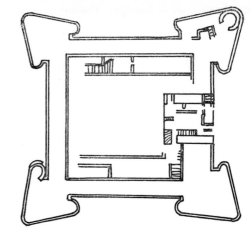

Fortress of Nettuno (1501–2).

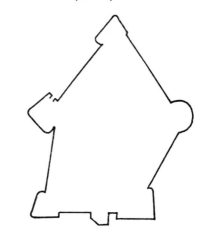

Fortress of Civitacastellana (1494–7).

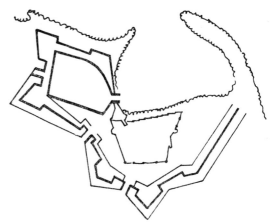

Fortress of Civitavecchia (1515).

to show the slightest curiosity of a general kind, such as was to make for the reputation of Leonardo da Vinci.

His pupils maintained the same tendency and were subject to the same limits. They were, as it were, too specialized in their work as architects or military engineers at the very moment when scientific humanism was opening up far wider horizons. Perhaps they should have had less success in their careers and less work to do. It may be said that, unlike Leonardo da Vinci, they had no time to read and they did not study the manuscripts of Archimedes. Practitioners rather than humanists, engineers rather than artists, they could not disengage themselves from a craft that was too absorbing.

The San Gallo, although they were not the direct heirs of Francesco di Giorgio, were subject to the same influences. This may be sensed in their art, which becomes a little cold and is an architect's rather than a painter's art. They are easily overshadowed by Bramante or Michelangelo.

The following generations soon lost part of the activity of their predecessors. Fortification and mechanics rapidly became the province of specialists. The architect remains an architect and no more. These various activities were occasionally to be reunited in one man, but the bond was to be tenuous and incidental. Galileo, who was a mechanic, was never an architect.

Leonardo da Vinci – we have been constantly tempted to invoke his name. We have come close to him on many occasions and yet each time we have pushed him away. Now we must try to bring him to life.

Already, probably, we have acquired a clearer picture of him. His environment seems to be better defined, its contours more precise. We know the hopes of all these men, their major preoccupations and also the limitations of their thought. They exist on a level which is not that of pure technique, which has few connexions with industrial techniques or with techniques in common use. They are concerned with these only indirectly, through the use of mechanisms which they borrow from around them. Coming from different quarters of the globe, they have gradually acquired a kind of uniform education to which is added the whole movement of ideas stirring in western Europe. They take these disparate, sometimes contradictory, elements and try to fuse them into a synthesis, though this remains imperfect. The taste for power over nature, of which men have now become aware, and a mania for disputation, no doubt a distant legacy of scholasticism, are both mingled in the minds of these technocrats of the Renaissance.

Leonardo da Vinci fits perfectly into this environment. There is perhaps no need to recall predecessors he may never have read, but whose ideas are not unfamiliar; there is no need either to believe in a genius of infinite inventiveness, because in this field, as in others, there are notions which float in the air, successes which become topics of discussion and instructive set-backs. Icarus did not think of the melting point of wax, Elmer of Malmesbury, in the eleventh century, had forgotten the tail. Even if Bacon was somewhat sceptical, many had already flown, at least in spirit, before this last quarter of the fifteenth century. And there must be many other facts of which we know nothing.

Some would say that the 'climate' was favourable, but the period was equally propitious for the dreams of some and the ambitions of others. At a time when the engineer becomes pre-eminent and technology supremely important, the Jules Vernes of the day write works which others seek to illustrate. Very often, and this is true of the period that interests us, we have no novels, but drawings have come down to us, or at least the sketches for the drawings. And one must surely not be tempted to take too literally these imaginative products of a time when men were beginning to think that everything was possible. The idea of progress, which perhaps is imperfectly expressed, impressed itself on the mind. These engineers' notebooks express a very obvious faith in techniques.

No doubt it is somewhat pretentious and vain to wish to return to the case of Leonardo da Vinci when so much celebrated work and patient research has been done. And this aim will appear even more surprising after further affirmations of our shortcomings and new examples of our incomprehension. But this essay on the engineers of the Renaissance would have appeared singularly incomplete if we had not at least recalled the figure of this great Florentine. We have wished to proceed with extreme care and within the narrowest limits of our subject. It is useful to recall the story of Leonardo da Vinci from this angle; we shall see him emerge as the very type of the engineer, as he will appear to us from now on. Without recalling in detail the 'career' of Leonardo, it seems worth while to underline a few facts that will enable us to place him more accurately in the environment to which a number of his predecessors have belonged. For the analogies are striking.

Leonardo was the illegitimate son of a man of good family, born in 1452 at Vinci, in the heart of Tuscany, and hence somewhat younger that Francesco di Giorgio, but exactly contemporary with his pupils. There is no doubt that Leonardo received a much more careful education than many others. This 'unlettered' man was certainly not illiterate. One only has to look at his writing which is neat and practised, rapid and certain. Shaky spelling shows, however, that there were gaps in this education: in any case it was not a university one. He showed such talent when he was still very young that in 1466 he was taken to Florence where he entered the workshop of Verrocchio (1435-88). The latter was a sculptor, painter, and founder and although not, perhaps, an artist of genius, he was a professional and appears to have trained excellent pupils. He seems to have begun as a goldsmith. As a sculptor he had to conform with

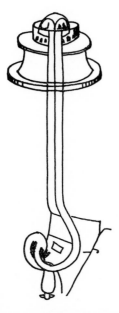

Leonardo da Vinci: underwater breathing apparatus.

casting techniques of a time when bronze was fashionable. He had travelled, been to Rome, before returning to work in Florence for the Medici. His fame was appreciated by Matthias Corvinus, the King of Hungary, who, as we have seen, was interested in technical writings. Verrocchio's culture must have been wide and it is known that he took part in some of the discussions presided over by Alberti.

It will always be one of the most serious gaps in our knowledge that we know nothing of the stages of the education that was given in these workshops. It was certainly not a strictly professional education whatever else it was. Many artists from this time onwards studied the sciences as a kind of auxiliary subject in connexion with their artistic apprenticeship; these included anatomy and the problems of perspective. They also had to familiarize themselves with precise techniques, in particular those of casting and as well as casting statues or bells they might also cast guns. And no doubt it was easy for this assembly of young people to escape the strict discipline of the workshops. We have the example of the previous generation, that of Francesco di Giorgio: artists had become famous engineers and treatises were being printed, the manuscripts of which must have circulated widely in all these circles.

The moment had come, as we have seen, when mathematics appeared to be the key to all practical problems and to the technical problems that faced artists as well as engineers. Some elementary knowledge could be acquired in the abacus schools which were then becoming more numerous. Leonardo, according to Segescu, acquired a knowledge of algorism during his apprenticeship in Verrocchio's workshop. Leonardo quotes two Florentine exponents of abacus, Paolo Toscanelli del Pazzo and Leonardo Chernionese. Luca Pacioli had followed the same route: we have already stated that part of his *Summa de matematica* came from an abacus manual. Leonardo appears to refer to the *Nobel opera de aritmetica*, by Piero Borgi, printed in Venice in 1484, which well represents the science of these schools.

An unlettered man, assuredly. Leonardo's knowledge, when he left the workshop, does not constitute an organized system such as is required at a university, and contacts with enlightened circles in Milan showed him all the gaps in his education. But nor is it the knowledge of a self-educated man. It was a practical education, which included a smattering of everything, perhaps superficial, no doubt distorted, and certainly badly assimilated. Men educated in this way were ready to quote authors whom they had never read and to pride themselves on resembling certain heroes of antiquity. And there was no better model for these engineers than Archimedes.

Taccola had already acquired the nickname of the Sienese Archimedes. Alberti had spoken of him, and Toscanelli, the abacus master, taught him by means of the Latin translations, which were not very accurate, of Gerardo of Cremona. Although Euclid was not used, at least fragments of his work were known.

Leonardo joined the corporation of painters in 1472 and appears to have stayed in Verrocchio's workshop until 1476. Although he carried out a very few paintings to order, Leonardo almost at once showed himself to be an engineer. In 1478 he offered to raise the octagonal church of San Giovanni of Florence, the present Baptistry, without causing any damage, in order to add a sub-foundation with steps; we know this to have been one of the favourite problems of our engineers. Leonardo, the principal trait of whose character appears to have been curiosity, an almost morbid curiosity which made him unstable, already possessed, in common with all the artists among his contemporaries, extensive but incomplete, diverse but uncertain, knowledge. He also had a craft: he was probably clever with his hands, attentive to questions of material, and already aware of techniques, that is to say of engineering techniques.

Up to 1482 we do not know much about Leonardo's activity. He did not practise much as an artist and, as far as we know, he did not use his technical knowledge. We may suppose that he was interested in all that was published: Valturio in 1472, Pliny in 1476, Petrus de Crescentiis, the agricultural economist, in 1478, in Florence, the *Sphaero mundi* by Sacrobosco in Ferrara in 1472, Frontinus in Rome in 1480, to mention only the authors cited by Leonardo himself. His first technical drawings are from this period.

In 1482 he was called to Milan by Ludovico Sforza, not as a painter, but as a sculptor and founder. His reputation in this domain must thus have been well established. He was required to execute the statue in bronze of Francesco Sforza, which in fact he never cast. But when he arrived in Milan, Leonardo showed a different side of himself. It is difficult to say whether the famous letter in the *Codex Atlanticus* is really by him, and whether it was ever sent. We must perhaps grant this, since other facts later on confirm, at least in part, Leonardo's wish to be an engineer as well. This text should be read after a re-reading of that of Roger Bacon: the similarities are striking; apart from a few differences, the tone is identical. We could, with Leonardo's text in our hands, resume our perusal of all the notebooks we have quoted: those of the Germans, of the first Italians, from Kyeser to Taccola; all the subject-headings are there and any of the drawings could illustrate it. We are thus well within the line of tradition: the plan, the curiosities, the investigations are still the same.

'Most Illustrious Lord, having now sufficiently considered the specimens of all those who proclaim themselves skilled contrivers of instruments of war, and that the invention and operation of the said instruments are nothing different from those in common use: I shall endeavour, without prejudice to anyone else, to explain myself to Your Excellency showing Your Lordship my secrets, and then offering them to your best pleasure and approbation to work with effect at opportune moments on all those things which, in part, shall be briefly noted below.

(1) I have bridges of a sort extremely light and strong, adapted to be most easily carried, and with them you may pursue, and at any time flee from, the enemy; and others, secure and indestructible by fire and battle, easy and convenient to lift and place. Also methods of burning and destroying those of the enemy.

(2) I know how, when a place is besieged, to take the water out of the trenches, and make endless variety of bridges, and covered ways and ladders, and other machines pertaining to such expeditions.

(3) Item. If, by reason of the height of the banks, or the strength of the place and its position, it is impossible, when besieging a place, to avail oneself of the plan of bombardment, I have methods for destroying every rock or other fortress, even if it were founded on a rock, etc.

(4) Again I have kinds of mortars; most convenient and easy to carry; and with these can fling small stones almost resembling a storm; and with the smoke of these cause great terror to the enemy, to his great detriment and confusion.

(5) Item. I have means by secret and tortuous mines and ways, made without noise, to reach a designated spot, even if it were needed to pass under a trench or a river.

(6) Item. I will make covered chariots, safe and unattackable, which, entering among the enemy with their artillery, there is no body of men so great but they would break them. And behind these, infantry could follow quite unhurt and without any hindrance.

(7) Item. In case of need I will make big guns, mortars, and light ordnance of fine and useful forms, out of the common type.

(8) Where the operation of bombardment should fail, I would contrive catapults, mangonels, trebuchets and other machines of marvellous efficacy and not in common use. And, in short, according to the variety of cases, I can contrive various and endless means of offence and defence.

(9) And when the fight should be at sea I have kinds of many machines most efficient for offence and defence; and vessels which will resist the attack of the largest guns and powder and fumes.

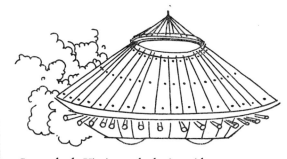

Leonardo da Vinci: assault chariot with guns.

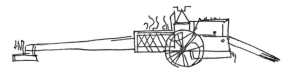

Leonardo da Vinci: super cannon.

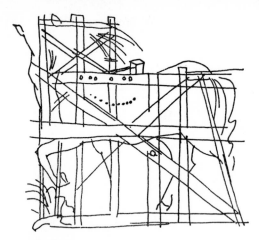

Leonardo da Vinci:
study for the casting of the horse of the Sforza statue.

(10) In time of peace I believe I can give perfect satisfaction and to the equal of any other in architecture and the composition of buildings public and private; and in guiding water from one place to another.

Item. I can carry out sculpture in marble, bronze, or clay, and also in painting whatever may be done, and as well as any other, be he whom he may be.

Again, the bronze horse may be taken in hand, which is to be to the immortal glory and eternal honour of the prince your father of happy memory, and of the illustrious house of Sforza.

And if any of the above-named things seem to anyone to be impossible or not feasible, I am most ready to make the experiment in your park, or in whatever place may please Your Excellency – to whom I commend myself with the utmost humility, etc.'

From now onwards Leonardo was to live and work as an engineer. His other activities appear to be little more than general curiosity, scholarly or artistic investigation. His drawing of flowers, his study of geology, his dissections and anatomical illustrations, are sure proofs of his interest in all that he studied with Verrocchio. Francesco di Giorgio also painted pictures. But Leonardo and he are engineers. Let us limit ourselves to understanding the engineer.

We know little about Leonardo's activities, although recent discoveries in archives show that our hypothesis is well founded. He is shown on the list of engineers of the Sforzas; when he was sent to Pavia he was styled *ingeniarius ducalis*. His talents as a draughtsman were also used, apart from the *Last Supper* which dates from his Milanese period. We have the evidence of Lomazzo to the fact that Leonardo executed for Gentile dei Borri, Ludovico's armourer, a series of drawings for studying methods of defence of horsemen and foot soldiers: some of these are in the Louvre and at the École des Beaux-Arts. Such collections, as we have said, were made at the same time, or even before, in southern Germany; there are some good examples in the Armeria in Vienna. A sheet of drawings in Venice shows complicated and decorative halbards which may have been projects for the ducal guard. At a time when ornamental arms, side-arms, and even pieces of artillery were highly prized, decorative motifs were often requested from artists. Francesco di Giorgio and Leonardo both produced examples.

Drawings, relatively numerous, from the Milanese period show that Leonardo was at that time interested in civil and military architecture. He probably worked in the open workshop of Milan, but he certainly did not have any great influence there. We know the engineers employed by Il Moro for the direction of his works. They were Bramante and Bertola da Navate; Leonardo may have occupied a secondary position. A sketch shows that he was, at all events, interested in the Sforza castle. We know that he took part a number of times in discussions or in competitions for the completion of the Duomo. Thus, in 1490, when Ludovico asked Siena to send him Francesco di Giorgio, the latter met Leonardo and later took him with him to Pavia together with Giovanni Amadeo and Luca Fancelli. Leonardo also had the opportunity of seeing Giuliano da San Gallo. Leonardo is thus mentioned, but his exact role, which was not that of architect in chief, remains obscure.

It is equally difficult to say whether Leonardo worked on the canals around Milan. Bertola da Navate, who was in charge, had drawn up the plans and was completing the diversion of the Martesana canal. Here again drawings show the attention that Leonardo gave to these, but he was certainly neither the instigator nor the main executor of the work. He may, to put a broad interpretation on certain hints in the *Leicester Codex*, have worked on the draining and reclaiming of the very insalubrious region of Vigevano. A document of 1498 names him as engineer in charge of operations on the rivers and canals. During the course of the same year he also probably assisted in the repairs to the mole at Genoa and the improvement of the citadel of Ivrea. All these fleeting and fragmentary notes appear to agree with one another. But we need further information.

Leonardo certainly contrived, probably with great success, those entertainments which delighted the men of the Renaissance. It was necessary to be a skilled and ingenious mechanic to regulate automata and water displays. In 1489, for the marriage of Gian Galeazzo Sforza and Isabella of Aragon, Leonardo was entrusted with the mechanical side of the entertainments. The heavenly regions were represented by a hemisphere dominated by the signs of the Zodiac. A machine made the seven planets sing and caused Apollo to appear and was thus both a reminiscence of Timaeus and the last flowering of the School of Alexandria.

This first Milanese period was certainly fertile as regards Leonardo's scientific curiosity. His scientific knowledge is exactly analogous to his technical culture. His attitude, notes Sergescu, is comparable to that of engineers who look not for absolute solutions, but for an approximation to truth which can be used without danger in practical applications. His calculations were and always remained very simple. His work on fractions was hesitant.

Milan, under the influence of the Sforza, was a brilliant city and Leonardo certainly gained much by frequenting the famous men and serious thinkers whom he was able to meet. Fazio Cardano, born in Milan in 1444, a jurist, father of the celebrated mathematician, commentator on Peckham's perspective, the second edition of which was published in 1490, was one of his friends and discussed with him the problems of perspective which were exciting scholars, artists, and engineers. Stefano Caponi was a doctor, enamoured of Euclid. Vicenzo Aliprando was an authority on Vitruvius. He used to consort with the two Marliani, sons of a doctor who died in 1482. In a note, Leonardo indicated what each of them had to offer: 'the algebra that the Marliani possess; a book dealing with Milan and its churches, may be obtained from the last bookshop on the way to Corduso: have Messer Fatio (Cardano) show you the book on proportions; have the friar from the Brera show you the *De ponderibus*; the book on proportions by Alchino, annotated by Marliano, belonging to Messer Fatio; the work by Giovanni Taverna which Messer Fatio possesses; a treatise on the celestial bodies by Aristotle, translated into Italian; try to see Vitolone, which is at the library of Pavia and deals with mathematics; a nephew of Gian Angelo, the painter, possesses a book on water which belonged to his father.' It was by meeting all these men who were concerned with new ideas as well as by being familiar with the work of their predecessors that Leonardo added to his knowledge. Much was still missing, the gaps remained serious, his ideas were often uncertain. It was always to be the same.

The weakness of Leonardo's texts as far as mechanics are concerned, the imprecision of the terms, the internal contradiction of certain propositions, have been emphasized. De Santillana thought, rightly, that Leonardo probably read less than he questioned or listened. Not only does he search for works, but he also has to have them explained to him. 'Ask brother John to show you the *De ponderibus*.' He noted everything, sometimes misunderstood and, concludes Santillana, because of this he was right in the end. At each difficulty he had to consult his friends, to work the problem out laboriously. He ignored important things and dwelt on obscure and irrelevant points. His sure instinct saved him and his intuition guided him to results which 'Galileo, encumbered with all his old books, would take thirty years to discover'.

At the end of his time in Milan, Leonardo studied anatomy with Marcentonio della Torre. What he had learned, doubtless very roughly and superficially, in Verrocchio's workshop, was suddenly confirmed, corrected, and extended. It was in 1496, after a long stay at Urbino, that friar Luca Pacioli arrived in Milan. He and Leonardo at once became friends and Leonardo executed for him the engraved plates of the *Divina proportione*. Paciolo had carefully studied Archimedes and knew Euclid.

It all looked as though, in the absence of opportunity to practise any branch of the engineer's art on a large acale, Leonardo was making efforts to extend the theoretical knowledge which he judged necessary to reach any kind of perfection. Of this he retained, at least in the beginning, only those elements that were directly and practically usable. He transformed himself, as it were, into a kind of research department. But without a solid basis this knowledge was not ordered into a coherent system. This was because of the uncertainty, the variations in the solutions of problems, and the confusions of language. During his time at the Sforza court the *De architectura* of Alberti appeared, also the *De re militari* of Vegetius together with the *Stratagems* of Frontinus.

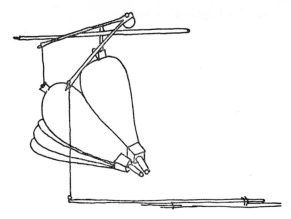

Leonardo da Vinci: bellows.

The whole of Leonardo's work and the whole of his thought show that from 1482, when he left for Milan, his career was marked out; it was to be that of Taccola and of Francesco di Giorgio. A remarkable observer, as his anatomical work attests, Leonardo achieved less than he studied. He could only work by setting out from what he already knew, that is to say, from the immense technical experience that he derived partly from Verrocchio, partly from all the engineers that he had read or frequented. He was trying throughout his stay in Milan to integrate the new science that was in process of formation not so much as an exercise in pure and exact research, but for practical purposes unimpeded by subtleties, precise language, or formal exactitude. It would appear that he wanted to substitute something else for the system of prescriptions that had been passed down to him, something more rational but perhaps not much more systematic. It was like a mutilated mosaic; the isolated, fragmentary spots of colour represented the ideas of his apprenticeship, snatches of conversation, and, also, the major preoccupations of his career.

Leonardo da Vinci had, from 1494, made certain contacts with the French. He was a member of the entourage of Ludovico Sforza when he went to negotiate in the castle of Pavia. In 1499, after the entry of the French into Milan, Leonardo entered the service of the Comte de Ligny, Louis de Luxembourg; Ligny hoped to recover the inheritance of his wife, the Duchess of Altamura, whom he had married during the first campaign of Charles VIII at Naples. He asked Leonardo to prepare him a report on the state of military defence in Tuscany: he was thus engaged as an engineer. The sudden return of Sforza changed his plans. But Il Moro was handed over to the French and Leonardo left Milan. In February 1499 he took refuge in Mantua.

In March 1499 he entered the service of the Venetians, still as a military engineer. The latter feared an attack by the Turks and were looking for an Archimedes who would protect their city. He studied the watercourses of Friuli and proposed that the course of the Isonzo should be diverted by means of locks so as to be able to flood a whole region covering the approaches to Venice.

In April 1500 he returned to Florence, without employment, since the Florentines had their own engineers in the San Gallo, and took up painting again. He then wandered from place to place. Isabella of Este recalled him to Mantua and we have the letter in which Pietro da Novellara answers the Duchess of Mantua, on 4 April 1501, and discloses the failure of his mission to Leonardo: 'His mathematical studies made him disgusted with painting.' Leonardo was certainly pursuing his dream.

In 1502 Leonardo joined the service of Cesare Borgia, still as a military engineer. His letter of appointment, which has been preserved, entrusts to him the inspection of fortifications, with such repairs and alterations as might be necessary, and with the drawing up of plans. It was in his capacity of engineer that Leonardo was present at the siege of Urbino and the looting of its magnificent library. Moving from fortress to fortress, inspecting and designing, Leonardo traversed the whole of central Italy. We can follow him thanks to notebook L, which is oblong and easy to put in the pocket and in which he jotted down anything that interested him. On 30 July he left Urbino. On 1 August he was at Pesaro, where he visited the library and studied in the manuscripts there designs of machines. On 8 August he was at Rimini, the home of Valturio, where he studied the fountains and the water distribution system. On 11 August at Cesena he designed a vehicle and noted a certain way of cultivating vines. On 6 September, at Cesenatico, he surveyed the bastions for the defence of the coast. It is said that he outlined the plan of a port linked to the sea by a canal, which was executed much later. It would be tedious to pause at each of his stopping-places: Buoncevento, Casanova, Chiusi, Perugia, Foligno, Piombino – where he studied waves and drew up a plan for draining the swamps – Siena and Orvieto. In all these visits it was Leonardo the engineer who took notes for reports, who noticed anything of interest for his occupation, and who made drawings. Drawings of fortresses, bastions, bridges, machines, flowers or human heads, fine maps like that of Imola, all these are mere travel notes, working notes, and perhaps ideas that were suggested by the shape of some curtain-wall, the plan of some rampart that he had seen. Between 1503 and 1506 Leonardo remained in Florence where he worked as military architect and hydraulic expert. At the same time he re-entered the guild of painters. We must not forget that this period, a particularly active one, is that of *La Gioconda* and the ill-starred *Battle of Anghiari*. It was at the beginning of this period that he presented to the city of Florence his project for the diversion of the Arno for which numerous hydraulic investigations had been made. It was desired to create a navigable canal which would link Florence to the sea and make the city a seaport. This was part of the whole plan to eliminate the possibility of catastrophic floods, to drain the lower parts of the valley, and to harness the power which was required by Florentine industry. It would seem that the Florentine administration was tempted by the grandeur of the idea and the scope of the programme. The war between Pisa and Florence interrupted the study of all these grandiose projects.

This period was also important for Leonardo's scientific education. Not only did he pursue certain projects of pure research, but he was able to experiment on a wider scale. His experiments were still limited and partial, certainly, and were not detailed from technical aims, but they show a development in working methods. We have only to think of his researches on the formation of river beds and all the hydraulic studies connected therewith. The drawings of birds in flight and the first sketches of flying machines also date from this period. Observations, experiments, and *a posteriori* constructions follow each other in rapid succession.

The ill-success of the *Battle of Anghiari*, commissioned by the Signoria, for which a number of cartoons were made and which was never completed, led Leonardo to leave Florence. The invitation of Charles d'Amboise, Comte de Chaumont, came at the right moment – in May 1506. In 1507 Louis XII mentions Leonardo as his painter and staff engineer. He joined the royal corps of engineers which was then making its appearance within the French military organization and which, at the time, was recruited from Italians. He was extremely well received in Milan, where the governor had him lodged in his own quarters and tried to intervene to calm the angry Florentines.

Leonardo was asked to organize the entertainments on the occasion of the entry of Louis XII into Milan. He may have devised more of those marvellous machines that so much delighted the onlookers. He returned to Florence for a time to settle certain family affairs; and he remained for some time, engaged upon drawing anatomical plates. But he was anxious not to lose his position or his salary; he wrote to his pupil Francesco Melzi to ask him to recommend him to the 'Water commission'. He was hoping to be given charge of some great hydraulic works in the Milanese countryside, probably irrigation canals, since he hoped to use it to the benefit of the vineyard which the French had given him. He returned to Milan in July 1508, where he was pleased to find his pension, the regular payments of which he recorded in his notebooks.

Louis XII soon returned to Italy and entered Milan in May 1509. Almost at once he directed his armies against Venice and Leonardo followed the king as military engineer. He assisted at the Battle of Agnadel. He was always anxious to learn from his friends what was new in the way of gadgets, prescriptions, and scientific explanations, and he covered the pages of his notebooks with these. He noted everything he could recall of conversations with the miniaturist Jean Ferréal, who was also greatly interested in mathematics and science.

It has been noted that this second Milanese period, which lasted until 1513, marked for Leonardo a profounder study of pure research, science, and a new love of disinterested investigation. Receiving regular payment and probably with little to do in his position of engineer, Leonardo had leisure to resume, with difficulty and much hard work, his scientific education. He acquired much new and rich material from Giorgio Valla's *De expentendis et fugiendis rebus* based on Archimedes and Euclid, which appeared in 1509. The whole of Greek geometry, with solutions different from those he was used to, opened up before his eyes. The work undoubtedly had a very great influence on him.

The French soon began to suffer reverses. Charles d'Amboise, his immediate protector, died in 1511. The years 1512 and 1513 mark the beginning of the French withdrawal. Leonardo left Milan on 23 September 1513 to go to Rome at the request of Cardinal Giuliano de' Medici.

He remained in Rome for three years, from 1513 to 1515. He had come once again as an engineer. But the San Gallo were the big names in Rome and Leonardo was only entrusted with small missions such as inspections. He does not appear to have taken part either in the building of all those Roman fortresses that were to mark the final development of the art of fortification, or in the completion of all those monuments with which the city was being embellished. In this circle of artists, who were full of truly monumental ideas, even Leonardo's painting had no place. He was made to feel this. And the sarcastic remarks that were passed about the statue that was never cast and the *Battle of Anghiari* which was never completed must have made him very unhappy. Some paintings which have been lost and a treatise on singing which has never been found were the only works executed in this period by Leonardo the painter and scholar.

He took refuge in another speciality, perhaps his favourite subject: hydraulics. Giuliano de' Medici had acquired the unhealthy region of the Pontine Marshes south of Rome and hoped to develop it. The task was naturally given to Leonardo and to Fra Giovanni Scotti of Como. Leonardo studied the terrain and drew up a plan. It was a question of canalizing the waters of the lower part of the swamp and of draining them towards the sea. He used for this purpose an old Roman canal which ran parallel to the Appian Way. In order to make the water flow he planned to introduce into his canal two rivers, the Portatore and the Amaseno. Work began under the direction of Scotti, but the death of the cardinal interrupted the project.

It is possible that the cardinal had also employed Leonardo on architectural work, in particular his palace in Rome and his stables. He was also given the task of inspecting the fortifications of the duchies of Parma and Piacenza.

The Medici have created me and the Medicis have destroyed me, wrote Leonardo, in somewhat enigmatic fashion. Perhaps he wished to stress the disappointments of his sojourn in Rome. Wherever he went Leonardo found men holding the important positions who undoubtedly had more practical experience than he: Bramante, and Bertola da Navate in Milan, the San Gallo in Florence, Bramante again, Michelangelo and others in Rome. He had reason to think that he would never be allowed to show his abilities in an important workshop or that he would never be given a great work to carry out. Perhaps, also, patrons were aware of his instability and his tendency to be rapidly discouraged, which almost amounted to incapacity to complete what he had undertaken. In Rome he even abandoned his usual researches to devote himself to a new science – alchemy – which he learned from two German servants of the Cardinal de'Medici. It is true that he stripped it of its element of greed – the search for gold – that he tried to harness it to other ends. But his hope was always the same, to find a rational basis for technical procedures.

Francis I, to whom the victory of Marignan had again opened up Italy, met Leo X at Bologna in December 1515. Leonardo may have been there, and in Rome when the King of France went there a little later. Francis I continued the policy of his predecessors and summoned numerous Italians to France, including not only artists, but also engineers, most of whom were asked to build solid and impregnable fortresses along his frontiers. It was Italians who, during the years immediately following, built the great tower at Toulon and the tower at Le Havre; it was Italians who, at the same period, built the characteristic Château d'If. We shall be returning to this aspect of military technique.

Francis I also invited Leonardo to settle in France. The court of France was perhaps more interested in the painter, in the artist, than in the engineer. Up to that time the French were the only ones to have engaged the great Florentine as an artist. In Italy he had never been engaged as anything other than an engineer.

Leonardo, accompanied by his pupil Melzi, left for France and was installed in the Château du Cloux, near Amboise. He was often consulted, but never asked to do any actual or real work. He was consulted over the alterations to the Château d'Amboise, which gave rise to some reflections on the solidity of the buildings and on the comfort of these dwelling-places which were being adapted to a new mode of life. He was also asked for ideas about the canal system round the castle at Blois, but he seems only to have called attention to the work of his predecessors who were also mostly Italian.

Still preoccupied with hydraulic matters, Leonardo began to study a vast programme of river control centred on the small city of Romorantin, which was for the time being a royal residence. The canal, which he planned, was to join the Loire at Tours or at Blois and in the other direction, passing the Allier and the Loire and crossing the hills of Charollais, to flow into the Saône, near Macon. This may have been a *jeu d'esprit* rather than a serious study, as was the dream of draining and cultivating the marches of Sologne which so long occupied the minds of the central authorities in Paris. The drawings which he made are, moreover, only fairly rough sketches, but they show, at least for part of the project, considerable geographical knowledge.

He was also asked to organize entertainments, that is to say to make decorations and to set up 'marvellous machines'. At the beginning of October 1517 he was the master of ceremonies at a great entertainment given by the king in honour of his sister, at the Château d'Argenton. Melzi tells us that Leonardo contrived a lion with a bristling mane, led by a hermit, which made the women draw back in terror, but when the king touched the lion three times with a magic wand, handed to him by the hermit, the automaton opened and spilled mounds of fleurs-de-lis at the king's feet. One can well imagine Leonardo devising the mechanisms required for such an automaton. Many of the drawings in his notebook, the significance of which is not always understood, must relate to these preoccupations.

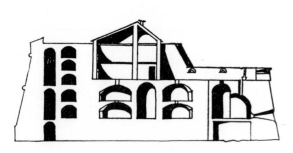

Section of the great tower of Toulon (1514–24).

Château d'If – fifteenth century.

It is possible that Leonardo was asked to organize the entertainments given at Amboise, in May and June 1518, for the baptism of the Dauphin and the marriage of Lorenzo de'Medici to Madeleine de la Tour d'Auvergne. The taking of a citadel under siege, defended by the Duc d'Angoulême, and a kind of astronomical fairy entertainment, reminiscent of the pageant of Paradisi mounted in Milan for Isabella of Aragon, were greatly admired.

On 2 May 1519 Leonardo died at Amboise.

We shall probably be accused, in this very rapid outline, of having distorted the generally accepted classical image of Leonardo da Vinci. We have attempted somehow to integrate him with our engineers without taking account of his true personality, that of an artist and philosopher. How many biographers write about him without mentioning this scientific or technical activity, except to show the extent of a knowledge regarded as universal, but which can efface neither the smile of the Gioconda nor the enigmatic thought of the man ignored by contemporaries ill-fitted to appreciate his genius?

The experts, whom we are not equipped to criticize, have admitted none of the sculptures attributed to Leonardo. They are in full agreement on half a dozen paintings considered to be beyond question his. We know, from documents and from contemporary evidence, that the volume of Leonardo's painted work was very small. Was he an artist? This cannot be gainsaid; that he was one of the greatest and one of the most celebrated is beyond all doubt. But it was not his 'profession'. It is true that he was a member of the Florentine guild of painters, but Spinoza polished spectacle lenses and Borodin was an infantry officer.

There is no doubt that from 1482 onwards the career of Leonardo da Vinci was that of an engineer. Like all his predecessors he had received an artistic education, though his was probably more complete and was certainly wider in scope than theirs. But he presented himself as an engineer to Ludovico Sforza and an engineer he wished to be. His notebooks with their preponderance of drawings of machines and engineers' projects are a clear witness to the fact.

Leonardo the artist has always been magnified and it would not be easy to refute universal opinion. A recent symposium on Leonardo held in Paris began by expressing certain reserves about his scientific thought, or at least by restoring it to its just proportions. Leonardo's mechanics are of his time, with its weaknesses, uncertainties, and errors. And it would not seem that he brought many discoveries to this field. His physics are somewhat confused and vague; his chemistry is limited to the preparation of an alembic and to certain works of alchemical research which he carried out in Rome.

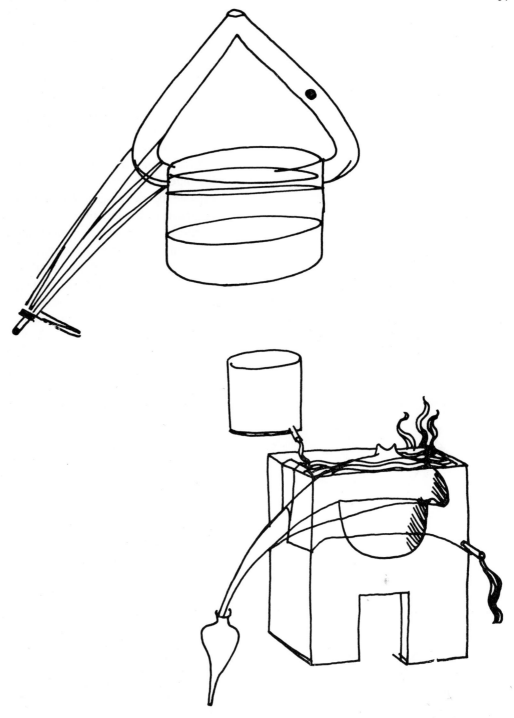

Leonardo da Vinci: alembics.

His science, as many have strongly emphasized, is all practice and observation. Such is the case also for his anatomy which is remarkable for its drawing, but which overlooked many important elements. Leonardo was insufficiently knowledgeable or his knowledge was not well enough organized to enable him to discover the circulation of the blood. His mathematical culture was that of a practical man: it had the limited objectives of the abacists of his time. Following Pacioli, he studied lunulae and with difficulty mastered the geometry of the Greeks. His perspective is the same as that of all the theoreticians of his time.

Leonardo, the admirable but only occasional painter, the intelligent scholar who lacked adequate education, who was incapable of defining a concept with precision, was certainly an engineer, of the line of engineers of his time. He tried, no doubt, to outstep the stage of clever mechanics, of slowly developing principles of fortification or architecture, of more or less avid traditions: he probably succeeded to the detriment of the efficiency which some of his contemporaries had managed to retain in dealing with the same problems. It is not the mind that changes here, it is more the mode of thought, the mechanism of reflection.

All this was achieved with great difficulty, through constant reference to what the ancients and his immediate predecessors had written. And Leonardo found himself a little lost in this world which emerged from past centuries. At each line that he discovers, at each phenomenon that he reveals, he has to lean on others for explanation and for commentaries on texts only half understood by many.

And, through ignorance of this whole past by which he was formed, Leonardo has been presented as a fertile inventor, when in fact nothing new stemmed from any part of his environment. An immense and attentive curiosity and an imaginative grasp of the whole epoch has led to the belief in an inventive genius which these men did not possess. At the end of October 1902 an historian, today forgotten, presented to the Académie des Sciences a paper on Leonardo, engineer and scholar. In it he extolled the role of Leonardo in the progress of science and technology. Berthelot, roused to indignation, maintained that all this was imagination, illusion, and error. Berthelot knew many of the notebooks which we have examined and saw in them 'the origin of a large part of Leonardo's work'. Many of the ideas, according to him, were also part of the technical virtuosity which the circle of engineers had made its speciality: winged flight, perpetual movement, and the whole increased desire for mechanism which is the mark of the time. The writer who reported this dispute added some years later: 'This

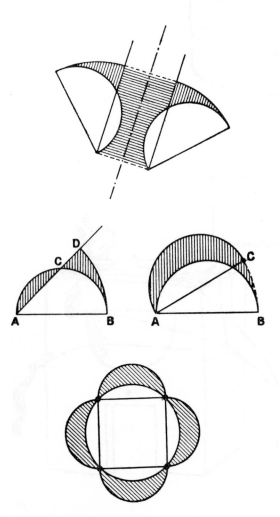

Lunulae by Leonardo da Vinci.

opinion of Berthelot did not arouse any interest and did not affect in any way or in any sphere of his reputation the fame of Leonardo da Vinci. I shall therefore, in the course of my exposition, follow quite calmly what may be called the traditional ideas of so many critics and scholars.' Our study may be taken as a belated echo of the opinion of Berthelot.

It would surely be surprising if Leonardo had been the incomparable precursor that he has been described, that he should have had no pupil. Let us reject the image of a man hiding his discoveries in order not to frighten the world, and forget about his famous inverted writing. As he himself wrote, this was a form of false vanity, in which he himself did not believe. Before him, Fontana had written in code. Taccola had made similar reflections. In a world in which knowledge was still for the most part transmitted orally, writings were of no great importance. Or rather, their importance was only beginning: Matthias Corvinus had the treatise of Valturio recopied when it had already been printed. Leonardo da Vinci was at the turning point of a period in which tradition was beginning to lose its authority. As early as the beginning of the fifteenth century, methods which had been transmitted through architects' lodges were beginning to be discussed. Disputes, such as took place even in Leonardo's time, regarding a monument in construction, whether it were the Duomo in Milan or the Cathedral in Pavia, are not new phenomena. Similar disputes had taken place during the first quarter of the fourteenth century, when the vaults, which were badly constructed, were threatening to fall down.

A new support element emerged during the course of the fifteenth century, which stemmed from the newly rediscovered world of antiquity. Only the discovery of a manuscript of Vitruvius could give rise to new hopes. Valturio and, after him, Leonardo had adopted from the ancients a whole machinery of war which could not hold its ground in face of the progress of artillery. It was the fashion of the time. L. Febvre recently quoted the competition organized at the beginning of the sixteenth century by the Republic of Venice on the best shape for ships. The master of eloquence, steeped in Greek tradition, carried off the prize in the face of the experienced builder.

Leonardo is difficult to classify, and it is in this sense that he has appeared exceptional. But the reason undoubtedly lies in our ignorance of the life and of the exact thought of his predecessors. We do not know much about the life of Fontana or of Taccola. Francesco di Giorgio is already more familiar to us and his resemblance to Leonardo seems clearer and more precise. At a time when the education of engineers embraced the most diverse and extensive knowledge and when scientific curiosity was deepening, the case of Leonardo is easier to explain. Francesco di Giorgio was not a negligible painter. His work as an architect is appreciated more highly today. His talent as an engineer equalled that of Leonardo. His writings, some of which have certainly been lost, are merely less well known. Alberti also left important work in a multitude of fields. His scientific and philosophical thought, now more highly appreciated than before, forms a ready parallel to that of his compatriot.

What would Leonardo have been without his masters? Duhem, having investigated the problem with praiseworthy thoroughness, believed that he had found them in Oxford and Paris in the fourteenth or early fifteenth century. Perhaps, but Leonardo only knew of them through the writers we have cited who had retained from their works only the very precise problems related to their own curiosity and preoccupations. We see in Leonardo the same distortions, the same conceptions, the same hopes, and the identical limitations.

It would be extremely suggestive to seek not totally original ideas or flagrant errors, but the common scientific and technical basis of a generation, with its zones of uncertainty and its admitted truths. One could then uncover the almost imperceptible gaps, the rigidity of methods, and the evolution of reasoning. We have tried, with small success, to isolate the experience of the Renaissance engineers and to underline what we today would call their problems. The documents we have used and the texts available to us are doubtless insufficient to give us full knowledge of them. In contrast to such illuminating testimony as that of Alberti, for example, there are obvious obscurities. It would be interesting to know what Francesco di Giorgio knew of this matter or that, or what he had read or knew about Nicholas de Cues, and if he also had studied the *De ponderibus*.

This tradition, though fluctuating, was, Koyre noted, present in the teaching of the universities, which Leonardo did not follow but of which he must have heard echoes both in popular literature and in works in the vernacular, the riches of which Olschki made available some years ago. The links are not made by famous names, and they merge into each other on all sides.

The influence of Leonardo has been denied: for a long time his manuscripts remained inaccessible. Is this in fact the reason? The thought of his period was transmitted by the same unknown or imperceptible channels. As Koyre has again very rightly pointed out, Baldi, Cardan, Piccolomini, and Benedetti did not need the writings of Leonardo in order to carry out their researches. All this knowledge was still living around them. The academic disputes, the workshop conversations, the so-called manufacturers' secrets, the marvellous machines, all these were as much present as was the most trivial piece of news spread today by our newspapers.

And precisely because he had not acquired this university knowledge, because he was an unlettered man, because he was perhaps aware of the uncertainties of his knowledge, the unsuitability of his language – otherwise why should he have taken a whole page to copy out the scientific terms he had culled from Valturio? – because, in short, he had no vestige of established doctrine, Leonardo, doubtless like all the engineers of his time and his immediate successors, gave a new impetus to the scientific and technological conceptions that had been passed down to him. Tradition is not necessarily a question of routine, and technical progress was, probably more than anything else, apt to lead those who practised it along untrodden paths.

It should now be possible to remove the hypothesis which has for so long overshadowed the history of this period, of a Leonardo da Vinci who was a fertile and universal inventor, greatly in advance of his time and whose discoveries would have remained unknown for as long as his notebooks lay hidden. It would be tedious to criticize each of Leonardo's drawings, to trace the sources or to differentiate those that were mere dreams from those which could have been carried out. The celebration, in 1952, of the quincentenary of his birth gave rise to exhibitions, the catalogues of which showed a selection of the machines which Leonardo is supposed to have invented and most of which were reconstituted for the exhibitions on a small scale. It would be possible to show from this selection, which was certainly quite arbitary and gave a false idea of the activity and of the mind of Leonardo, that apart from the flying machine, some textile machines and the machine for polishing mirrors, everything is borrowed, often directly, from his predecessors.

Whatever may have been said, Leonardo's quest was not universal. It was limited almost exactly, at least in the field of applied techniques, to the preoccupations pursued by all the engineers of this period. The only difference, in the long run, was the spirit in which certain investigations, to which we shall return in the next chapter, were conducted. Architecture and town planning, armament and fortifications, and hydraulics constitute the great majority of the subjects of Leonardo da Vinci's technical designs and correspond to the chapter headings of all the treatises which we have mentioned. The letter to Il Moro, like the decree of Cesare Borgia, shows beyond doubt the great interest Leonardo took in military problems. This technique, practised by all engineers, which was their principal reason for working, had two sides: the question of armament and that of fortification with all its accessory problems arising from the conduct of armies in the field. It was felt, in a confused way, that a new art of war was on the point of being developed. The first French campaigns in Italy showed that a new technique had truly become the stake of the century. Both Taccola and Francesco di Giorgio had felt this. And Leonardo da Vinci was at the turning point in this important period.

We can identify Leonardo's sources both from the quotations that he made and by the striking analogy of certain drawings. He systematically studied the *De re militari* of Valturio: he copied him, annotated him, noted his terminology, and steeped himself in his ideas. He certainly used, in the first editions which were often issued together, the treatise of Vegetius and the *Stratagems* of Frontinus. It should not be forgotten that the first German editions of Vegetius which circulated in Italy were illustrated with the drawings of Kyeser. Vitruvius and Alberti had also written on fortifications. Among more modern authors, although he did not quote them exactly, Leonardo certainly used Taccola, Francesco di Giorgio, Il Filarete, and Fioravanti. It had become a commonplace to attribute to Leonardo a particular importance in the domain of military art. More recently, close research has considerably reduced his role in the development of military techniques.

The field of armaments is certainly the one in which Leonardo made the fewest innovations. Following Valturio and in the spirit that we have already mentioned, Leonardo was much impressed by the war machines of antiquity and his quest for Archimedes related as much, perhaps, to his military activity as to his scientific work. Sir Kenneth Clark has noted quite rightly that Leonardo's knowledge of military matters was not in advance of that of his time.

Leonardo's artillery is of the most classical type, the most common at that time. It is to be found in all the notebooks of which we have spoken. We have reproduced drawings which show all the types of lifts used by Leonardo (jack lifts, circle lifts, and screw lifts). Organs, those fixed or rotating multiple-tube cannons, already existed in Kyeser and are repeated from engineer to engineer and from notebook to notebook up to Leonardo. We have already come across the assault chariot, with which Leonardo has so often been credited. These chariots were, apart from certain variations arising from fantasy and from the art of drawing, the same as those of his predecessors. The movements of the endless screw and of the crank and pinion have often been reproduced after Taccola or Francesco di Giorgio. All the scaling machines, the ladders and mobile towers

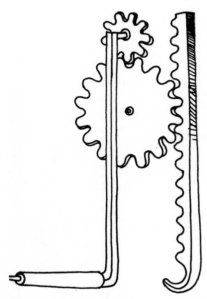

Leonardo da Vinci: lifting-jack.

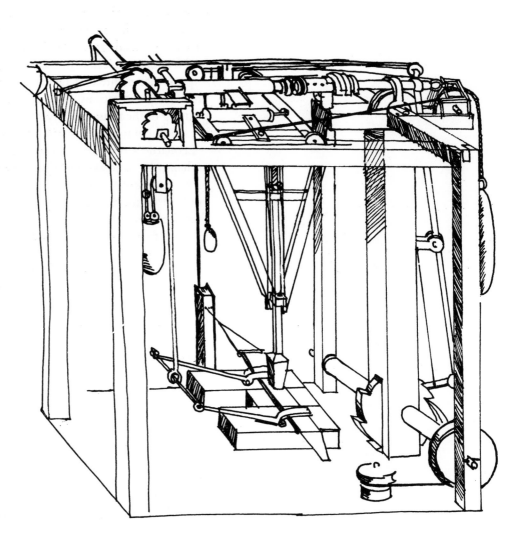

Leonardo da Vinci: forging machine.

were also part of this old common fund which goes back, as we have seen, to the period of early antiquity.

Nor is there anything original in the field of naval armament. Leonardo's drawings show quite clearly that all or nearly all have been borrowed directly from Francesco di Giorgio. The ship with wheels with lateral vanes activated by cranks is certainly very ancient; it is not impossible that this drawing is of Roman origin. It is already to be found in Kyeser and occurs regularly from Taccola onwards. The ships with mobile rams, or with large hooks for grappling with the enemy, are faithful reproductions of machines to be found in the treatise of Francesco di Giorgio. Moreover, despite his contacts – sporadic, it is true – with the sea in Venice, the drawings of ships and the notes on naval techniques to be found in Leonardo's notebooks do not show any great knowledge of the problems of naval construction. We should remember that the Venetians called upon the famous engineer only to defend their land frontier and it does not seem that they asked him anything about ships. Other painters of Leonardo's time have given us much more precise representations of ships: such, for example, as the famous painting of the return of Ulysses by Pintoricchio (1454–1513), which is exactly contemporary with the notebooks.

Leonardo's only real contribution to armament techniques was, perhaps, the exposition of founding processes shown in a few pages of his notebooks. This provides an interesting addition to the notebook of Ghiberti, which we have mentioned. It is not very likely that the latter showed any marked innovation either. The notes relating to the composition of metal are very brief and do not indicate an advanced technique: six parts of tin to 100 parts of copper is what he prescribed for artillery bronze. And he adds: 'The less you put (of tin) the stronger will be the mortar.' It is known that the normal proportion for a bronze of good quality in Leonardo's time was 12% tin. A few notes on the kind of earth to be used and a few prescriptions for the fusion of metal are all that are worth keeping. The information on calibres, the importance of which we shall assess further on, is very fragmentary. This is not so much a treatise as a collection of foundry recipes, or even fragments of a treatise on the making of cannons. We shall come back to all these questions in order to assess more exactly Leonardo da Vinci's position in this field.

Leonardo's role in the development of fortification has been and no doubt will continue to be much discussed. It is, however, difficult in the absence of any precise chronology, to show the stages of Leonardo's thought on the subject of fortification. The most that the latest historians who have closely studied the drawings of the

Ship, c. 1493.

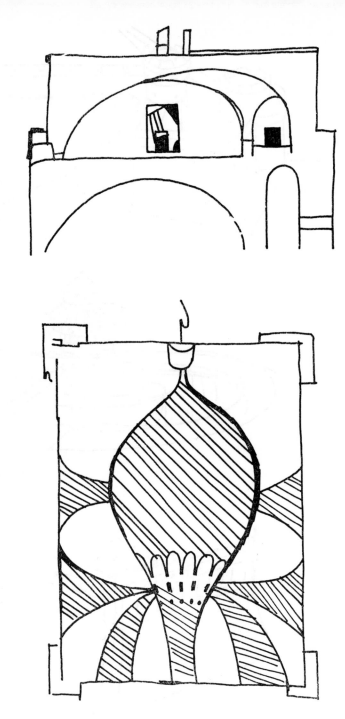

Early sixteenth-century ship.

Leonardo da Vinci: metal smelting furnaces.

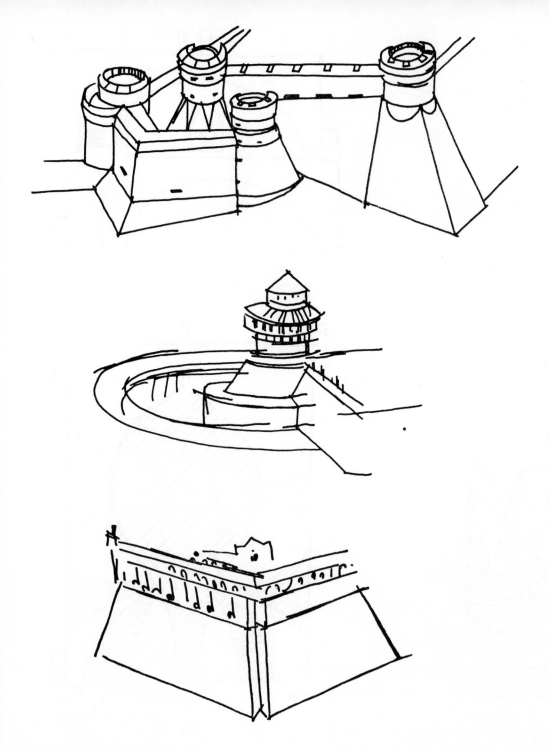

Leonardo da Vinci: types of fortification.

notebooks, particularly Ignazio Calvi, have been able to do is to note a relatively clear progression from notebook B, which appears to date from the beginning of the first Milanese period, to notebook L, in which are to be found all the notes taken during the voyage of inspection carried out on behalf of Cesare Borgia, nearly twenty years later.

If the drawings are grouped according to similarity of subject it is possible to distinguish, very broadly speaking, three main types in his conception of the fortress, all three dominated, it should be said, by persistent echoes of tradition. The first two types appear to have been borrowed from immediate predecessors. The first conception shows a type of intermediary fortress, still with high walls and oblique bases. The salients usually only have towers with machicolations. In many respects, these drawings are the same as those of Francesco di Giorgio. Sometimes, however, as also with Giorgio, we find salients with triangular works of the tenaille type.

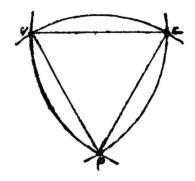

Another series of drawings shows us triangular ramparts placed in front of straight high walls which are still feudal in character. This is the same idea that the famous captain François de Surienne wished to carry out at Dijon in 1461. In one of these drawings, in the *Codex Atlanticus*, we see, clearly marked, the firing plan of the high batteries, placed at the top of the wall, and the plan of the rampart, no doubt much lower.

In notebook L, Leonardo's technique is much closer to that of the San Gallo and probably of a number of their contemporaries.

The final stage appears to have given rise to curtain-walls with counterforts or a series of salients, topped not by machicolations and crenellations, but by rounded shapes, such as we already see at Salses, in Roussillon, a castle which was built at the very end of the fifteenth century, in 1497 to be exact. With Leonardo, as with most of his contemporaries, we should note the general tendency to lower the fortifications and to adopt bastion shapes, the only ones capable of supporting heavy artillery.

Even if we do not know what exactly Leonardo carried out in the way of fortification (perhaps in fact he was dealing more with repairs than alterations, or new building), it would seem that he was employed in this field rather than in the making of implements of war. It is true that in many engineers' notebooks these new implements are fruits rather of the imagination than of reality. It would be surprising if Leonardo had enjoyed any considerable fame in these fields with princes who were readier to use the services of other engineers. We know the names of the Italians who worked in the south of France at Toulon, on the Château d'If, or at Le Havre at the

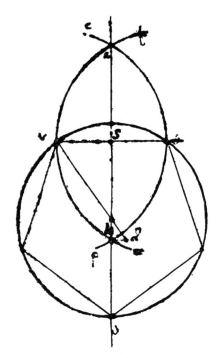

Pentagon for laying-out fortifications by Leonardo da Vinci.

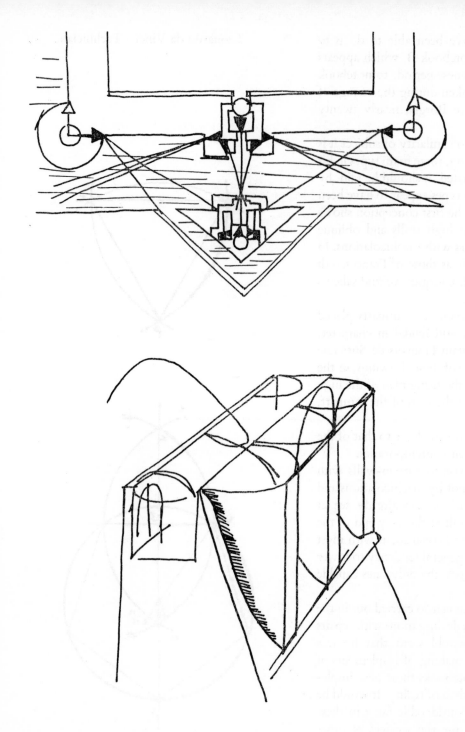

Leonardo da Vinci: types of fortification with field of fire.

very time when Francis I invited Leonardo to follow him to France. There were other engineers of the period, whose names have been lost or who did not go to the trouble of consigning to treatises or to loose sheets of notes the essential elements of their techniques, prescriptions, and specialities.

Pedro Navarro (1460–1538) enjoyed a great reputation in mining and floating batteries. From 1485 he served as a mercenary in the Italian wars which stimulated so much progress. He took part in the wars, which lasted fifteen years, between the Genoese and the Barbary pirates. Between 1500 and 1503 his experiences of mine-laying on behalf of the Spanish, in Sicily and in southern Italy, led to the production of a type of explosive which remained unchanged during the following 400 years. In 1515 Navarro deserted the Spanish cause to join, as Leonardo was to do some months later, the service of the king of France, Francis I.

The same comments could be made in regard to architectural techniques. If we set aside the purely artistic aspect, with which we are not concerned, and certain problems of construction, to which we shall return at greater length. Leonardo's investigations show but little originality. Domes were in fashion and several had been built since Brunellesco. Leonardo had observed the methods by which the cupolas of Florence and of Milan had been constructed. It was the work of others that he noted, not his own. Moreover, the development of these affected external appearances more than the building processes themselves.

The implements, in particular the lifting apparatus, which Leonardo presents are largely taken from his predecessors. This is the case with the double cranes, the machines for lifting heavy weights

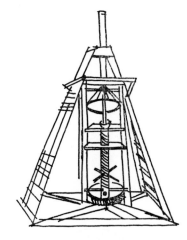

Leonardo da Vinci: drilling machine for wooden beams.

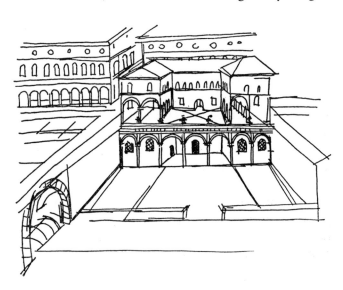

Leonardo da Vinci: building on different levels.

and those for moving large bodies, most of which are to be found in previous work. The endless screw apparatus, or the jacking apparatus to raise columns, are taken, line for line, from the book of Francesco di Giorgio, as is the hydraulic saw. The large number of *Trattati delle leve e tirari* of this period lead us to believe that Leonardo found in these the major part of his inspiration. Alberti himself had written one and, as it were, brought into being the whole of this movement.

No doubt the same could be said of Leonardo's more purely architectural ideas. No one, certainly, has attributed to Leonardo the merit of having 'discovered' functional architecture. Leonardo's designs, several of which deserve the interest that has been shown, have not, however, the variety and the system of the drawings which Francesco di Giorgio devoted to different types of building. The stables which he outlined have been identified either as those of the Medici in Florence or those of Urbino. We found here, as in other connexions, rather an assortment of practical notes on details than general views.

His town planning is also extremely fragmentary and very uncertain: he has not the breadth of approach of Alberti or of his immediate successors. Lavedan, in his excellent history of town planning, has noted some drawings for an ideal city, which are of smaller merit than those of many others. It would seem that he was in favour of a spindle-shaped plan, with canals. Leonardo had certainly been struck, after the epidemic of plague that ravaged Milan while he was there, by the unhealthiness of Italian cities of this period. He made certain deductions from this, and it is a pity that he did not carry them further. Although he produced plans of superimposed roads to resolve a traffic problem that must have been very difficult, his effort seems to have been limited to the plan of certain quarters and the surroundings of certain monuments, so that these are only incomplete ideas.

It is known that in 1492 Ludovico Sforza ordered the inhabitants of Vigevano to demolish the old market place and to rebuild it according to the plans of his engineer Ambrogio de Cortis. This, seen in retrospect, becomes the first systematic town planning enterprise. Bramante worked on the façades. It is said that Leonardo was there also, but we cannot be certain. He also appears to have given advice to Cesare Borgia on the reconstruction of Cesena and the development of Cesenatico.

It is undoubtedly in the field of hydraulics, in which many of his predecessors had engaged with varying degrees of success, that Leonardo appears to have had the greatest number of ideas, if not to have carried out the most work. Possibly he worked in the beginning

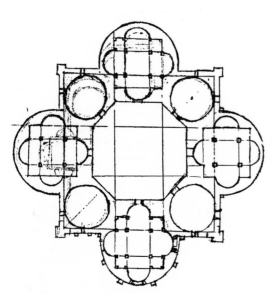

Geometrical plan of a basilica by Leonardo da Vinci.

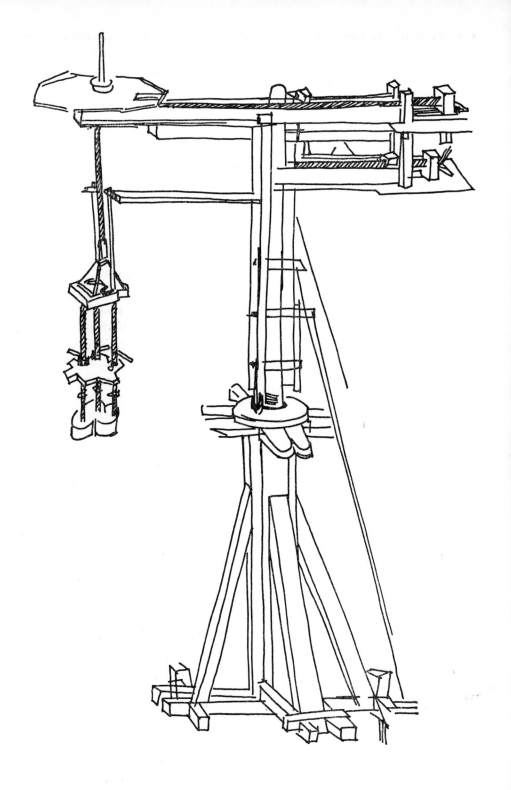

Leonardo da Vinci: hoisting apparatus.

under the great engineers who conceived and constructed most of the extensive canal network of the district of Milan. We possess more information about Leonardo's work in this field. Thus, in 1493 Leonardo seems to have worked on the improvement of the Lomellina and the systematization of the canals around Novara. In 1498 and 1499, in the service of the Sforza, he must have taken part in the drainage and cleansing of the region of Vigevano, where the dukes of Milan had built one of their residences. It is only after his second stay in Milan that Leonardo appears to have become interested in the problem presented by the inadequacy of the Martesana Canal. He proposed a certain number of changes in the arrangement of this canal, in particular the water influx and water losses along the route. Leonardo thought that the only possible solution was to divert the course of the Adda. He drew up a number of plans along these lines.

Leonardo also travelled the entire region of Tuscany around Florence, as we have already indicated. His great plan for the regulation of the Arno had a number of aims. By regulating the river it was hoped, first of all, to avoid both the devastating floods which had already occurred and the periods of very low water which were so damaging to the crops. Leonardo's plan also included the drainage of the region between Chiusi and Arezzo. We have seen how he tried to use all the elements at his disposal, in particular certain lakes, in order to avoid too much construction work. The canal was, in short, both to provide water as the motive force for the industry of Florence and to facilitate a link between Florence and the sea. This was what we today would call a 'preliminary plan'. Leonardo did not enter into details of execution as he did, for example, with the Martesana Canal.

The plan for draining the Pontine Marshes was of the same nature. It is limited to a map of the Marshes with an indication of the canals

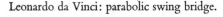
Leonardo da Vinci: parabolic swing bridge.

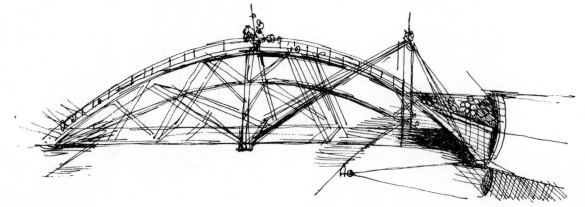

required. This drawing, preserved in Windsor Castle, represents no more than a simple idea. The same may be said for the famous Romorantin canal of which we have a few rather vague sketches. As he conceived it, this canal would have raised a number of enormous difficulties, about which Leonardo had nothing to say. It was perhaps in this connexion that he conceived the canal bridge, a sketch of which is to be found in the *Codex Atlanticus*.

Here again, Leonardo tackled the parallel problem of the gear required both for the work and for the equipment for the water-courses. The suggestions for the apparatus required for digging the canals are very numerous. These machines are perhaps not as original as some have suggested. In many cases Leonardo only adapted existing systems of lifting and of removing debris, in particular his great excavator, so often reproduced. A design for a dredger shows more imagination than sense of reality; Fontana's rock-clearing machine was certainly more efficient.

In regard to pumps, Leonardo was not called upon to offer innovations; suction and force pumps, only practical if they are combined with a rod and crank system, had been known and demonstrated since Taccola. The problem of siphons and aqueducts had been resolved as long ago as Roman times. We have seen elements of these in the notebooks of Leonardo's predecessors. He had, moreover, studied Frontinus's book on aqueducts, as is shown by a note. It is remarkable to observe that all the engineers of the period studied the work of their Roman predecessors and tried to bring them up to date or to adapt them as far as was possible, We have said that in order to drain the region of the Pontine Marshes Leonardo had thought of resuming an operation begun by the Romans; shortly before that, Nicholas V had commissioned Alberti to restore the Aqua Virgo, one of the great aqueducts of Rome, which, in so doing, he slightly altered.

Leonardo da Vinci: Archimedean screw and noria.

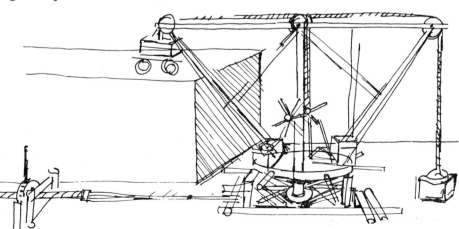

Leonardo da Vinci: machine for earth moving.

Other facts might be mentioned to show that Leonardo was aware of everything that his predecessors did and that he carried on from their sketches when it seemed that certain alterations were required. Thus Leonardo has left fairly numerous drawings of locks with movable gates such as already appear in Alberti. Although he took the machines for raising columns from Francesco di Giorgio, Leonardo never borrowed from him the machines for driving in the piles which were used to consolidate the banks of canals.

He often made numerous sketches not of general views of an operation or of a machine, but the detailed drawings on which the success of some engineers may be based. Even for canals we have many of these notes of detail, some of which are of secondary importance, such as, to take only two examples: work on canals should be undertaken between mid-March and mid-June, the slack time for agricultural work, when the days are long and the heat is still bearable, and willows should be planted to secure the banks.

The subjects with which we have just dealt form the largest part of the technical work transmitted to us through the notebooks of Leonardo da Vinci. We are thus concerned with the same preoccupations and the same enquiries that we have seen in the case of Leonardo's predecessors. No doubt each had his preferences, and if we must clasify them we may see Francesco di Giorgio more as a military, and Leonardo more as a hydraulic, engineer. It is also possible that in the first quarter of the sixteenth century this type of engineer was disappearing. Specialization seems to have been set up among the various technical activities and it was becoming impossible to deal with everything. This period saw the appearance of the first great technical treatises, as we shall see further on. Military engineers now dealt only with fortifications and hydraulic engineers confined themselves to hydraulic constructions.

Leonardo da Vinci: dredger.

In addition to this they all claimed to be mechanics. This is the final element linking them with the traditions of antiquity. Delight in automata was common to the School of Alexandria, to Fontana and to Leonardo da Vinci. This interest enjoyed a revival in the fifteenth and sixteenth centuries. Hydraulic and pneumatic automata were very much sought after during the period of the Renaissance. The art of garden layout and fountains was in process of development at this time and inspired the construction of artificial bushes peopled with moving silhouettes of birds, the song of which was activated by air expelled by a current of water. Here we have a whole tradition which had been preserved from the earliest times. The aims had been slightly modified, the mechanism had developed but the quest remained the same and magic was still sometimes associated with it. Unhappily, Leonardo, who took part, as we have seen, in certain masquerades in which automata had an important place, has not left any notes or drawings that would enable us to assess his knowledge. Nor does he appear to have been concerned with clockwork as was Francesco di Giorgio.

Although he was an able designer of all kinds of machines it is very difficult to say whether Leonardo was also a clever mechanic. We have seen that he was interested in the machines required by the engineers of the time. He made many drawings of them in his notebooks. And it would seem that in this instance his curiosity was wider than that of some of his elders. Moreover, these drawings are evidence not so much of profound knowledge, but of imagination and sometimes of fantasy. Except in some fields which we shall study further on, the mechanisms shown by Leonardo da Vinci were in common use.

No doubt he was aware, as were others, of the material difficulty of realizing correctly the connecting-rod and crank system for the transformation of a continuous circular motion into an alternating rectilinear motion, or vice versa. He devised a number of solutions, some of which are not valid. The most original is a wheel toothed round only half its circumference, engaging with two lantern wheels disposed at the two extremities of a diameter of this wheel and fixed to the same axle. Each lantern wheel thus turns alternately, one going one way and the other the other way, and a continuous circular motion has been transformed into an alternating circular motion. All that is now needed to achieve the rectilinear alternating motion is a jack or ratchet. We would also mention an articulated chain for the transmission of motions. We have seen that Taccola had also thought of it but Leonardo's design, very similar to a modern bicycle chain, is, in this instance, much superior to its predecessor.

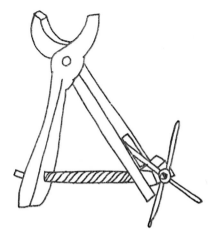

Leonardo da Vinci: pincers.

The utilization of natural or animal energy is frequent with Leonardo. He has been credited with the water turbine which he took from Francesco di Giorgio, whose designs in this respect are better. We note that he is one of the first to have drawn windmills with a turning turret, which were, however, known to exist at this date. Whereas Francesco di Giorgio was particularly interested in gears using the worm-screw and employed them at every opportunity, Leonardo frequently used jacking systems. It seems that the jack, which was afterwards to become very much used, made its appearance at the end of the fifteenth century. He already used it, although the chronology in this matter is not very well known, to extend the cord of a crossbow: certain paintings of the end of the fifteenth century, particularly those depicting the martyrdom of Saint Sebastian, illustrate this very clearly.

Leonardo's drawings do not show many lathes, which is perhaps surprising for a man who showed such desire for improved machinery. One lathe, on a treadle and rod and crank system, is shown in a somewhat clumsy drawing. Elsewhere there are bow-lathes, such as were to figure in Diderot's *Encyclopédie*.

There is no question but that Leonardo possessed this desire for mechanization to the highest degree and more strongly than his predecessors. And it was without doubt this immense mechanical curiosity that allowed him to transcend the relatively narrow sectors of interest of the others. It is also clear that in this field virtuosity can be given free rein. Any automatic machine, executing a limited number of operations, can be imagined. What child, possessing something of a mechanical mind, has not imagined splendid machines, the first, or one of the first, of which will certainly have been concerned with perpetual movement? And Leonardo, of course, like most of the others has his solution to perpetual movement, which is exactly the same as the one which Villard de Honnecourt had presented years earlier.

If all mechanical difficulties, such as friction, wear, instability of the various parts, are being eliminated – and it is easy to do this in a drawing, since the pen or pencil is in any case unable to render them – all becomes possible. And this hope, of which we may sense the presence, of more general mechanization of many industrial operations, is among the more important aspects of Leonardo's thought. There are limits to all things and it would be difficult to attribute to Leonardo everything which has been so generously laid at his feet, even in the field of virtuosity. The difference between the articulated chain shown in one of his drawings and its realization by Galle at the beginning of the nineteenth century are of the same order

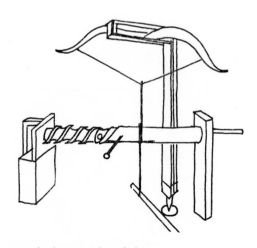

Leonardo da Vinci: bow lathe.

as the difference between Icarus and a Caravelle. Other differences may be noticed. It is known that there is no fundamental difference in conception between the highly developed automata of the end of the eighteenth century and modern automatic mechanisms. The cam systems have facilitated the execution of an almost unlimited succession of different movements. The automata of Jaquet-Droz and of Leschot, preserved in the museum of Neuchâtel, the tympanum player of Kintzing, made for Marie Antoinette towards the end of 1784, belong to modern times. This conception of the machine, which appeared at the end of the eighteenth century with De Gennes and continues with Vaucanson, shows a totally different mechanical attitude from that of a man such as Leonardo. Leonardo's machines entailed the execution of one elementary mechanical operation only, such as powering a shearing machine, cutting files, etc., linked to a drive. This was the same principle as that of Villard de Honnecourt's saw.

Leonardo was undoubtedly one of the first of this circle of engineers to be interested in the mechanical working of metal. No one will deny that the rolling mill was quite simple to think of. But in practice there was the difficulty of making polished and precisely calibrated resistant cylinders. Wire drawing and cutting machines were also easy to imagine. All that was necessary was to pass the piece to be worked into a matrix of the appropriate shape, doubtless after having heated it to render it more malleable. The driving systems are constituted by endless screws and gears linked to water turbines. These machines must have been very difficult to construct.

The principle of the hydraulic tilt-hammer is known in the form in which it has existed since the thirteenth century. The handle of the hammer can pivot around an axe. A wheel, fitted with cams, is fixed to the shaft of a mill. The cams, resting on the end of the handle, raise the hammer which falls back by its own weight. The tilt-hammer has been used in the forge for a very long time. It is a semi-automatic instrument, since it is driven by water power without any other assistance. All Leonardo's automatic hammers are based on this very simple principle, among them the machine for cutting files for which he has been given so much credit. An excellent principle, simple, known since early times, but impossible to realize in practice, even from an identical diagram. The same can be said for the machines for making sheets of beaten metal. All that was required was that the system driving the article to be worked should be co-ordinated with the movement of the tool. Transmissions generally are made by weights, the drop of which is blocked by stops which allow the tool to move. We would also note something

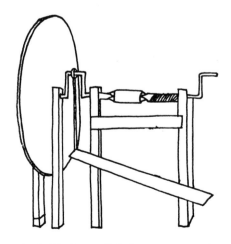

Leonardo da Vinci: treadle lathe.

which has not been noticed by everybody, that the majority of these machines are intended for working metals which are usually very malleable, such as precious metals and gold in particular.

There are also a few aberrations. The idea of grouping a number of hammers on one machine is of no interest. The force required to power six hammers, as indicated in the drawing in the *Codex Atlanticus*, would never have been obtainable. There is an element of mere frivolity in this. We do not, however, find with Leonardo, as with some of his predecessors, machines for boring or for filing cannon. The great and famous drawing preserved in Windsor Castle does not give us any information on this subject.

Screw-cutting machines have often been cited and reproduced, and there are many examples in the notebooks of Leonardo. It should not be overlooked that these were wooden screws and thus easier to work: there could have been no question at this period of thinking of metal screws. The cutting chisel is at G; the crank M, by means of the gears F and S, advances the tool-holder which slides on two screws. The tool is fixed and the crank turns the piece to be cut while pushing the tool forward. The thread of the screw is thus a function of the gears which only have to be changed in order to obtain different dimensions.

The machine for boring wooden tubes is exactly the same as those that we have met in the work of the anonymous engineer of the Hussite War, and in the notebooks of some of his successors. Boring was executed horizontally to begin with but very soon became vertical. The men who controlled the apparatus were protected from the inevitable fall-out of shavings.

In our opinion the machines for polishing mirror surfaces are more interesting and presupposed the solution of a number of difficulties in obtaining regular surfaces. For flat mirrors the same crank gives an alternating movement to the surface to be polished and a continuous circular movement to the mill which carries the

Leonardo da Vinci: printing press.

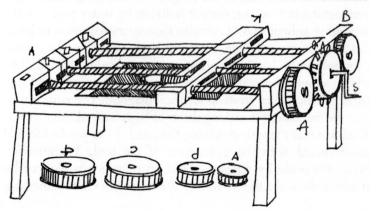

Leonardo da Vinci: machine for cutting wooden screws.

abrasive matter. Leonardo conceived of machines differing slightly from one another, for polishing mirrors with concave surfaces, according to the radius of curvature and according to the focal distance. The same crank turns, on two different planes, the surface to be polished and the mill. For Leonardo a good concave spherical mirror had to have a focal distance of F8. These mirrors were made during his time in Rome when Leonardo was studying the formation of images.

We thus see how limited are the mechanics of Leonardo. His applications are not very numerous, but he is the first to have as it were formulated the problems of industrial technology. However, he appeared to be little interested in machines which we judge to be very important; they had appeared recently and because of this might have engaged the attention of those who were preoccupied with technical progress. The most extraordinary example, which did not affect Leonardo alone, was that of printing. Again Leonardo is one of the first to give us a drawing, still very much simplified, of a printing press. We will return to this problem of the surprising omissions of these generally curious men.

Leonardo was also one of the first of his group to be interested in the textile industry. This industry was important in Tuscany and Lombardy. He applied himself to the study and the perfecting of a number of textile machines.

A certain ignorance, long cherished and still not completely dispelled, has attributed to Leonardo the important advances in the perfecting of the spinning-wheel. The spinning-wheel was, at first, a simple distaff with a spindle mounted on a turning axis. In order to make a true spinning instrument, the machine had to be given a device that brought about a second twist of the material before it was wound on to the bobbin. The invention of this was not much before the time of Leonardo: it is certainly shown with remarkable clarity in a German manuscript of about 1470. Part of Leonardo's imaginative effort was concerned with the relatively minor problem of the equal distribution of the thread on the bobbin. It could be achieved by a to-and-fro movement derived from the continuous circular movement of the wheel. The transformation was made thanks to the ingenious solution noted above: that of the wheel toothed along half its circumference, engaging two lantern wheels placed at the extremities of a diameter.

It does not appear that Leonardo sought to make his wheel completely automatic. Nevertheless he imagined a wheel with a number of spindles, the movement of which is very difficult to understand. The spinning of silk had been automatic since the end of

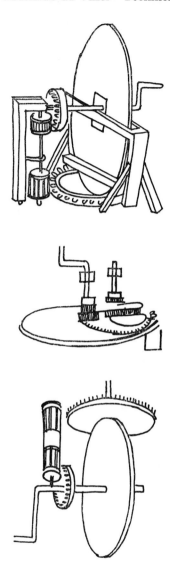

Leonardo da Vinci: mirror polishing apparatus.

the thirteenth century. This was because unwound silk thread is very long and spinning consists only of the twisting of a number of single threads. Leonardo thought of a way of stopping the machine as soon as the thread broke which was, indeed, one of the great drawbacks of the operation. He notes the importance of the crossing of the threads in the spinning of silk. Leonardo's 'inventions' in regard to spinning are thus only partial ones and do not in any way affect the organization of textile techniques of the period.

Machines for making rope, that is to say for twisting together a number of trands, were relatively easy to conceive, and there is no doubt that this industry had long been mechanized, at least in an elementary fashion. Leonardo shows a number of machines for rope-making: one with three strands, the other with fifteen. The essential was that the cord being made should be tightly and equally stretched. The stretching and twisting appear to have been very suitable. It remains to discover whether this very simple machine was not already in use at this date.

The question of the power loom is different. It is known that constant efforts were made, from the second half of the sixteenth century onwards, to mechanize the processes of weaving and that this did not really start until the flying shuttle was invented by Kay in 1733. Leonardo has given in the *Codex Atlanticus* a general plan of a weaving machine, accompanied by some detailed sketches of important parts. But this mechanism has to be interpreted, since much about it is obscure. The opening of the warp threads, the movement of the loom, and the movement of the textile were simple operations, but the passage of the shuttle was difficult to carry out. Leonardo used a number of elements for transmitting and cor-relating movements, including toothed wheels, chains, and mobile valves, the working of which must have been somewhat hazardous. The shuttle system indicated by Leonardo has in fact never been properly understood.

Other textile machines were designed by Leonardo, the conception of which was simpler. One of these was the machine for carding cloth. He imagines a continuously moving machine which passes the material in front of a frame to which the carding-brushes are fixed. The tension of the cloth, the two ends of which have been sewn, is regulated, which, at the same time, determines the force of the carding-brushes. He has another machine with a non-continuous movement: by movement of mechanical rollers the pressure of the material on the carding-brushes could be regulated. This last machine is very similar to the apparatus used at the end of the last century.

Leonardo's last textile machines deal with the operation of cloth

Opposite:
Various textile processes (fifteenth-century miniature).

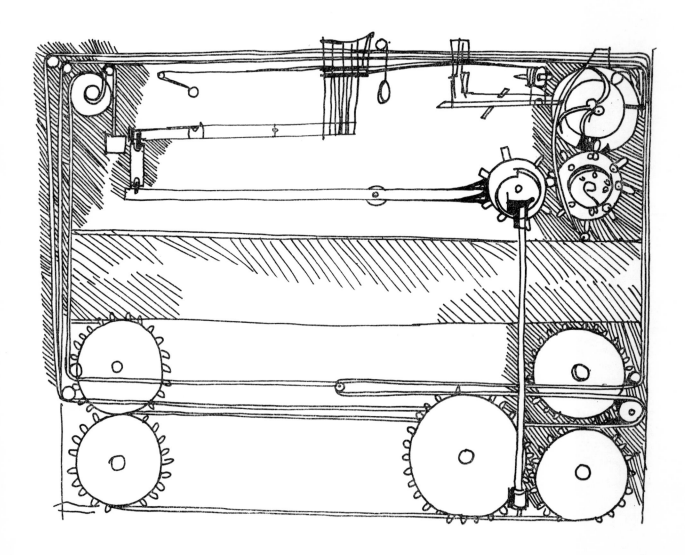

Leonardo da Vinci: automatic weaving machine.

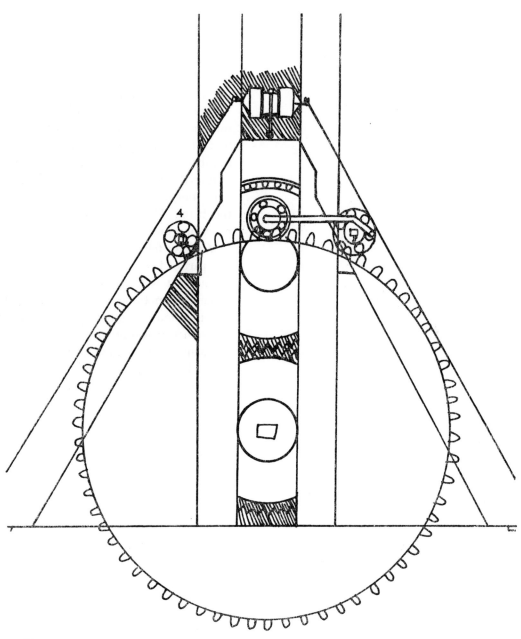

Leonardo da Vinci: cloth carding machine.

shearing. He imagined an apparatus operating simultaneously on a number of lengths. Three series of movements had to be carried out: that of the forces themselves which is done by a system of cams and cords, the lateral advancement of the frame holding the cloth which is achieved by the winding of a cord fixed on the axis of the cam system, and the progressive advancement of the cloth when the whole width has been sheared, achieved by an arresting device which is automatically unlocked when the entire width has been sheared. We also see that for many parts of the mechanism Leonardo hesitated between alternative solutions: a particularly striking case is the mechanism which brings together the shears and the heddles.

Leonardo pushed the difficulty further since he imagined a machine to be used for shearing the small woollen berets which were worn by Italian peasants and which were produced in fairly large numbers. The beret is placed on a revolving block of wood which enables the piece to be sheared to be turned. The shears, mounted on a pivoting axis, slide on a frame which corresponds with the shape of the beret. This was a much more delicate mechanism than the preceding one.

We have felt it necessary, for a number of reasons, to dwell upon this part of Leonardo's work.

The first is the fact that this interest in the textile industry is certainly something new. It is the first time that we see an engineer of this period trying to improve an industrial manufacturing process. Or, rather, it was not a question of improving the processes, but of mechanizing the operations which were in current use. Leonardo, as we shall see in the case of the flying machine, took as his point of departure concrete observations, the regularity of which permitted mechanization. Of all his machine designs, these are among the most advanced. He was not content with a vague and superficial sketch; he presented total views on a number of planes, he designed certain details and certain important pieces. In the case of certain mechanisms it is clear that he tried to find the solution which seemed best to him and he left us evidence of his hesitations. There is no doubt, as a single glance will be enough to show, that these sketches are, from the technical point of view of course, the best drawings of Leonardo da Vinci which have come down to us. We find in them the precision and clarity of some of the pages of Francesco di Giorgio.

It is also probably true to say that these machines, original in relation to the endeavours of his predecessors, are the best conceived. The carding and shearing machines, to a greater extent than the spinning or weaving machines, allowed Leonardo to give proof of his mechanical ability. If everything is not perfect, we can, however,

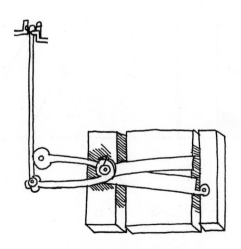

Leonardo da Vinci: cloth shearing machine.

see that he knows how to assemble an appropriate mechanism and calculate its effects. His combinations appear to be perfectly logical.

It seems impossible to speak of Leonardo as a technician without at least mentioning the flying machine, which is at least equal to the *Mona Lisa*'s smile as a source of its author's fame. The fundamental idea of the engineer was that human flight is possible by a mechanical imitation of nature. It is exactly the same principle that Leonardo applied to the construction of textile machines: he had observed the workman at his task and had tried to reproduce mechanically movements into which the mind does not enter. Leonardo's first observations on the flight of birds led him to some important conclusions. Thus he notes that the kite 'beats his wings moderately' and tries particularly to use air currents to keep him airborne. When he cannot find this support he replaces it by moving his wings more rapidly. When his wings are tired he can rest them by planing. We may say at the outset that the form of human flight envisaged by Leonardo was, in great part, what today we would call gliding. Observations then follow on wing positions, on the functions of feathers, whether they should be more or less open, on direction of flight which must be into the wind in order to rise. There is no doubt that the whole of this study is most remarkable.

The design for the machine itself certainly cannot be taken quite so seriously. For the wings he drew his inspiration from those of the bat, since these appeared to him to be the most logical and, no doubt, easier to create artificially than feathered wings. He then calculates the aerofoil required for given weights. It is easy to make similar calculations for birds: the wing of the pelican represents the square root of his weight. This analogy then led him to determine the shape of the wing, that is to say the ratios between length and width. The wing of the bat, which he took as a model, is not a rigid mechanism but is articulated. A series of sketches in the Museum of Valenciennes shows Leonardo's attempts to reproduce these movements with the aid of suitably chosen articulated systems.

The man must be placed vertically and move the wings with either his arms or his legs. The calculation of the force required was a much more difficult matter. Leonardo had come to the conclusion that a bird was a machine possessing superabundant power and that the availability of this power enabled it to attack and defend itself, which his flying man did not need to do.

There is no need to dwell upon a machine which has been abundantly reproduced and of which detailed studies have been made. Certainly there was some element of amazement in all these specifications which he gives on the materials to be used, on the

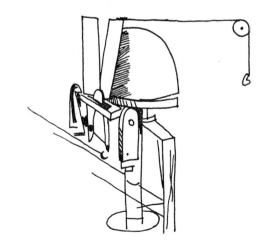

Leonardo da Vinci: machine for shearing caps.

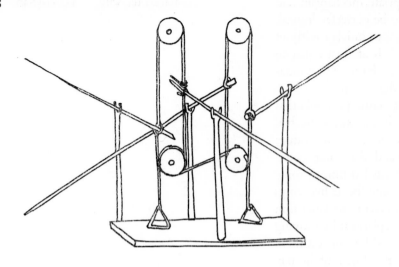

Leonardo da Vinci: studies for flying-machine.

probabilities of falling and on the means of escaping without injury. The idea was certainly not new and although mechanical reproduction of nature, which is the property of automata, had already been attempted, it is nevertheless true that Leonardo's observation was extraordinarily penetrating.

Leonardo da Vinci's curiosity led him also into a number of other fields in which he did not show himself superior to his predecessors. The mechanical chiming clock, of which he left a drawing, is a copy of the one already devised by Francesco di Giorgio. Leonardo was also interested in the problems of vehicles capable of moving by themselves. These were probably mechanisms applicable equally to combat chariots as to the enormous animals exhibited at the pageants of which we have spoken. Leonardo's design for an 'automobile' is far inferior to that of Francesco di Giorgio, but the principles are more or less identical.

The same could be said of the diving suit. We have seen that the idea was a very ancient one. Like flight, the descent of man under water is a very ancient dream. The miniatures of innumerable manuscripts of the History of Alexander illustrate apparatus which could be used for going to the bottom of the sea. From Kyeser onwards we begin to see individual outfits and on page 70 we have reproduced the design of a diving suit of very modern appearance from the manuscript of the anonymous engineer of the Hussite War. Leonardo's diver, a rapid sketch without detail, is by no means superior to those sketches of half a century earlier.

We have thus passed from the familiar to the original and from reality to fantasy. At the end of this very brief review of Leonardo's technical activity it is useful, however, to recall the essential elements and to remind ourselves of the proportion of this research.

If the last lines of this chapter have shown us some new curiosities and some that were original ideas in relation to those of his predecessors, Leonardo remains, nevertheless, well within the tradition which we have followed almost from antiquity. The Florentine is in no way a precursor on the strictly technical plane; he has the same preoccupations, he carried out the same investigations which, with inevitable deviations, had long been pursued. Certainly from the beginning of the fifteenth century we may say that there existed a school of engineers whose main centres of interest were the military arts and hydraulics. To this was added, at least in Italy, an undoubted interest in automata, taken in the very general sense of the word, which is also an ancient heritage, and a highly developed artistic sense due to a common education.

Any one of these engineers might bring to this knowledge and to these investigations a small personal note. The anonymous writer of the Hussite War had noted the details of a machine for polishing precious stones. Taccola had amused himself in the steam baths. Leonardo chose the textile industry and the flying machine. These are minor points and the underlying curiosity was the same for one and all.

There are certainly some differences and the discrepancies are obvious. This is incontrovertible on the level, first of all, of drawing: there is nothing in common between Kyeser's drawing and the sketches of Leonardo. The training of the Italian engineer of the second half of the fifteenth century counted for a lot in this development. The conception itself of processes or of machines remains the same, but the mechanism itself is modified as far as can be judged. There is progress in each part of each machine.

New ideas appeared which were certainly due to external factors. Thus the importance of the implements of war tended to diminish in relation to fortification which became the masterpiece of the engineer's art. The engineer is no longer 'master of the engines', he has become a true architect and builder.

Leonardo emerges in short as in every respect one of the Renaissance engineers whom we have tried to study. His life, at least what we know of it, and his work are exactly parallel to the life and work of Francesco di Giorgio. He fits perfectly into this environment that we have learnt to understand. It is a far cry from this to the universal genius who has so often been described. Alberti, Francesco di Giorgio, and Leonardo are certainly men of the same stamp.

No doubt the difference of period differentiates them. In place of the blunders and misunderstandings of the early days, more rational, more considered activity and thought gradually asserted themselves. And this was only natural. The ball governor conceived by Francesco di Giorgio shows that a feeling for mechanics could be accompanied by observation and deduction. Alberti had shown that the practice of science, at least of a certain mathematical science, combined well with technical activities. It appears that by the end of the fifteenth century this path had been pursued much further.

We would be neglecting an important part of our research if we did not add a few words on Leonardo in this connexion. It would seem that it was one of the main characteristics of his activity that he passed imperceptibly from methods used by many people with variable results towards that reflection which could be suggested by the use of different techniques. And it was in this respect that Leonardo da Vinci showed himself to be – to use M. Koyré's just distinction – more of a technologist than a technician.

It would be unjust and useless to define Leonardo only in relation to his profession of engineer. Beyond the suppositions of his biographers, beyond the guesses and the probabilities, beyond the illogicality and the prejudice of those who suppose that Leonardo necessarily influenced Bramante – because, for example, they do not wish to believe that Leonardo drew buildings Bramante had designed – it is difficult not to recognize in Leonardo something other than that which we have seen up to now. Not the philosopher or the mathematician: Alberti had been both and of a better strain. But the Leonardo with whom we are concerned endeavoured with imperfect means, which he doubtless knew to be imperfect, to construct a technique, to give it a validity other than that of mere efficiency or mere success.

Perhaps to the very extent to which he was never, properly speaking, a practical technician or rather, perhaps, because he never practised consistently, his real activity having doubtless been limited, like his painting, to a few works carried out at long intervals, Leonardo's technological research, supported by a remarkable spirit of observation, changed its direction. It is perhaps this which distinguishes him most clearly from the engineers of his time, the San Gallo for example, Francesco di Giorgio less so, possibly, and Alberti most of all. There is still a tradition here but it is more tenuous because we know very little about it. These are problems which are very ancient. The Greeks themselves had too much scientific intelligence and technical sense not to have raised them and, as we have seen in the case of the techniques themselves, the same questions are repeated throughout the centuries. The sagging of beams is one and ballistics is another.

If Archytas or Archimedes had, in their time, succeeded in com-

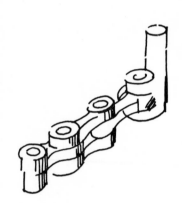

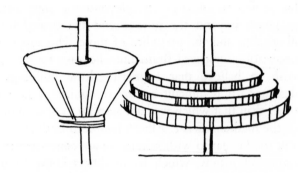
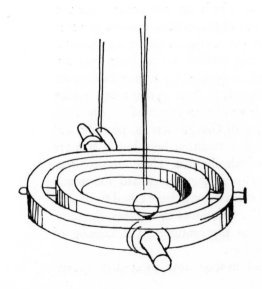

Leonardo da Vinci: types of gears.

bining scientific knowledge with technical experience, this union had weakened, although it would not be safe to say that it had totally disappeared. Beaujouan, as we have noted, has clearly demonstrated the interdependence between scholasticism which one would be tempted to regard as very pure and abstract and utilitarian techniques. The state of mind which we shall try to analyse in Leonardo da Vinci is thus not in itself a total novelty: it is only that we know little about the precedents, especially those which were closely related to utilitarian techniques. The scholars themselves are more familiar to us.

We would recall the words of Gundisalvo, written in the twelfth century:

'the science of engines teaches us how to imagine and to invent the manner of adjusting natural bodies by an *ad hoc* artifice that conforms to a numerical calculation in such a way that we can use it in the way we wish.'

We must not be misled by this numerical calculation. There was no formula – no kind of calculation to be applied to masonry, to the construction of lifting machines or to arms, all fields embraced by this science of engines.

The examination of certain facts of a technical order leads us to believe, however, that numerical relations were established. This was certainly the case in operating trebuchets, in the construction of certain vaulted buildings and in the erection of buttresses in particular. However, there was never any question, whatever the material might be, of building by reason based on precise calculation.

Advanced technological research was indeed carried out without the mathematical view of techniques, an aim which in any case had long been asserted. We have seen that Alberti was preoccupied with the nature of the materials which he used, and that Francesco di Giorgio exhausted all the possible formulae for constructing a machine for producing a given effect.

This quest was also pursued by Leonardo and often in a systematic manner. We will take only one example, the most significant. In the field of mechanics Leonardo was deeply interested in the problem of gears. Doubtless all the engineers of the period had come across problems in this connexion which were hard to overcome. Gears were made of wood, they wore out rapidly and absorbed a considerable amount of energy. Only two systems were used, both of which had long been known: toothed wheels and spindle-shaped lantern wheels. No one had dreamed of pursuing, or even of simply returning to, Pappus's mathematical calculations on gearing. Stepping-down was known but, it would seem, without any mathematical formula. Francesco di Giorgio added to these systems

Alignment of pinion axis in relation to the centre of the toothed-wheel and the effects of wear. Drawing by Leonardo da Vinci.

the endless screw, for which he appeared to have a decided pre-dilection. Finally, Taccola presented an example of chain trans-mission in a drawing which is still very tentative. Leonardo has left numerous drawings of gears. He must have understood that the solution of the problem would condition the whole future of machinery. A drawing in the *Codex Atlanticus* shows that Leonardo used geometry, of a very simple type, for determining the path of toothed wheels. He also tried to avoid the friction and wear we have mentioned. Although lantern wheels could not be altered, the shape of the teeth was of great importance. Designs and notes appear to show that the engineer was much concerned with this question and may have carried out certain experiments of which hints remain.

Leonardo also passed beyond the stage of improvements. He clearly tried to find other types of gears, more solid and more regular. Whoever has seen an old machine, fitted with toothed wheel and lantern wheel gearing, in operation will at once have noticed the jerky and irregular movement of such apparatus. Leonardo designed conical gears, which allowed motion to be transmitted on two perpendicular planes. He also thought of helical gears, which ensured a more regular motion, but did not reach the stage of the modern staggered gears which are, at least for certain types of motion, the most uniform. In notebook B a trapezoidal gear is shown.

This research is interesting but no outcome was possible. Despite a few trials, Leonardo does not appear fully to have applied the required geometrical knowledge for obtaining a perfect gearing path. The gears, furthermore, should have been of metal, but at that period neither metallurgy nor the working of metals had the necessary means of making them. The same could be said for the superb drawings of articulated chains in the *Codex Atlanticus*.

Leonardo does not appear to have enquired as far into the trans-formation of motion. Irregular gearings did not make their appear-ance until the middle of the sixteenth century. We have seen that he also tried to find simple and practical solutions for replacing the connecting-rod and crank, which was difficult to achieve in practice. One of these shows a certain originality. It is similar to the mech-anism devised for transforming pendular motion into continuous circular motion which provides an elegant and simple solution.

Always haunted by the hope of being able to construct a multiple-purpose machine, Leonardo soon arrived at the idea called, perhaps not quite correctly, 'gear change'. This is simply a lantern in the form of a truncated cone which was probably difficult to keep in contact with the toothed wheel with which it engaged.

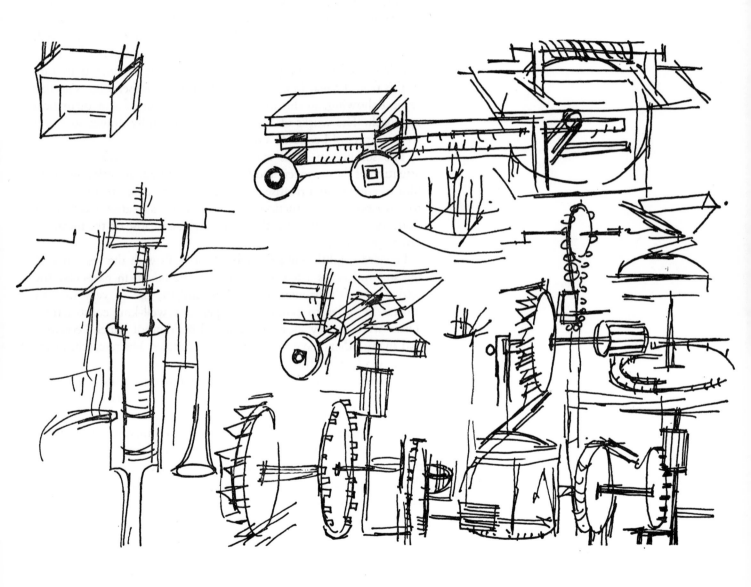

Leonardo da Vinci: studies of transmission mechanisms.

It is none the less true that this research in a sector of practical mechanics, which does not pass beyond the stage of practicalities, is already something new. Francesco di Giorgio had many times supplied a number of solutions for the same machine. Nevertheless we do not see him tackling a precise and specialized problem of mechanical technique as did Leonardo.

The stability of buildings has always been the main problem facing architects. This problem became more intricate when the number of vaults and arches increased. Existing methods of formulating the canons of solid construction were also undoubtedly improved. Unhappily we have no history of architectural techniques which will enable us to follow this progress. It may be that documents are rare in this field. Leonardo is one of the first to leave useful hints on this subject showing, in this instance, the beginning of a mathematical approach. The works of Sartoris have successfully drawn attention to this aspect of Leonardo's research.

The solidity of walls and the appearance of cracks drew the attention of the engineer, and Leonardo proposed, doubtless with the idea of compiling a treatise on architecture, to dedicate a few pages to this aspect of construction: 'first of all make a treatise of the causes of the crumbling of walls; then, separately, a treatise on the means of remedying this'.

Leonardo rightly links the solidity of walls with the resistance of the soil and notes a few precautions to be taken, in particular the setting up of horizontal foundations and the use of very smooth mortar in order to acquire a proper and well-knit construction. These were merely ideas about sound building of which Leonardo and many others have left numerous examples. His research, however, goes beyond this.

Leonardo's attention was even more powerfully drawn to the causes of crumbling than to formulating a doctrine of sound building. Like a doctor he must be able to diagnose correctly in order to indicate what remedies should be applied. Numerous observations enabled Leonardo to distinguish the direction of the cracks, whether they were vertical or horizontal, their form, according to whether the opening is wider towards the top or towards the bottom, and to attribute to each case an obvious cause: 'when the crack of a wall is wider at the top than at the bottom it is a clear proof that the cause of destruction is to be found outside the perpendicular of the crack'. Leonardo, however, does not appear to have given to these problems all the further ramifications that he had envisaged. All that remain are fugitive notes which are, however, sufficient to demonstrate the beginnings of precise methods.

The solidity of beams was, as we have said, a very old problem. Alberti and Francesco di Giorgio were concerned with this but none of them, as far as we know, had looked for mathematical formulae. By calculations that were still very approximate, and also perhaps by a series of experiments, Leonardo managed to establish the laws of the elasticity of beams, the norms of pressure-resistance in square and cylindrical beams and beams that were free or built in at either or both ends, and of the resistance of built-up beams, the builder's terror. He also broached the problem of a beam fixed at one end, and weighted, always regarded as Galileo's problem.

In regard to square horizontal beams supported at each end, Leonardo had found that the resistance varies according to the square of the side and inversely with the length, which is a fair approximation. Carrying his research further, he calculated the sag of beams of square section, weighted in the middle. This sag, he thought, was in direct proportion to the weight, but he did not go as far as to establish the relationship which is now accepted, that it is directly related to the cube of the length and inversely in proportion to the fourth power of the side of the square. He eliminated the modulus of elasticity and the moment of inertia which Nemorarius had mentioned.

We can see clearly that Leonardo carried out experiments to compare the resistance of prismatic and cylindrical beams in order to find out the effects of bending and traction, all investigations which were to be taken up later by Hooke (1635–1703). His reasoning, as can be clearly seen in these studies, was undoubtedly intuitive to begin with, then it proceeds by analogy and approximation. But there were also some elements and some kinds of development which are missing from his work.

Leonardo was also much interested in the practice and theory of the arch. He tried to evaluate the thrust on the shoulders of an arch, to formulate the laws to be observed in the spread of the load which an arch supports, as well as the resistance of columns. He studied square and circular supports, placed vertically, in which the upper fulcrum is uniformly weighted. He estimated that the resistance to pressure is proportional to the surface load in the case of a square support, which is correct, and inversely proportional to the relation between height and the side of the square or radius of the base circle, although it is in fact inversely proportional to the square of this relation. Thus, reasoning by analogy, he thought that if one doubles, at equal height, the side of the square of the base or radius of the circle of the base, the resistance would be eight times greater, although in reality it is sixteen times greater.

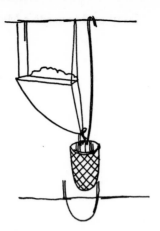

Leonardo da Vinci:
apparatus for measuring resistance to traction.

Thus Leonardo's analysis of statics revolved round masonry, the bearing of weighted arches, the cracking of stone façades. He apparently carried out many experiments concerned with the resistance of solid bodies to friction, pressure, and traction. He also carried out research concerning the centring and decentring of structures and calculations on scaffolding, and had set out static figures for cupolas, vaulting, and porticos. And the whole was often accompanied by the practical notes of which the engineers of the period were particularly fond. Thus in notebook A we find a number of recommendations on the construction of arches: avoid tie-irons, make sure that shoulders are secure and fill in angles well; if an accident takes place, undertake a serious examination that will show the cause of the errors that have been committed. Certain notes even concern earth tremors and the effects they can produce. And he devised certain structures to avoid the destruction caused by these phenomena.

Leonardo da Vinci's method certainly consisted in a search for numerical facts. These facts could be obtained only by a series of experiments; they were relatively easy to establish in certain cases, in that of beams for example, but much more difficult in others, as in that of masonry and arches. It is quite clear that the formulation of results could only be simple, that is to say expressed by ratios. As for the calculation itself, whether of measurements or formulae, there was no need for extreme precision, as Leonardo himself well knew. The engineer was easily satisfied with approximative facts or formulae. It is the first time, however, that we see the application of these methods in crafts in which people had long had to be content with traditional and unreasoned methods of appreciation.

He used exactly similar methods in the field of hydraulics, although here the use of mathematical formulae was less easy and consequently less generalized. Leonardo was looking above all for general information applicable to every case, which would enable an adequate solution to be found to any problem and, should the occasion arise, make possible the amendment of such elements as were inadequate to the end proposed.

It is certainly greatly to be regretted that Leonardo did not complete the treatise on water which he mentions so often and for which we have numerous highly interesting notes. In some places he indicates chapter headings, but the work seems to have been so vast in his head that it was unrealizable in practice. An attempt has, in fact, been made to collect these scattered notes that form the basis of an extremely advanced enquiry.

Leonardo's attention was especially attracted by three types of important problem. It would seem that the first was the formation of river beds: this was a problem suited to an engineer who had planned the straightening of certain rivers. The study of eddies could have a bearing on the construction and maintenance of canals and the installation of artificial objects in watercourses. All these researches led Leonardo towards more abstract questions, one of the main ones being the motion of water.

His ideas on the nature of water and on everything related to this question were only those of the period, vague, incomplete, and often erroneous. At most he was able to define the incompressibility of water, which was an easy observation. We must also leave out of account everything concerning the origin of rivers, which is more properly considered as a geographical than as a technological study.

It was certainly the right method, before engaging in the long and costly works of canalization which he was invited to undertake, to study the great laws of hydrology. Leonardo is one of the first, if not to have studied the formation of river beds in a systematic manner, at least to have put down in his notebooks some very pertinent observations. The notion of contours appears to have been unknown to him, but he reached conclusions on the age of channels, estimated according to the speed of the currents. An old river is characterized by the slowness of its waters. But Leonardo does not appear to have established any relationship between the courses of the rivers and the nature of the soil traversed. The formation of bends and sinuosities was an important matter, since the effort of the engineer would be mainly concerned with rectifying these. For Leonardo, tributaries were the cause of the first sinuosities (he had no notion of the possibility of the erosion of rocks by water). The water then leaves its straight course and strikes the bank in oblique fashion. It is thrust back at a similar angle. Thus are formed the sinuosities of rivers in soft earth. Leonardo also deduced the measures to be taken to rectify these. The confluence must be dealt with in such a way that the tributary makes a very acute angle with the course of the main stream. Leonardo observed, however, that this causes undermining, which makes for trouble: this happened with the river Po where works of this kind had been carried out. These meanders also caused the river to flow slowly. This could be proved by floods, which generally sweep away such obstacles, which, however, usually re-form after the floods have subsided. Thus, if one wants to avoid these difficulties, it is necessary to accelerate the flow of a river or of a canal. This Leonardo did in the Pontine Marshes: the drainage canal, which would naturally have been very slow, was accelerated by the introduction of two small torrents. Sinuosities, finally, are not permanent and 'rivers change their position'.

Apart from the course of the river, the shape of the bed was also an interesting problem. The sharper the fall, observed Leonardo, the deeper is the bed. Here again the age of a river can be determined: if rivers have an equal fall, the widest river will be the shallowest. The bed of a river does not form a regular channel; in straight watercourses the greatest depth is in the middle.

A river or stream hollows out its bed and also deposits alluvia. Here again Leonardo's observations are extremely precise. The engineer cannot neglect the formation and nature of alluvia. The most sluggish water, wrote Leonardo, discharges the material it carries most quickly. And again: 'Where the current is strongest, there are the largest pebbles'. His studies on eddies are the best known. Leonardo attached great importance to the origin and effects of eddies formed in running water. He certainly regarded them as one of the essential causes of the formation of the beds and banks of watercourses. Leonardo the painter was most certainly not insensitive to certain shapes observed in these eddies.

Pursuing his study further, Leonardo was led to the problem of the internal motions of water. His work on eddies led directly to this. It was easy to observe in a stream that the current did not flow uniformly. Thus, in a regular channel, he quickly recognized that water flows more swiftly at the centre than at the edges where it is subject to the friction of the banks. It was also possible to state that these various motions could give rise to counter-currents along the banks, generally affecting the solidity of the banks. The motions of deep water were much more difficult to observe, but for similar reasons it could be supposed that the current was more rapid on the surface than at greater depths.

Leonardo was also able to distinguish between the different streams of a waterfall and could reproduce in admirable drawings effects which only the most up-to-date photography has been able to show.

Leonardo da Vinci's observations cannot be too greatly admired. Although they do not deal with every aspect of hydraulic research, they contribute significantly to our knowledge of the motions of water. They do not, usually, contain measurements, despite the title of the book which was printed from his papers in the first years of the seventeenth century, but notes which are, nevertheless, very precise. The only law that Leonardo formulated was that of the flow of water. Pure observation by itself would probably not have enabled Leonardo to reach these results. There is no doubt that he must have carried out experiments on small models, in exactly the same way as modern hydraulic engineers. His apparatus was simple no doubt, but sufficient to reproduce effects which are sometimes not easily seen in nature. We have the drawing of small channels in wood, which Leonardo used for his experiments; some of these even show glass sides to give better observation, in particular of deep-water phenomena. It is also astonishing that Leonardo should have used for his studies of the motions of water, coloured water in which the different streams could be distinguished. The formation of waves, reflected waves, and interference also provided material for experiments that were perfectly carried out. We have preserved some illustrations of these experiments on models. We would mention the one which shows a deposit of alluvium around an obstacle placed at the bottom of a river bed. Leonardo constructed his small channel in wood. He put sand on the bottom and placed a stone in the middle. He sent sandy water through his model and observed that more numerous deposits were formed behind the obstacle. He observed at the same time how the water divided into streams in order to pass the obstacle. Leonardo usually made what we would call a primary observation. He then experimentally reconstructed the natural data, keeping only the essential elements, or at least those on which he wished to concentrate. He thus reached what he called a proposition, expressed in very general terms.

All these investigations have their limitations. The most serious lack, as we have already noted, would seem to be that of an adequate language that would have enabled him to express clearly in precise terms what he wished to say. Obscurities of language certainly constituted a serious obstacle to the development of some of his research. Thus elementary notions are often badly expressed and consequently block all possibility of correct reasoning. There are many phrases used by Leonardo that are difficult to understand. 'An entire mass of water', he wrote, for example, rather confusedly, 'presents in its width, depth, and height an innumerable variety of motions, as is shown by the moderately turbulent water in which bubbles and whirlpools constantly appear together with various eddies formed by the more turbid water which, from the bottom, rises to the surface.' Of all scientific techniques, language is perhaps the most precious.

Leonardo, however, was not trying to create a science. His observations were not systematic, and the ordering of his research was not logical. He wished to write not so much a scientific treatise as an engineer's summary. He was dealing with cases, not with laws. The chapter headings provide proof of this. 'Book on the various ways of equalizing the levels of waters, on the manner of turning watercourses when they cause damage, on the method of rectifying the courses of rivers which cover too much ground, on the method of making rivers branch out and of making them fordable, on the method of deepening river beds by means of different watercourses, on the method of controlling rivers to check at the beginning the erosion they cause . . .' The information given here is, in essence, utilitarian.

In his research into hydraulics, as before in his concern with practical architecture, Leonardo shows himself in the guise of a doctor – the expression is his – who wishes to prevent certain illnesses. The intellectual procedure is symptomatic and partly explains the methods chosen. There are few propositions which, although apparently general, are not followed by a practical application. Erosion of embankments caused by the presence of an obstacle at once becomes a warning against the presence of dead tree trunks abandoned by the banks of a canal. Banks are washed away by a narrow stream entering a river: this happens if a lock is narrower than the canal that follows. 'The bank which is moved back to widen a canal causes the sudden formation of an eddy which, at some depth below the surface, hollows out a deep concavity at the base of the bank thus causing it to collapse.' Obstacles placed at the bottom of rivers are also harmful. Leonardo had rightly noted that an obstacle 'placed on the smooth, level bed of a river causes it to be eroded and to become uneven'.

The studies of waterfalls and eddies could be applied to mills. Leonardo was interested in water power. Two aspects of the question drew his attention: both the form of the fall and the position of the wheel and design of the vanes. 'The mill water should strike the vanes of the wheels at right angles. Water with less fall strikes the wheel beyond the perpendicular of its fall.' And again: 'the percussion of water on the wheel reaches its maximum power when it strikes at equal angles. The percussion between equal angles will have greater power when the current of water and the motion of the wheel follow the same direction.' Finally: 'the water wheel turns better when the water which moves it does not rebound after striking it. The straighter and longer the motion, the greater will be the power of the shock it causes.' We could cite many more examples of a kind of technical doctrine arising slowly from observations followed by experiments.

In the field of hydraulic energy it was possible to take one step further and to try, as before in the field of building, to establish mathematical formulae. Although we do not possess the results, at least Leonardo stated the problems. 'Given the depth of a waterfall and its slant, as well as the power of the wheel which is its object, we try to determine what will be the height of the fall in order to equal the power of the wheel.' Such examples are not unique. 'Knowing the resistance of a wheel, as well as the slant and fall of a waterfall, we ask what would be the volume to equal this resistance. Given the volume of the waterfall, its length and its inclination, we ask whether the power of the wheel is equal to that of the water. Given the resistance of the wheel and the inclination of the water and its volume we ask what is the height of the fall.' These texts are extremely important. Not only is the problem stated in mathematical terms in relation to supposedly familiar laws, but it may be stated in all possible ways. All cases had to be envisaged. Only one element is missing in the face of such an admirable statement of the problems; this is the solutions and the mechanism of calculation. So that we are justified in wondering whether, after this excellent logic, Leonardo was not, after all, using poor traditional formulae derived from the narrowest empiricism. Perhaps this does not matter. At least we must record the development: it was to be heavy with consequences.

The fact is that there were fields in which his mental equipment showed itself to be sufficient. Did not Leonardo outline a theory of water pumps? But here he could measure easily: he knew the rate of flow through the pipes and the capacity of the cylinders. It was another matter to reason about natural phenomena that were not at all easy to measure.

The practical aim which was proposed, the only valid one, as we shall see, was certainly contemptuous of these scientific subtleties. From observation to observation and from observation to experiment Leonardo was able to state problems, purely technical problems, in general terms. We thus come to the final process, that of the reasoning which enables the engineer to relate his particular case to a general problem. When this has been accomplished, a true engineering science will be in existence. Thus the remarkable passage, too rarely quoted, in which Leonardo envisages the measures necessary to save his house, situated near a river, on a bank which is about to cave in. He defines his case by reference to established propositions and deduces from these the action required to remedy the situation. We owe it to Leonardo to quote his own words:

'I have a house upon the bank of a river, and the water is carrying off the soil beneath it and is about to make it fall in ruin; consequently I wish to act in such a way that the river may fill me up again the cavity it has already made, and strengthen the said house for me. In a case such as this we are governed by the fourth of the second,

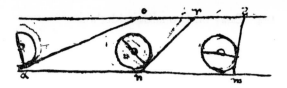

Action of falling water on a mill wheel by Leonardo da Vinci.

which proves that "the impetus of every movable thing pursues its course by the line along which it was created"; for which reason we shall make a barrier at the slant n m, but it would be better to take it higher up at o p, so that all the material from your side of the hump might be deposited in the hollow where your house is; and the material from the hump k would then do the same, so that it would serve the need in the same winter. But if the river were great and powerful the said barrier would have to be made in three or four attempts, the first of which, made in the direction that the water is approaching, ought to project beyond its bank a fourth part of the width of the river; then, below this, you should make another, distant as far as the summit of the leap that the water makes when it falls from the first barrier – for in this summit of its leap the water leaves the summit of the mound made by shingle which was hollowed out by the first percussion, made by the water when it fell from the first barrier upon its bed. And this second dam extends halfway across the breadth of the river. The third should follow below this, starting from the same bank and at the same fixed distance from the second as the second was from the first; and it follows its length as far as three-quarters of the width of the river. And so you will proceed with the fourth dam which will close the whole river across. And from these four dams or barriers there will result much greater power than if all this material had been formed into one barrier, which in uniform thickness would have closed the whole width of the stream. And this happens by the fifth of the second, where it is proved that the material of one single support, if it be quadrupled in length, will not support the fourth of that which it used formerly to support, but much less.'

We apologise for having quoted this lengthy passage which is valuable less for the exact terms in which it is expressed than for its form which faithfully reflects the method used. We may admire this collection of empirical formulae of which some are numbered, surrounded by general formulae, which are relatively vague. The whole of Leonardo da Vinci, the whole of his method, is revealed in this text from the *Codex Atlanticus*. In searching for new ways forward, it is difficult to disentangle oneself from the old procedures, or, to put it another way, the new outlook is not yet capable of covering all exigencies of action.

There is no question but that we have now reached a point of development beyond that of Leonardo's predecessors or contemporaries. Neither Francesco di Giorgio nor San Gallo built up such a system of reasoning. When Francesco di Giorgio designed his ball governor, which is better in its practicality than the rather confused measures suggested by Leonardo in a particular case, he was not even led by the intuition which assumes a problem to have been stated and a solution to have been found immediately, without intellectual analysis; it was instinct.

Leonardo is no longer at this stage. His knowledge – let us be clear about this for we are dealing with engineers – his theoretical experience, form, so to speak, the sign-posts, sometimes few and far between, which mark the way forward and which embrace all the empirical deductions of previous generations.

If, in the end, technique is designed to meet scientific standards, two conditions are required. First, a condition of measurement, which will enable the technician to establish formulae and to know whether the reality which confronts him corresponds effectively to the formulae or how it can be made to correspond; this is exactly the question which Leonardo asked himself earlier in relation to mills. Secondly, a condition of ideation, which is to know the reality of certain facts, their nature, their place in a more general system of knowledge. Leonardo da Vinci understood this, no doubt, but very incompletely.

The problems of measurement are situated halfway between technique and science. Leonardo, as is generally known, concentrated on these fields and produced some valuable solutions. Some indicate the practical approach, such as the articulated instrument devised to construct mechanically the solution of Alhazen's problem, essentially a technical problem (to find the point of incidence on a spherical mirror of a ray proceeding from a luminous source so that the reflected ray passes through a given point; it is necessary, in fact, to construct an ellipse tangential to the circle and having its foci on the two given points). This instrument, writes Sergescu, indicates a profound knowledge of the properties of conical shapes.

We must not be deceived. All Leonardo's measuring instruments show the same technical preoccupations which are approximative. The proportional compass and the parabolic compass are also engineers' instruments. There are numerous designs of scales in his manuscripts, notably a diagram of hydrostatic scales. The podometer, for the use of surveyors, ideas on hygrometry and notions on water levels, together with the anemometers, all form part of an equipment that was, if not in common use, at least already thought of at this period. Nor are Leonardo's astronomical instruments in any way different from those that had already been in use for a very long time.

The compasses are doubtless the best of these. The simplest

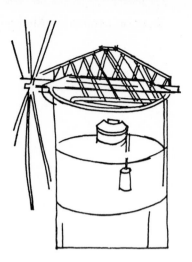

Leonardo da Vinci: windmill.

Leonardo da Vinci: mechanical spit.

compasses, those with a flat hinge, are the ones which were used at this period. Daumas has, however, mentioned the beam-compass, the essential tool of the great constructors of scientific apparatus: the section of the beam, the shape of the points or of the slides, reveal an obvious desire for improvement. Leonardo even conceived the idea of a beam-compass with an adjustable screw. There are other, even more remarkable, instruments. Among these are the ones to be used for measuring the resistance of wires to traction, but the idea of this is relatively simple.

Even in this field it was difficult to think of innovations. Practitioners had at their disposal neither the material means nor the scientific solutions that would have enabled them to make the decisive progress that was not achieved until two centuries later. Leonardo's equipment is not, properly speaking, measuring apparatus. It consists mainly, as one may well imagine since he was an engineer, of mechanical implements of geometrical construction.

There is no better yardstick for determining the scientific limitations of men like Leonardo da Vinci than their studies on steam machines. The links had been established for some time. We know that the point of departure, of which the Middle Ages never lost sight, was the aeolipile of Hero of Alexandria which we find here once again. The differences between steam, air, and warm air are very difficult to distinguish. The aeolipile, the windmill, and the automatic spit, of which we have designs prior to Leonardo, appear to proceed from the same principle.

Leonardo knew the work of Hero, if not directly, at least through commentaries or references. He mentions the *Pneumatica* as well as the *Spiritalia*, which he probably knew only by way of Giorgio Valla, whose commentary, a work that was certainly a revelation to Leonardo, was published in Venice in 1501.

Hero's 'fountain' was much reproduced by Leonardo. At least eight complete drawings have been counted. He also borrowed from Hero a considerable number of siphons. All this had already been seen in Fontana's *Bellicorum instrumentorum liber* and in Francesco di Giorgio, in particular in the Laurenziana manuscript annotated by Leonardo. Leonardo also knew some of the devices of Philo of Byzantium. Thus Leonardo's ideas on steam follow a perfectly traditional line. It would be interesting to discover in detail why Leonardo was unable to advance upon his predecessors, why his method proved to be unworkable in the face of problems, the mechanical solution of which was to appear much later.

The point of departure seems to have been an experiment which had been known for many years and the explanation of which long remained obscure. This is the phenomenon 'of the water which rises in a vessel turned upside-down on a container full of water when a candle or a burning coal is introduced into the latter'. The same thing happened with oil lamps with automatic feed, of the type which were later to be called 'bouteilles de Mariotte', sketches of which are shown in Leonardo's work.

It is quite clear that the notion of steam is a mystery to Leonardo da Vinci. On this subject he has the ideas which Vitruvius demonstrated in his first book, in which he compares wind with the 'air' which comes out of the aeolipile. Leonardo, however, went further and formed a theory of the generation of a vacuum by the condensation of water vapour. This theory was derived from two series of observations: the one of an experimental nature, and the other concerning the phenomena of nature. The experiments are those of the upturned vessel which we mentioned above: the water vapour expels the air and then by condensation forms the vacuum. Then, thanks to the atmospheric pressure, the water in the basin into which the neck of the retort was plunged rises. There was certainly a vacuum because the rising water replaces the air which was there before.

The natural observation is more doubtful. It concerns rain which is condensed water vapour, and which leaves a vacuum in the place where this condensation occurred; the vacuum is filled by the surrounding air, as may be seen from the wind or currents of air formed at the same time. Thus steam has a double mechanical effect, its own, as may be seen in the aeolipile, and that which results from condensation. From Hero to Leonardo da Vinci, to Della Porta at the end of the sixteenth century and to Huygens at the end of the seventeenth, the differences are very slight. All this is also mingled with certain quite erroneous theories. If Leonardo in fact possessed certain information on the nature and the potential power of steam it led him, by way of some perfectly correct opinions, to certain totally incorrect conclusions. In one passage he shows us the origin of rivers in volcanic heat. The earth, according to him, functions in some way as a gigantic distilling apparatus. These are some of the contradictions which we have already mentioned.

Since observation was insufficient, Leonardo, using a method with which he had been successful before, tried to advance by means of experiment. He thought it necessary to measure what steam was and we shall see that in so doing he, as it were, by-passes the steam-machine. The experiments appear to date from between 1504 and 1509, during his second stay in Florence. They appear in the *Leicester Codex*, at least as far as he pursued them.

The drawing is most striking. One would swear, if one did not see the explanations on the same page, that it was indeed a primitive steam-machine. In fact it was nothing of the kind.

Leonardo was trying only to measure steam. He thus took a square vessel which he half-filled with water, and over this water he placed the skin of a new-born calf which was to be filled with the steam which would be released when the bottom of the container was heated. In order to prevent any escape, a cover, strongly resembling a piston, was placed on top. But since this piston could, by its weight, alter the result of the experiment, it was counterbalanced by a weight to which it was tied by a cord and two pulleys. It was thus not, as it was with Huygens, a weight to be lifted when the atmospheric pressure acted after condensation, but simply one to counteract the weight of the cover. There are a number of sketches of this curious apparatus, the oddity of which lies mainly in its similarity to others. Leonardo in this way hoped to measure the quantity of water that disappeared and at the same time the quantity of steam that had been formed.

Such experiments could not lead very far. They, and some others, led Leonardo to conceive the war machine, which he called the *Architonitro*, and which he attributes, it is not known why, to Archimedes. It would appear that it is only, in fact, the famous experiment of the seventeenth century of making a cannon explode after having filled it with water and heated it. Leonardo used steam to expel a cannon ball. 'The *Architonitro* is a fine copper machine invented by Archimedes which throws out iron balls with great noise and violence. It is used in this way: a third of the instrument is placed in the midst of a great quantity of glowing coals. When the metal is white hot, turn the screw D which is in the upper part of the water reservoir abc; when the upper screw is closed, the reservoir will open at the top and all the water which it contains will descend into the heated part of the instrument. There it will immediately be transformed into such abundant 'smoke' that it will astonish the onlookers and even more so when they see with what force and noise this will happen. This engine threw a ball which weighs one talent to a distance of six stadia.'

Reti, who has studied with great care the texts of Leonardo concerning steam, points out a drawing in notebook F, which many admirers of Leonardo's technique have not mentioned. In this text Leonardo says quite certainly that it is an apparatus for raising weights. Reti considers it to be a cylinder and piston machine absolutely identical to those which were constructed at the end of the seventeenth century by Huygens and Papin and which worked

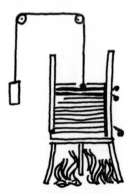

(above and opposite) Leonardo da Vinci: stages in the construction of a steam engine.

with powder. It is almost a hot air machine which acts directly by means of a piston-rod and not by the intermediary of a cord or a pulley as in the machines of Louis XIV's time.

Despite his good intentions, despite his experiments and his measurements, Leonardo nevertheless remained unable to penetrate the mysteries of steam. This clearly made it difficult for him to apply it, except in Hero's plaything, which was part of the pseudo-scientific folklore of that period, and in the famous *Architonitro* which has been the subject of so much discussion.

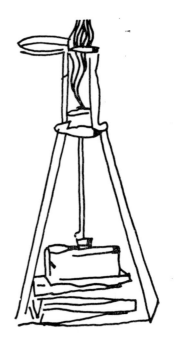

We hope by now to have reached a better understanding of Leonardo da Vinci's method. If this term implies coherent research, there was no method. Such coherence can only come from a scientific mind skilled in relating notions one to another and in constructing scientific systems of the kind that were to appear shortly after Leonardo da Vinci. Leonardo's technical knowledge is extremely fragmentary; it appears not to go beyond a certain number of particular problems which are treated very narrowly. It is even possible that its truth was more than anything else natural or experimental and not fundamentally abstract. 'In talking about water', he writes in notebook H, 'remember to call upon experiment and then on reasoning.' He does, however, wish to link together some of his propositions and through them to arrive somehow at a system, as in notebook G. But we feel that his mind is working very slowly and, without a hypothesis to support him, he sometimes falls into errors of observation. The approach is undeniably that of a practical man for whom theory is too far removed from reality and who constructs, using more or less general formulae, a system of prescriptions which are sufficient for his purposes. It is possible that Leonardo recognized that there might be something more beyond this.

His finality has nothing scientific about it, it is all pragmatic, real, almost down to earth. He admits this at the beginning of notebook F, when he writes: 'If you co-ordinate your notes on the science of the motion of water, remember to write below each proposition its applications, so that this knowledge does not remain unused'. Could any text be more symptomatic, more antiscientific, or, indeed, more a-scientific than this?

The gaps are thus too great, whatever may have been said, for Leonardo to appear in the final analysis as a true scientist. His learning and his scientific investigations bear only on those subjects with which he was familiar as a technician. It is true that Leonardo was never an artillery expert; he had no knowledge of ballistics, he does not mark a stage between Buridan and Tartaglia, and his dynamics were uncertain and vague.

A good approach would have been to find out whether Leonardo, even in those aspects where he appears to be an innovator, had not, in these fields also, taken over from others the slow work of investigation and progress. His quest for certain books surely shows that he was looking for confirmation of his suppositions. In certain subjects the books he records having used or asked for were numerous. In his study of hydraulics, to take only one example, we may follow him in citing Pliny the Elder, a small work of Aristotle apparently called *The Flooding of the Nile*, a work of Avicenna on liquids, the book by Frontinus on aqueducts, a treatise of Galen on the movement of liquids, a work of Theophrastus on flux and reflux, on eddies in water and water in general, and a treatise on water by the Bishop of Padua. But it is difficult to know what is concealed behind these more or less fanciful names or titles.

We must not deprive Leonardo of his true merits. His need to rationalize what until then was unknown to technicians must be granted. Technique was no longer the concern of artisans, of ignorant persons and of more or less valid traditions, more or less understood by those who had to apply them. Leonardo tried to define technical truths by the setbacks, mistakes, and catastrophes he experienced, just as doctors have acquired their knowledge of men only through the expedients of their illnesses. A crack in a wall, the undermining of a river bank, a bad metal alloy, are so many opportunities for learning the correct methods, which can then be established as principles on which future generations may act.

A scientist would have been preoccupied with fame, would have been aware of the enormous gaps that existed and would have tried to build up a scientific whole. Leonardo was an engineer who was concerned only with efficiency and whose efforts brought him no more than a means of acquiring power over the material world.

We have marvelled at the imagination shown by our engineers. Their increasingly improved powers of draughtmanship – there have been few studies of this kind on Leonardo da Vinci – and their undoubted faith in technical progress justify, in our opinion, the attention that we have given to it. Theirs was not a diversion for dilettantes. The engineers effectively carried out their profession, to which they brought a kind of passion and, sometimes, vain hopes. It was tempting, since the intellect never loses its rights, to end with Leonardo's astonishing quest, in which he endeavoured to put technique on to a higher plane. We might consider our curiosity gratified and our intellect satisfied, having reached a point where the possibilities of knowledge were ever multiplying.

We did, however, warn the reader at the very beginning of this study that it would be essential and, since there is no reason to spare our regrets, disappointing to examine the true technical situation of the period. In spite of this it may be permissible to believe that our efforts have not been useless, even if such influences are difficult to discern. We know enough about oral traditions to attach too much importance to the fact that certain manuscripts were unknown to the author's contemporaries. Leonardo was aware of the manuscripts of Taccola and of Francesco di Giorgio; it would be surprising if two men so attentive to what their neighbours were doing had not gathered the sense of Leonardo's own researches, even if we have no absolute proof of this.

We cannot give a general and precise picture of the techniques of the Renaissance which our fragmentary knowledge would also prevent us from presenting in bold outlines. We must, therefore, limit ourselves to indicating a few tendencies. The double aspect of this parallel between our engineers and the technique of their time has already been stated: on the one hand the considerable gaps that would exist in their work if we considered them as promoters of technical progress, and on the other, within the limits of their technical horizon, the place that they in fact held in the movement of ideas of this period. The term gaps which we have used is no doubt inappropriate. Our engineers had to occupy themselves neither with the many craftsmen's techniques nor even with a number of industrial techniques. Several volumes would not be enough to show all that they did not know. It has seemed suitable to isolate certain general tendencies and to concentrate on the fields which were their own. Although their curiosity ranged widely, none of them, including Leonardo da Vinci, were universal technicians.

This was the period, and no doubt our engineers are one of the most remarkable proofs of this, in which technical literature, with its specialization, its continuous research and its sometimes spectacular discoveries, was making its appearance. Even today this literature is not much studied and has had no attention drawn to it. We have mentioned, among first impressions, that even before the end of the fifteenth century there were important technical works, reflecting the curiosity of the period, certainly, but also indications of more profound, more systematic and better organized knowledge. The writers of antiquity and the authors of the Middle Ages had received the honour of being printed. Among contemporaries, Valturio and Alberti represent the technicians of the Renaissance and their major preoccupations. We have seen that they enjoyed considerable success.

In the first half of the sixteenth century there was a veritable avalanche of these treatises, in nearly all fields. New works were written, mere drafts received universal acclaim; all these books, mostly well illustrated, some of which contained echoes of classical work, shaped as it were contemporary techniques. Some of them maintained their interest for the public right up to the very end of the eighteenth century.

Of the works of Petrus de Crescentiis, the mediaeval agricultural economist, there were, between 1471 and 1550, six Latin editions, nine Italian editions (the first in 1478), seven French editions (the first in 1533), and one in German (in 1518). There was also a shortened version of a treatise on sheep-farming by Jean de Brie, a humble shepherd from the environs of Coulommiers, which he composed for a friend of the King of France in 1379 and which was published in the first years of the sixteenth century. Of the classical agriculturists there were thirty-one editions between 1470 and 1550,

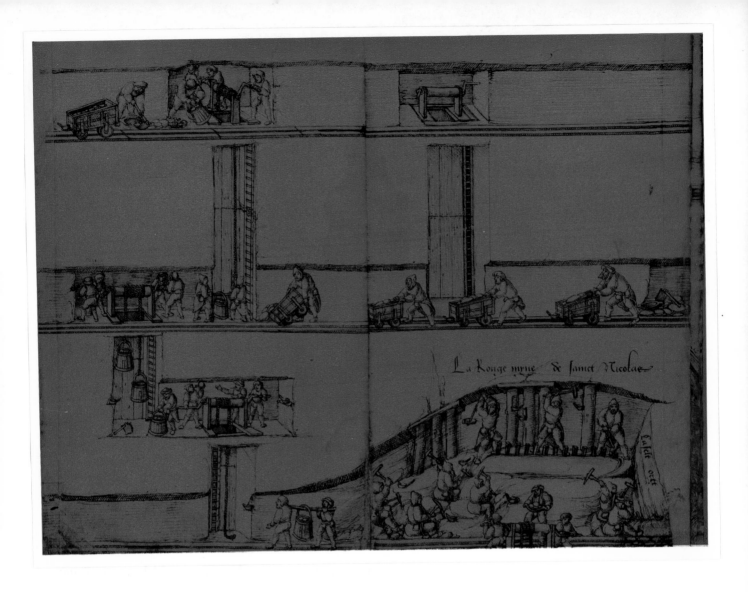

The mine of Sainte-Marie-aux-Mines by H. Gross – sixteenth century.

in Latin, French, Italian, and German. The treatise on agriculture by the Englishman Fitzherbert appeared in 1523 and went through eight editions before 1550. The *Libro de agricultura*, by the Spanish writer Alonso Herrera, appeared in 1539. *La coltivazione*, by the Italian Luigi Alamanni, was published in Padua in 1546. The first parts of *La maison rustique* which had so much success was published shortly after 1530. The whole of this unparalleled movement in agricultural economy, which developed from the beginning of the sixteenth century immediately after the period which we have been studying, did not arise from a vacuum. This was a real advance, based on a tradition to which our engineers did not belong. The Sforza library of which we have a catalogue of about 1470 shows this most clearly.

In regard to mining or metallurgy, where development was equally notable, we would mention the *Bergbüchlein*, published for the first time in 1505 and which quickly went through several editions (five appeared before 1540). It is the beginning of a tradition that in a few decades was to lead to the *Pyrotecnica* of Biringuccio and the famous *De re metallica* of Agricola, the former published, the latter written before 1550. The admirable drawings of the book of Sainte-Marie-aux-Mines, of which we show a reproduction, date from the same period as Leonardo. The critical reader will compare certain clumsy sketches by our engineers with these astonishingly precise drawings.

Chemistry also had its triumphs. The *Liber de arte distillandi* by Brunschwig was printed at Strasbourg in 1500. An anonymous book on dyeing, *Mairegola dell' arte di tintori*, appeared in 1510. Rossetti's great treatise on dyeing was printed in 1548 in Venice.

It is hardly necessary to state that both civil and military architecture followed similar paths. Books on guns and the art of war came after our engineers. Fave has identified a small manuscript treatise on guns, dating from about 1430, which was the source of numerous works from the end of the fifteenth or the beginning of the sixteenth century: it inspired the *Art de la guerre*, by Philip de Clèves. But the treatise on the militia by Orso d'Ascoli of 1477 and the one by Machiavelli of 1512, the book on fortification by Albrecht Dürer, which appeared in 1527, and that by Battista de la Valle of which there were ten editions between 1524 and 1558, are in the same vein as the notebooks of our engineers.

There is surely no need to quote further examples. The movement that we have been examining is certainly part of a great movement which carries with it all the techniques of the period. Each element had its own traditions and its own original aspects. But all the

Mine working by Gassen, 1544.

tendencies were similar. People were now searching for the cause of things, for those universally valid explanations which alone justified the belief that progress and perfection were possible in each occupation. They enabled rules to be drawn up, principles to be demonstrated, and, in brief, made it possible to substitute sound doctrine for the innumerable fragmentary prescriptions. And whether we like it or not, whether or not Diderot succeeded, the *Encyclopédie* is at the end of this road.

All these books clearly show that specialized research had taken place. It is certainly more difficult to find any direct evidence. But it may be supposed, to take only one example, that the hydraulic machine with reversible movement of which Agricola has an admirable drawing, existed before his time, since he reproduced it. A single glance at the engraving will show that it consisted simply of two wheels side by side, the vanes of which are inversely inclined. The same water supply feeds the two wheels and one person can work the vanes to produce either of the movements. It is ingeniously simple, worthy of our engineers, but in this case easy to carry out and doubtless it was in fact carried out, since Agricola was an observer, and neither a technician nor aware of the astonishingly theoretical nature of certain projects. The small wagons on rails, also represented by Agricola, had already figured in the manuscript of Sainte-Marie-aux-Mines.

This taste for mechanization, which is perhaps not confined to our engineers or to their period, nevertheless developed quite remarkably. All that had once been mere fiction, dreams, or literary imagination, began to be realized. It is this effort which is noticeable above all in the technicians whose acquaintance we have made. It existed also in those fields which they ignored. We may recall the machine for polishing precious stones, of which we have seen a somewhat maladroit and incomplete sketch, in the work we have called the anonymous manuscript of the Hussite War. The realization of this principle is not generally dated before the seventeenth century, the first illustration occurring in one of the works of the French architect Félibien. But we find this machine in a manuscript which may be dated to about 1475, in a drawing remarkable for its clarity and precision. It is, moreover, in a collection together with some very interesting notes on the construction of clocks which appear to date from the first half of the fifteenth century and are the work of an extremely colourful personality, to whom an important study has recently been devoted. So that it forms both the sequel to Dondi's treatise on clocks and the continuation of this modest notebook.

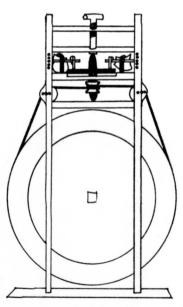

Apparatus for polishing precious stones (*c.* 1470).

Agricola's reversible hoist (sixteenth century).

Biringuccio: reduction furnace.

A few references will enable us to follow the mechanical progress made during the period of our engineers. We have reported the appearance of the blast furnace and of the new metal, cast iron, which changed even the methods of working iron. The sheet rolling mill, more practical than the 'inventions' of Leonardo, was difficult to construct although it was a comparatively simple idea. The casting of the rollers, which could only be of iron, their finishing and polishing, all required advanced techniques. To cut the iron into bars the mills were formed of rollers which were linked one to another. These instruments are mentioned, though very briefly, in the region of Liège at the beginning of the sixteenth century. They date, perhaps, from the very end of the fifteenth century. Hydraulic wire-drawing dates from the same period and is illustrated by Biringuccio.

The textile industry made slower progress, despite Leonardo's work. The loom, said to be by Jean le Calabrais, which made it possible for the silk industry to produce figured materials, made its appearance in France, under Louis XI, at the end of the fifteenth century. It is what is called a button loom, which can be used only for small-scale designs and is worked by one operative. A certain Anton Muller appears to have seen in Danzig in 1529 a machine for weaving four or five textiles at a time. The invention of this machine appears to have caused such unrest in the working population that the magistrates of the city demanded that it should be suppressed and the inventor drowned. Doubtless this is a legend, but it denotes a curious reaction which was subsequently to grow. The great printing riots in France in the middle of the sixteenth century were no doubt caused by technical modifications of the printing presses, which in fact led to a reduction in the number of workers. Lee's stocking loom of the end of the sixteenth century represents the first successful attempt at mechanization in the textile industry.

In the field of clockmaking, in which there was probably the greatest degree of mechanization, the principles remained constant, as was inevitable, but the execution was always being improved upon. Dondi describes the way he made the clock of Padua. The early fifteenth-century manuscript by Fusoris, whom we have already mentioned, describes the construction of the clock of the cathedral of Bourges. A manuscript in the library at Augsburg, written in about 1477–8 by brother Paulus Alemannus, also shows some interesting designs. Thus, by comparing one manuscript with the other, we may measure the obvious improvement of construction methods, the continuous discoveries of solutions to every problem, and the slow growth of a technique which is becoming increasingly self-aware. Thus it became possible to make smaller and smaller clocks, of which some, in the first half of the fifteenth century, could be called watches, although the regulation of the mainspring was at first very clumsy.

During the second half of the sixteenth century, at the very moment when technical advance was tending to slow down, a return was made to formulae similar to those of our engineers. Thus originated those 'theatres of machines', the numerous editions of which, in many languages, show how popular they were.

We do not know much about Besson. Born at Briançon, in about 1540, he was – and this title is symptomatic – engineer and mathematician to the king. Before 1570 he was professor of mathematics at Orléans. He seems to have taken refuge, for religious reasons, in Geneva, where he died young in about 1576. He wrote a treatise on instruments for observing the stars, a book on chemistry and the famous *Théâtre des instruments et machines* which appeared in Lyon in 1569. It was translated into French with a commentary by Béroalde, and into German and Spanish. 'Besson,' wrote Béroalde, 'engineer and mathematician to the kings of France, exposed himself to many dangers, made many tiresome journeys to a number of countries, spent his whole life and worked in many ways to discover at the hidden sources of mathematics and the mechanical arts, divers much needed secrets.' We are thus within the tradition of our engineers.

Ramelli was born in 1531 near Como. A military engineer, he was attached to the armies of Charles V, then came to France, where he was in the service of Henri d'Anjou, King of Poland, the future Henri III. He was engineer to the Italian troops at the siege of La Rochelle and died in 1600. He had composed a treatise on fortification but lost the manuscript; later he wrote the *Livre des diverses et artificieuses machines*, which appeared in Italian and French in 1588.

These two works are a collection of the most varied kinds of mechanics. Often a number of solutions are given to the same problem. But there is still a certain amount of theorizing in all this. Salomon de Caus, the early seventeenth-century engineer, noted: 'Besson, Ramelli and a few others have given us machines invented by them on paper, but few of them can be at all effective'.

Although these works, as was observed by Father Russo, are not without seriousness, and although they proclaim their wish to be of service to professionals, the emphasis is on play, amusement, the desire to satisfy a wide public which was at that time much attracted by curiosities, mechanical inventions, automata, and 'marvellous' ways of making water rise, of harnessing the power of rivers, of

Silk mill (Florentine MS. 1487).

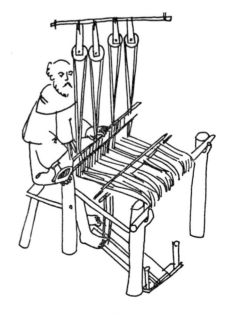

Loom (Nuremburg, end of fifteenth century).

combining motions, of crossing deep moats with ingenious ladders, and of unhinging doors with implements using screw combinations. This is the same picture, if a somewhat distorted one, that we may also have of our engineers. It is not certain, for that matter, that the public being addressed was not, with a few differences, the same as that of Besson and Ramelli. If great public works were not an innovation at the time of the Renaissance, at least they took on a new importance and a new aspect. Certainly the birth of centralized states had favoured the development of planning. But the techniques were also strengthened and if there was now the possibility of thinking big, it was also possible to achieve finer results.

Ever since Eupalinos at Samos had driven a tunnel a kilometre long through the Castro mountain which dominated the city in order to bring water, nobody had seemed to wish to repeat this exploit. Although our engineers appear to have practised mining they had, so it would appear, neither the opportunity nor the desire to embark on such large-scale works. The well of Orvieto, by San Gallo, is a remarkable construction, with its double ramp for the donkey to pull up the full jars, but he was spared the difficulties of a tunnel which would have required both levelling and support. The Marquis of Saluzzo wished to carry out such a scheme to link his states with Dauphiné, with which he had active trading relations which were hampered by the barrier of the Alps. For this reason he wished to drive a tunnel through Monte-Viso. After agreement, in 1475, with the French authorities, the work was begun, under the direction of two Italian engineers, Martino di Albano and Baldassare di Alpeasio. The work was begun at both ends so that the tunnel has a slight bend in it. Tunnelling was carried out at 2400 metres above sea level. The tunnel is 72 metres long, 2.47 metres wide and 2.05 metres high, large enough for mules to pass through it. No doubt this is modest work, but for the year 1480, when it was carried out, it denotes an act of will and material means which were both out of the ordinary.

There had been less timidity in matters relating to hydraulics, as we have already shown. Nevertheless progress continued during the whole of the second half of the fifteenth century. It appears that the engineers of western Europe were not inferior to their Italian contemporaries. The works that were achieved in some places were on a scale which far exceeds the projects of a man such as Leonardo da Vinci. The techniques utilized were thus already advanced, so that there was no need to call in 'specialists' from the Peninsula. Others, especially the Dutch, very rapidly acquired a mastery that was universally recognized.

Opposite:
Well at Orvieto constructed by San Gallo c.1530.

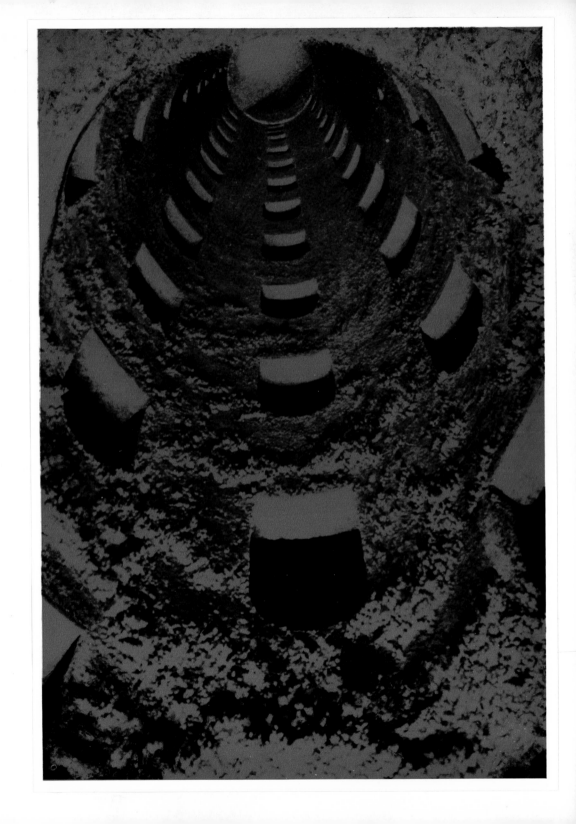

The achievements of the Dutch go back to very early times, since records of the first dikes raised against the sea date from the end of the twelfth century. The problem was indeed complex since it was a matter of obtaining protection not only against the sea but also against the great rivers which flow into this country, with their immense volume of water and formidable liability to flood. It had also been learned that terrain that had been drained and reclaimed had a tendency to subside, thus lowering a level that was already dangerously low. The region of the Zuider Zee, which was perhaps drained naturally, had, for this reason, been newly flooded at the beginning of the fourteenth century. The works were also carried out without any general plan, which could put those regions which were not protected into a bad position. A disaster of 1421 enabled stock to be taken of the programmes to be carried out. The whole of the region between Bergen-op-Zoom and Moerdijk, between the mouths of the Escaut and the Maas, had been partially reclaimed and protected by a dike constructed in the fourteenth century. The neighbouring region of Dordrecht was not protected. The setting up of the barrier across the River Maas probably caused the disaster. During the night of 18–19 November 1421 the waters flooded a tract of country which included sixty-five villages, causing the loss of about 100,000 lives. A drawing which we reproduce records this drama: we can clearly see the sea rushing through the breach, the unfortunate people hastily trying to save what they can and the bodies floating on the water.

This disaster probably led to the idea of collective planning to avoid the repetition of such events. The network of dikes with different water levels by which the water was progressively raised above the dikes and directed towards the sea or into the rivers probably dates from this period. But the need then was for new means of pumping, which had not previously been available. Some historians suggest the date of 1408 for the first use for this purpose of windmills, which originally worked only by Archimedean screws. The problem could then be resolved by increasing the number of these instruments, thus fixing the traditional aspect of the Dutch countryside. The region flooded in 1421 was thus reclaimed between 1430 and 1460. The 'polders' were systematically constituted from 1435 onwards. Towards the middle of the fifteenth century these techniques appear to have been finally perfected, together with the processes of dredging necessitated by the silting up of the river-mouths which caused the risk of flooding rivers. During the second half of the fifteenth century the importance of these reclaimed regions continued to increase.

Opposite: floods in the region of Dordrecht in 1421.

Protection against the sea was continually extended. The region of Alkmaar was protected from the end of the fourteenth century. At the end of the fifteenth century it was possible to envisage the protection of the island of Walcheren. About 4 kilometres long and 100 metres wide, the dikes were higher by nearly 5 metres than the high tide, and by more than 8 metres than the low tide. Progress was such that in the middle of the sixteenth century it was possible to set up a body of specialist engineers for such work.

There was the same long history of coastal drainage in the marshes of Poitou. The same difficulties had arisen, although on a smaller scale. Political disturbances had led to the abandonment of certain installations and between 1438 and 1443 work of repair and maintenance had to be carried out. From 1525 a large programme was put in hand and was followed throughout the century, sometimes with the help of Dutch experts.

The region of Venice had slightly different but no less demanding problems. In addition to the protection of embankments attacked by the sea as well as by the waters of all the rivers which flowed into the sea at this point, there was the danger of sandbanks forming, which was particularly damaging to a city which lived for the most part by its navy. As is not surprising, various solutions were submitted by the Venetian Senate which hesitated a long time as to what steps to take. As early as 1335 there was talk of setting up an embankment 3.50 metres wide and 1.36 metres above the level of the water. This matter was again raised in 1372. As early as this period an attempt was also made, by means of a canal parallel to the shore, to divert the mouths of the rivers, such as the Marzenego and the Musone, which flowed into the sea just opposite Venice.

Finally, a dike was constructed. It was made by a single line of small, short oak piles, the bases of which were reinforced with stones. This dike was completed in about 1359 and was several times extended in various directions. Erosion and the passage of time made fairly short work of it, so that the piles had to be replaced on average every five or six years. After 1359, a second taller line was erected, little more than 2 metres from the first. The two lines of piles were linked by traverse structures and the space between them was filled with stones and branches which held the sand. In 1416 a third line of piles was set up. Tamarisk shrubs were planted everywhere to stabilize the sand. In order to break the force of the sea, groins of Istrian stone were placed in front of this dyke.

In the second half of the fifteenth century the problem of rivers appeared to be uppermost. Two possible solutions were discussed: that of diverting the rivers at some distance from the shore and that

Dredger by Breughel the Younger – sixteenth century.

of diverting them near the mouth. The first was advocated by the engineer Antonio Carraro. Finally it was decided to divert them near the mouth, along the slope of the shore, in spite of the fact that the slope was not great enough. The diversions begun at this period and in some instances re-worked later, were designed to divert the waters of the Piave and the Brenta to beyond the Venetian lagoon.

Problems of harnessing rivers were equally great. We need only mention the French case of the Loire, where flooding was relatively frequent. Here, again, problems had been discussed for centuries but had been put into operation only in a piecemeal manner. It would seem that the *turcies* or river-walls of the Loire were begun in the region of Saumur in about 1160. Natural or artificial hillocks had been joined together. These works had been resumed and extended at the end of the thirteenth century. In order to maintain the walls, people had been asked to live inside the area of these primitive earthworks. Other dikes were constructed in the region of Orléans, where, as early as 1415, a dike of about 50 kilometres in length protected the surrounding countryside. At the end of the fifteenth century, on the orders of Louis XI, this work was resumed in its entirety and at the same time the embankments were modified so that they became bare, uniform structures. In 1468 Guy Farmeau and Guillaume Baudet were commissioned to straighten the Loire and to eliminate sandbanks and dangerous channels. In 1480 active work was in progress in the Val de Cisse, traces of which work are still to be seen, under the direction of Hardouin de Maillé, Antoine de Galles, and Jacotin le Mercier.

The avoidance of flood damage was a consideration but it was also desired to control the watercourses in order to facilitate navigation, as Leonardo had done for the Arno. Palisaded banks and locks had already been used in many places. In 1455 work was in progress on the Eure, between Nogent and Chartres, on the setting up of locks and a tow-path. During the same period the Juine and the Essonne were canalized, with water diverted from other streams. Further on, the navigability of the Sèvre at Niort and, in 1462, that of the canal from Luçon to the sea were improved.

It was planned to create a vast navigable network in the valley of the Loire by using the tributaries of the river: the Auron was to link Bourges with the main river, the Brenne was to be used to transport wood to Tours, the Clain was to link Poitiers with the whole of this network. The Brenne was made navigable from Château-Renault to Tours by Nicolas d'Aubigny. After it had been dredged and cleared of weeds, locks were set up long the Clain. In 1460, on the orders of Louis XI, the Loire, the Maine, and the Sarthe, on which works to increase the navigability had recently been completed, were visited. The sluice-gates at Nouâtre on the Clain had broken and a certain 'Messire Antoine Martin', probably an Italian, was summoned to direct the work of repairs.

We must not forget the work carried out in northern Germany, at a period prior to ours. At the beginning of the fourteenth century the River Stecknitz had been canalized and made navigable from Lake Mölln to Lübeck, a distance of 30 kilometres with a drop of about 40 feet. This canal was later continued and joined the Elbe at Lauenburg. For the first time the country between two sea basins, that of the Baltic and that of the North Sea, had been crossed. This work was carried out between 1391 and 1398.

Thus the work of our hydraulic engineers can be seen better when it is set against a vast number of works, which were begun well before their time, and continued during their period with improved techniques and in pursuance of far-reaching programmes. When Leonardo da Vinci was dealing with his famous canal of Romorantin, there is no doubt that he knew about all the efforts that had been made half a century earlier in this region. Our engineers perhaps contributed more to the improvement of certain techniques and to the deepening of experience in certain fields than they actually realized in these great projects. It is not impossible, though we do not possess the precise documents to prove it, that investigations of this kind were carried out by the actual men who worked on the projects. Only they, at all events, could define the difficulties which they encountered and perhaps sketch out solutions. It is noteworthy that although, from the end of the fifteenth to the beginning of the sixteenth century, we have treatises on a large number of techniques, nothing has come down to us in the field of hydraulics. Belidor's *L'architecture hydraulique* of the early eighteenth century was to be the first great book on this subject. Thus, there is no doubt that the problems were infinitely varied and numerous and that no one had the courage to tackle them as a whole. Leonardo da Vinci was a precursor.

The art of war was certainly among the main preoccupations of our engineers. No doubt in this field they were more often closer to reality than in others. We know that a great part of the work which they presented was in fact used. There are numerous allusions to all the ladders, towers, chariots, and rams of which they gave illustrations. They are to be found in the miniatures of manuscripts as well as in literary texts, and are always presented as something marvellous and powerful.

The end of the fifteenth century certainly marked a considerable turning point in military techniques. The implements and types of fortification which had originated in the early Middle Ages were very rapidly abandoned. Artillery was slow to oust the survivals of a period which was now finally past. There are still allusions to the use of trebuchets at the end of the fifteenth century, that is to say at a period when artillery was being largely employed, as, for example, at the Siege of Burgos from 1475 to 1476. The 'descent' of Charles VIII into Italy in 1494–5 marked the end of a period.

The endeavours of our engineers in relation to firearms is certainly interesting. From one drawing to the next we see the cannon being transformed and becoming in the end an instrument that was easy to handle, if not very efficient. Its evolution may be followed from the notebooks of the Germans to those of Leonardo da Vinci. It remains to ascertain whether this evolution, largely an Italian one, represents the essential progress achieved during this period.

There can be no doubt about this. When the French artillery appeared in Italy in 1494 it caused great terror among the enemies of the king of France. The French had assembled many guns, many more than made up, for example, the fine artillery corps of Charles the Bold, and their effects appeared to be far greater than anything which had been seen hitherto. The landing at Rapallo, under cover of naval guns, and the Battle of Fornova, in 1495, showed the superiority of French techniques in the matter of artillery. Assuredly it was not yet terrible and Commines tells us that at Fornova this fine artillery succeeded in disabling a dozen men. But there was an impression that a new world had come into being and that the cannon was for many centuries going to decide the fate of battles. Proof of this was indeed to be seen, some years later, at the Battle of Marignan, when the action of the artillery was much more decisive.

Primitive artillery was made of forged iron and fired stone balls. The barrels were made of iron sheets placed on a cylinder and welded, and were held by hoops which covered them completely. We still possess arms of this type. Advances in metallurgy had made possible considerable improvement in this type of piece. The powder chamber which fitted into a groove and was fixed by clips which often broke had been abandoned. In the first half of the fifteenth century the powder chamber had been wedged into an opening in the barrel shaped like a trap, but this quickly wore at the muzzle in use. After this there were pieces with a single holder, which were charged from the front. In order to transport them more easily – we have noted the difficulties of transporting artillery – chamber and gun were screwed together and could thus be separated. We can see on pieces of this type the openings used for putting in the wooden handles which formed a kind of winch to operate this screw.

There are some examples of this artillery still in existence. The Basle cannon, dating from the third quarter of the fifteenth century, is forged from one piece. The bore is composed of a number of iron sheets 0.03 metre thick and 0.06 metre wide. A series of iron rings encloses it. The Edinburgh cannon, made at Mons in 1486, is much larger but of the same type.

Firing technique had also been improved, as is shown in the anonymous writings which have come down to us. It was understood that there was a relationship between the weight of the ball and that of the powder, between the dimensions of the chamber and the length of the bore and the calibre. The usefulness of very exact calibres began to be appreciated. Notable advances were made in the first half of the fifteenth century. The powder was now measured out better, in proportion to the resistance of the gun. More importantly, iron bores were being abandoned. Copper bores probably originated in Italy, while elsewhere there was some tendency to cling to iron bores. The arsenal at Basle has a copper piece dated 1444. During this period some attempt was also made to improve gun-carriages.

We are thus led to a form of artillery which strangely resembles both that of Charles the Bold, of which there are examples still in existence, and that which figures in the last notebooks of our engineers, those of Francesco di Giorgio, of Leonardo da Vinci, and of Ghiberti.

Although this artillery was not made of pure copper, the other components were present only in small quantities. We have noted this before, in connexion with Leonardo da Vinci; Francesco di Giorgio declares that bronze bursts and that only copper and iron may be used. Francesco di Giorgio's artillery is very clearly defined: he notes the proportions between the thickness of the metal and the diameter of the bore, the proportion between the dimensions of the piece and the calibre, and the proportions to be observed in the use of the powder. Thus for a piece using munitions of 100 lb, two calibres are required for the length of the chamber, and five and a half for the bore; 24 lb of powder must be used. Thus rules were carefully formulated, although measurements were still uncertain and the composition of powder was still very variable.

Other advances were made in France, probably during the reign of Louis XI. The first change was the substitution, probably more general in France than in Italy, of the cast-iron cannonball for the stone ball. The problem at the time was to give more speed to lighter projectiles. This was achieved with bronze cannons. French engineers succeeded in finding the exact composition of metal that was required. The artillery of Charles VIII was entirely made of bronze.

The illustrations we have given show the difficulty of aiming. The gun was placed in a kind of wooden trough attached to the carriage. This arrangement was not easy to handle. By casting their cannon all in one in bronze the French founders again succeeded in adapting them to being mounted on to turn-tables made in one with the mass of the bronze. Therafter mounting on to the carriage and aiming became much easier. While the artillery of Ghiberti is superior to that of Charles the Bold, that of Charles VIII outstripped all the others. It was quickly copied and from 1497 Venice had similar artillery.

It is difficult to ascertain the exact origins of this body of artillery, which began to be assembled under Louis XI. The latter employed bell-founders as well as foreign masters from Germany, Switzerland, and Liège. These cannon-founders in ordinary to the king worked under the orders of the masters of artillery, the most famous of whom were the Bureau brothers.

It is possible that another important advance was made at the beginning of the sixteenth century. It was realized that it had become much easier to obtain regular calibres. From then on it was possible to think of reducing the calibre in order to ensure a better and more abundant supply of projectiles. It appears to have been in about 1525 that castings in France were reduced to six or seven calibres. At the same period, Tartaglia listed twenty-six different calibres for Italy. Ordinances issued by Henry II were finally to regulate, in a very logical manner, both the number of calibres – six in France – and the dimensions of the pieces. Modern artillery had come into being. Francesco di Giorgio had clearly understood the advantages of such steps: he had strictly defined a dozen calibres; but his example had not been followed.

So here again our engineers participated in a movement which was general. Doubtless they were not situated at the point where the most outstanding advances were made. In the writings of Leonardo da Vinci, for example, there is no sign of development even after the discovery of the French artillery.

Our engineers were still encumbered by a whole mass of apparatus which no longer had any military value. Everything connected with the assault of strongholds was to become useless. The most symptomatic phenomenon was the return to antiquity, which had been apparent since Valturio and is encountered in many other fields.

The sources of inspiration of the Renaissance led technical activity astray. Leonardo da Vinci, to take him as an example again, was unaware of portable firearms. All that he shows us are various types of crossbow, though those form an admirable page of drawings. There is no doubt that, despite what has been said, Leonardo's arms show no originality. These portable arms already existed, although, it is true, still in a very primitive form. The arquebus did not make its real appearance until about 1520 and achieved its true strength only when the Spaniards invented a gun pan for it.

It is curious that our engineers were not interested in shipbuilding, except for the imaginative drawings of Leonardo. Here again profound changes were in progress. Although ships' hulls did not change much, the sails took on an entirely different appearance. The drawings also show a certain attachment to the galley, although for more than a century ships from northern Europe had been seen in the Mediterranean. It was one of those domains in which our engineers were not interested.

Fortification was certainly their chosen field, to which they gave unwavering attention. Francesco di Giorgio and the San Gallo were very great fortification builders. It was the subject of detailed and general discussion, which perhaps explains the fact that the Italians were masters of this art and took it to the threshold of the most modern techniques.

It is true, as we have already stated, that the builders of castles and fortresses had clearly understood that the development of artillery would lead to a profound change in fortification. Fortifications had to provide both a defence against artillery and a position on which to mount guns and the high mediaeval crenellated walls were no longer suitable. The first reaction was the simple idea of burying the walls so as to render them less vulnerable to cannon. This idea was adopted in many places; the castles of Nantes and of St Malo are perfect examples in a region far from Italy where, as in Milan, castles of the old type were still being built. The first changes were made to enable artillery to be used; those that followed were for defence against it.

An attempt was made to protect the bases of the walls by making them thicker and giving them a slope. This could have been seen before its destruction in the castle of Ham in Picardy, built in the third quarter of the fifteenth century, and it may also be seen to some extent in the castle of Ostia and in the drawings of Francesco di Giorgio and Leonardo da Vinci.

The abandonment of machicolation, sporadic at first, marks another tendency, that of bringing defence down nearer to ground-level. Low fortifications, either old, brought up to date or new, were becoming essential, whereas hitherto they had been considered merely as adjuncts. Where it was not possible to adapt ancient works, new ones were constructed in front of the old; the old fortresses were, as it were, surrounded by new constructions. This was advocated by François de Surienne at Dijon, as early as 1470. The barbican of the castle of Bonaguil in Périgord is a good example.

A period of trial and error followed. It was now necessary to avoid the direct fire of the enemy. Francesco di Giorgio had already taken a first step. What we today call the bastioned front cannot be attributed to him. He used an irregular line of curtain walls in such a way that they would present only an oblique front to enemy fire. Whether or not he knew the tenaille bastion, he flanked his salients only with the traditional elements, in which Leonardo followed him.

Although the works themselves preserved their mediaeval exterior appearance, with round buildings still largely dominating the scene, their structure had totally changed. They had thick walls, vaulted casemates, and a terrace that could be used for the gun battery. The tower of Langres, built at the end of the fifteenth century, the towers of Toulon and of Le Havre, the latter since destroyed, which date from the reign of Francis I, and the central part of the Château d'If are of this type. Such layout was gradually replaced by triangular ones, as at Ostia and the Castel Sant' Angelo in Rome.

It was necessary only to combine these various elements in order to create a modern style of fortification. Some historians attach great importance to the gate of St George at Rhodes. A great square tower had been constructed, between 1421 and 1431, in front of the curtain wall. In 1496 the grand master, the Frenchman Pierre d'Aubusson, had constructed a rampart around the work, the layout of which corresponds to that of the tower, from which it is separated by a moat. This was then judged to be insufficient. The Italian engineer Basilio della Scuola, of Vicenza, filled in the inner moat of the rampart and linked it to the scarp. The bastion has a low listening gallery, casemates, gun batteries, and an immense terreplein which lay only slightly higher than the counterscarp. By giving these works the layout of orillon bastions, an idea which may already be discerned in the work of Francesco di Giorgio, their builders had found the essential elements of the modern ground-plan of a fortress.

Which were the first perfect examples of these new formulae? Historians tend to quibble about dates. However, they seem to agree in naming the bastion of the Maddalena, at Verona, built by San Michele in the year 1527. The Verde bastion at Turin is slightly

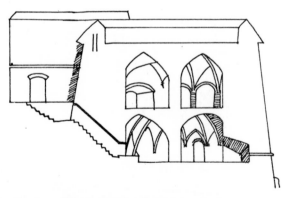

Section of the Langres bastion (about 1495).

later (1536 or 1538). If we accept a plan of Troyes, which seems to have been executed at the time when Francis I ordered the alteration to the walls of this city (1524–9), this type of fortification must have been known at more or less the same date in France. The fortress of Navarrenx, in the Pyrenees, built by an Italian engineer, Fabrici Siciliano, between 1540 and 1544, is the most magnificent example in existence.

The last point concerns the actual construction of these buildings. It was the tradition to build fortresses and castles in freestone which was almost always bonded. Such walls had the major disadvantage of being vulnerable to artillery fire. Another solution, therefore, had to be sought and it was found quite naturally at the same time as the others.

The bastions of Verona, built by San Michele and his successors between 1527 and 1548, are no longer built solely of stone. The materials also include earth, in which enemy projectiles became embedded without doing any damage. From then on, all parapets were made of well-packed earth. This was done at Turin, in 1538, in the fortress which was so highly praised by Tartaglia.

Whereas Dürer's treatise of fortification, which appeared in 1527, was still relatively traditional, that of Battista della Valle, which appeared in 1524, mentions some of the modifications of which we have just spoken. His bastions have three firing floors. For the construction of earthworks he recommends alternating faggots and well-packed earth, topping them with a vertical wattle fence and a timber frame. He recommends rams and mines as well as the use of scaling ladders.

There is no doubt that it was to the development of fortification that our engineers contributed most. They did not arrive at the right moment, when the development of firearms demanded a radical change in systems of fortification. It was left to the succeeding generation to accomplish the fundamental changes which lead directly to Vauban. Francesco di Giorgio and his imitators were content to sketch out solutions, which in their time were not yet required. This time they put their successors on the right path.

In the first decade of the sixteenth century all the ideas which were about to pass into practice were seething below the surface. In 1503 the Spaniard Ramirez completed the fortress of Salses, in Roussillon. None of the essential elements of the defence stood much higher than the level of the glacis of the counterscarp. It is the first great sunken fortress in France. In 1503, soon after completion, Salses was besieged and resisted: mines were sprung at the moment of attack and the assault was stopped short. In 1503 Pierre de Navarre took

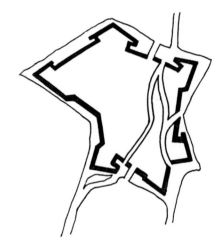

Fortifications of La Fère (1540).

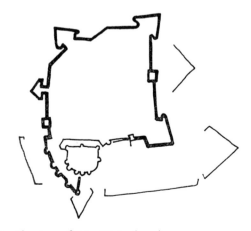

Fortifications of Saint-Dizier (1544).

the two castle of Naples, which were held by the French, thanks to a mine which remained long in the memory of military historians. He performed a similar feat at Milan in 1515, this time on behalf of the French. Thus immediately after his death, Francesco di Giorgio's techniques, which he had recommended and which he probably did not have the opportunity of putting to use, were successfully applied.

We have seen that our engineers were born of a long tradition which slowly changed, but which, nevertheless, preserved some of the characteristics of its origins. We have seen what were their basic preoccupations, the limits of their curiosity, and the direction of some of their investigations. We have set them against the background of the techniques of their time and have dwelt especially on those which they actually employed. It is undeniable that to some extent this very tradition from which they stemmed, and their own education, constituted obstacles to the blossoming of their ideas. It may be that Plato's ideal city, catapults and *ballistae*, took up too much space in their discussions and blinded them to some of the true realities of technical progress. No doubt those around them did the same and encouraged them along these lines. Men were required to organize festivities and humanists were wanted to hold discourses. But perhaps there were, in addition, simpler beings who knew how to cast cannons and to construct bastions without becoming involved in apposite reminiscences.

These were the men who really made technical progress. But they left no written or pictorial evidence of their hesitations or their successes. Even later, it was for the most part not they who edited the treatises which, as we have seen, appeared in such great numbers. Agricola was a doctor and not a technician.

But these men also had their traditions, their prescriptions, of which they sometimes made collections. Forgotten, taken up again, altered, changed beyond recognition, often at the whim of circumstance, these prescriptions also constituted technical progress. But it was necessary to regard them objectively as our engineers had to regard their own formulae. The men we have been describing, the engineers, were men of ideas. The first idea was of progress, which comes out on every page and in every drawing, and takes the form of unrealizable anticipations. Theirs also was the desire for systematic mechanization. This technical endeavour, by which power and fame were to be achieved, was somehow passed on by our engineers to their contemporaries, especially to those engaged upon practical tasks. The books, the conversations, the discussions in the workshops, the reputations, even the bluffs, were all fuel to the sacred flame from which modern technique has arisen.

This in itself would not have been enough. In setting up a new faith, our engineers also offered their period new ways of thought and untried methods. Reasoning took the place of empiricism, experiment replaced the rule of thumb, scientific calculation ousted elementary relationships. Could any generation have received a finer gift?

And while their contemporaries were catching the ball in flight and creating a new material world, our engineers retreated once more into those ancient dreams through which they acquired knowledge.

The debate on the origins of classical science has been in full swing for some time. We cannot hope to adduce here – nor is this the proper place to do so – any new features or unexplored perspectives. But it seemed that this essay would be extremely incomplete if at least some allusion were not made to the problems which were certainly the prime concern of our engineers. It would have been impossible for them, frequenting as they did the very circles in which this new knowledge was emerging, to remain indifferent to questions which often closely affected their own domain. If, in this subject as in technique, they were not true pioneers, their influence was perhaps not totally negligible.

The knowledge which they had received from their predecessors, and which, no doubt, had reached them only in an incomplete, and perhaps even distorted, form, had already undergone important changes. The peripatetic system had received some hard hits. The Oxford school had begun, somewhat timidly it is true, to submit the theses of Aristotle to mathematical treatment and were already in a position to undermine the basic data. The nominalists of Paris, more heretical in this respect, began to rest the whole of their knowledge on new foundations, one of the main ones of which appears to have been the observation of nature and of the phenomena of current life. Jordanus Nemorarius, towards the end of the thirteenth century, was one of the upholders of this tendency and his *Liber de ratione ponderis* (or *De ponderibus*, as it was more often called) was perhaps the key work for our engineers, since it combines scientific pre-occupations with practical technical problems to so great a degree. Nemorarius was a great admirer of Euclid, as Beaujouan has related, and was concerned with demonstrating mechanical theorems by geometrical proofs stemming from a few explicit postulates of a physical character. He was the first western thinker to formulate the theory of inclined planes; he presented a formula of the *gravitas secundum situm*, bringing in the concept of moment. He applied the principle of virtual displacement to the equilibrium of bent levers. Passing from statics to dynamics, he put forward, in Book 4, a whole series of propositions, some of them inexact, in which we detect an undoubted interest in the work of engineers. The mathematician Gérard de Bruxelles had similarly parallel interests. During the same period the Dominican Guillaume de Moerbeke translated Archimedes.

Our engineers are very close to this whole development. The importance of *De ponderibus*, of which the author's name had by this time been lost, the enthusiastic research into Archimedes or Euclid, prove, if proof were needed, how greatly they wished to follow these new paths which lead to classical science. Although two centuries separated them and they had the benefit of all the exact information brought to bear by the Parisian school of the fourteenth century, we recognize the same state of mind trying to free itself from Aristotelian doctrine.

However systematic it may have been, the scientific knowledge at the end of the fifteenth century still consisted of a body of disparate elements. Mathematics was only used in certain limited cases, and it could not have been otherwise, given the undeveloped state of mathematics. Physics was strictly linked to astronomy. And it would still have appeared paradoxical to establish close links between scientific knowledge and practical experience.

Although such links had long existed and it had been possible, as early as the twelfth century, to state that there was 'interdependence between scholastic science and utilitarian techniques', and although the Parisian nominalists, as we have just said, were concerned with a more concrete and more directly accessible reality, techniques were incapable, as we shall see, with the intellectual mechanisms then available, of producing scientific notions as we know them today. Technique intervened, almost in the same way as a Gospel parable, only in order to refute or affirm propositions constructed in quite another manner, and to appeal to common sense in a discussion that threatened to lose sight of the point. Although the firing of trebuchets or of cannon often found its way into discussions on impetus, in general these matters were kept separate from their purely material environment.

But the moment the scientist began to seek to rid knowledge of a certain formalism, of inappropriate language, and of its links with an abstract universe, he was fated to encounter the technician, whose investigations were, though for different reasons, similar to his own. This conjunction of two modes of thought, which were at first, despite occasional confrontations, diametrically opposed to each other, constitutes perhaps one of the determining moments of scientific evolution. Neither mode by itself could have achieved such results.

We know that historians dispute the exact role of technical activity in the birth of classical science. Some deny any obvious influence, others attribute pre-eminent importance to it. Indeed, Koyre may be right in presenting this thesis. The appearance of the cannon did not give rise to the new dynamics; on the contrary, it was on the experience of the artificers that the endeavours of Leonardo, Tartaglia, and Benedetti came to grief. The needs of navigation, of the calculations of the ecclesiastical calendar, of astrology, could and should have led to an effort to correct astronomical tables, but this did not happen; they did not impel Copernicus to reverse the order of the celestial spheres and to place the sun in the centre of the universe. The demands of commerce, the extension of exchange and banking connexions, certainly caused the spread of elementary mathematical knowledge and accountancy: they could not explain the spectacular advances of the Italian algebrists during the first half of the sixteenth century.

Crombie, for his part, offers less clear-cut opinion. In regard to the history of sciences, their evolution has come about because men have asked themselves questions susceptible of experimental answer, have limited their investigations to physical rather than metaphysical problems, concentrating their attention on the exact observation of the kinds of things to be found in the natural world and the correlation between the behaviour of one with that of another, rather than on their intrinsic nature, on immediate causes rather than on material forms, and in particular on those aspects of the physical world which could be expressed in mathematical terms.

Assuredly, technical intuition has no connexion with scientific discovery and it would be vain to credit Francesco di Giorgio, the inventor of the ball governor, with the discovery of the law of inertia. Experiment, which is one of the fundamental features of classical science, has no relation with the kind of experiment which is concerned with direct observation, and with common sense, which for a long time was actually an obstacle. This common-sense observation could and did produce only somewhat confused ideas, like that of impetus, for example, because there was no means of isolating all the component elements. Classical experimentation is directed and actively brought about; technical experimentation is submitted to, with all the confusion and complexity that this entails. Thus, in principle, let us not forget there is no common ground between the two.

It is important, therefore, to be careful about the exact meaning of the words used. Some historians have rightly made a stand against the oversimplified identification that has often been made of common-sense experience with the experimental observation of the scientist. But although technical experimentation was probably at first, to a large extent, a matter of common sense, was it still so in the middle of the fifteenth century? We ourselves think that technicians had also sorted out their problems, isolated the component elements, made a preliminary classification of the notions, not to say the concepts, which presented themselves in daily practice. It is in any case curious to note that during the course of the fifteenth century the essential problems of the scientists and technicians coincided very closely. The incomprehensions of the one side corresponded to the hesitations of the other and the problems which confronted everyone were to some extent concentrated on well-defined points.

A science with a liking for reality, ready to check its results against experiment, and a technique anxious to obtain explanations that would be more general and of greater validity, and which, moreover, had become increasingly able to make its own calculations, must inescapably have had close contacts with each other. And as soon as the one abandoned some of its abstraction and the other looked for generalization, an encounter became inevitable. There are two clear proofs of this. The first is that scientists and technicians had begun to base their hopes on a common ideal: Archimedes, the great Greek scientist who himself had been an engineer. His outlook was exactly the same as that of all these men who, towards the end of the fifteenth century, were concerned either with science or with techniques. His research had been centred on problems which were both defined and limited. He formulated hypotheses which, in the manner of Euclid, were raised to axioms which were self-evident or which he could verify by simple experiments. His science was certainly, like that of Leonardo, the science of the technician.

Because science was no longer constituted as a system, as it had been while Aristotle still dominated the scene, it only tackled difficulties in a fragmentary fashion and, for this reason, found itself almost inescapably linked to the analogous questions being asked by the technicians in general terms. Nearly all the problems of statics and dynamics, which were at the basis of the scientific renewal, turned out to be, at the same time, matters of technical incomprehension. Although methods of thought were different, at least they were brought together, on the one hand by certain parallel formal difficulties, in particular those of measurement, and on the other by identical objectives. The common Archimedean ideal thus becomes easy to explain.

It was therefore plausible to predict that these overlappings would take place, that, in other words, the engineers would participate in the movement that gave birth to classical science. When Koyre declares that Benedetti came near to the truth not because he was an artillery expert and an engineer, but because he had a knowledge of Archimedes, he is simply denying the existence of this remarkable agreement which was at this time coming into being between the two orders of thought. Tartaglia's dialogue between the cannoneer and the scholar, which is a literary formula, also represents this identity of objectives which is accompanied, to a greater or lesser degree according to temperament and to each man's culture, by an identity of logic. This identity, furthermore, was to persist for a long time and up to the end of the eighteenth century scientists continued to be concerned with technique while technicians prided themselves on their science. The two great scientific academies, those of London and Paris, were created for a technical purpose as much as a scientific one. Desargues, Roberval, and Blondel were still engineers, as was Monge, to quote only a few examples among many.

Interdependence and links; both these terms certainly imply close connexions and the overlapping probably went still further.

The classical science is mathematics. Although mathematics had been used sporadically, thus providing material for interesting developments, it was universally regarded as the special domain of technicians. Aristotelian physics had only slight need of mathematics, which was, or should have been, in constant use by surveyors, architects and engineers. After having declared that 'no human investigation may be called true science if it is not subjected to mathematical demonstration', Leonardo da Vinci could write: 'mechanics is the paradise of the mathematical sciences'.

There is no doubt that if certain discoveries or certain improvements were made by scientists, it was perhaps because precise problems had been presented to them by technicians in search of solutions. The development of trigonometry is due essentially to questions of measurement and surveying. When the *De trianguls libri V* by Regiomontanus, published in 1533 in Nuremburg, demonstrates for all triangles the proportionality of the sides to the sines of the corresponding angles, the author applies this fundamental theorem to concrete numerical cases. The work on arithmetic (*Abaco, ossia maniere facile per apprender ogni conto*), published in Treviso in 1478 had been written for young people embarking on a commercial career. This is essentially a technical work; all the operations are shown by using the proof of nine. A German book of arithmetic published in 1483 and the *Bamberger Rechenbuch* of the same date are exactly similar. The manual of John Widman, published in 1489, has the same purpose. It forecasts the alliance between arithmetic and algebra, the plus and minus signs indicating a premium and a rebate.

The later works known to us, such as the manual of the Parisian doctor Chuquet, written in about 1484 but not published, and even the *Summa aritmetica* by Pacioli, completed in 1487 and published in 1494, although they show important developments arising from a scientific attitude, nevertheless still have a clearly practical character. Both these manuals, in fact, expound a system of commercial arithmetic. Arithmetic and algebra were developed in order to deal with practical problems; only double entry book-keeping could provide the concept of negative numbers. The increase of questions connected with accountancy was certainly the origin of more abstract mathematical speculations. We shall find other examples. Algebra played no practical part in the development of science in the seventeenth century.

Assuredly, engineers were still too ignorant of most scientific notions for advanced mathematics to be necessary to them, or even useful, and Leonardo da Vinci's sally appears to have been more a wish than a reality. They still used extremely simple formulae and employed only an approximate system of reckoning, which was quite sufficient for them. Leonardo da Vinci makes no allusion to algebra and his arithmetic is no more advanced than that of the abacists of his time. When scientific knowledge became more profound our engineers returned quite naturally to pure mathematics. Again it should be noted that for a long time algebra was of no more use to them than to the scientists. It is quite contrary to the truth to say that Simon Stevin (1548–1620) was a mathematician who utilized his talents as an engineer; he was rather a professional engineer who practised mathematics. He was employed in his youth as an accountant – traditional association, this – and later entered the corps of engineers employed on the dikes of Holland. His first work had been devoted to interest tables and his practical preoccupations never ceased. If Stevin was a good mathematician – and Renaissance mathematics reached their culminating point in him – it is because he had learned to formulate in mathematical terms the problems that he had to resolve. His mathematics is, properly speaking, a tool

Diagram of a conical section after Dürer.

and not a system of pure knowledge. His technique was no doubt merely a point of departure, but in this case it seems to have been the essential impulse to scientific development.

Geometry appeared to be essentially a technical subject. The engineers lived in a concrete geometrical space which had no connexion with astronomical space. The geometry of Leonardo is a fairly faithful reflection of this. His researches on the centre of gravity stem, to some extent, from technical needs. And if by chance he came upon some problem stated in abstract terms, it was resolved with technical solutions. Albrecht Dürer's *Underweysung der Messung mit dem Zirckel und Richtscheyt* (Instruction on measurement with compass and rule), published in Nuremburg in 1525, is essentially a technical work; its aim is to teach technicians how to construct geometrical figures. If he sometimes goes further than this, it is because he wishes to establish his technique on a scientific basis. It is in the capacity of a technician who wishes to represent figures correctly that he comes near to the descriptive geometry of Monge, another technician. This development did not stop here and Desargues (1591–1661), the great geometrician of the following century, was, to begin with, interested in the possible applications of geometry to architecture, painting and sun-dials.

Hollow polyhedron by Leonardo da Vinci.

We do not wish to suggest that abstract mathematics, algebra or Euclidian geometry, had only technical bases, nor that either of them would have been inconceivable without a technical point of departure. But if we wish to put into chronological order the changes in intellectual outlook which enabled abstract mathematics to come into being, we are obliged to recognize that the technical element was important. None of the celebrated geometricians of the sixteenth century was completely detached from technical preoccupations; Stevin is again a good example. John Napier also had a technical aim, which was to facilitate calculation in trigonometry and astronomy. His love of cones and enjoyment of sun-dials were closely parallel. Descartes and Fermat were perhaps the first to reason completely in the abstract, or, it would be better to say, to have abstraction only as the essential objective. The question of spectacles remained an important one for Descartes but, by that time, a beginning had been made.

It was clear that mathematical apparatus could be used by technicians, at least in its most advanced forms, only to the extent that their knowledge of physics was well based. Archimedes had transmitted only a theory of statics, which was later developed, especially within the framework of an Aristotelian tradition represented by the book *Quaestiones mechanicae*, an anonymous work of the school of

Hollow polyhedron by Leonardo da Vinci.

Aristotle. The work of Jordanus, which we have mentioned earlier, remained in the tradition which made use of virtual velocity and virtual displacement. It was at the end of the fifteenth century that an attempt was made to return to Archimedes, as Stevin was also to do, while Galileo proceeded from the two movements. Leonardo da Vinci shows perfectly that the technicians of his period knew how to utilize this system of statics. Dynamics, and particularly kinematics, were still encumbered with notions which were difficult to apply to real situations but were also very difficult to get rid of. If today we were to try to question a person who had no precise scientific knowledge about the exact definition of inertia, we would obtain answers similar to those of the Middle Ages. Dynamics could be practically employed only in a few cases, of which ballistics, whatever the means of projecting the missile, was the most important and therefore the most often called upon. When first those in charge of the engines of war and then the gunners began to examine a little more closely what they were doing, the inadequacies of traditional dynamics were perceived. This criticism of theory by reality constituted an indispensable stage; it was bound to involve the emergence of a new system of dynamics. The problem of the 'fall of heavy bodies' had the effect of introducing other verified and still more complex notions which were also to become the concern of ballistics.

The Middle Ages had introduced the theory of *impetus*, which was, indeed, part of Aristotelian physics. This theory, which was gradually improved upon by the Parisian nominalists of the fourteenth century, offered certain usable elements. It became possible to distinguish motion, velocity, and even acceleration, as did Oresme, without bringing in the idea of impetus. Toward the middle of the fifteenth century the Italian masters knew the laws of uniformly accelerated or uniformly retarded motion although, since no one had yet had the idea of associating the motion of the fall of heavy bodies with a uniformly accelerated motion, they applied them to a fictitious motion. The practice of artillery, both of the old counter-weight artillery and the new fire artillery, had led to the formulation of certain rules of proportionality between velocity and motive force (the importance of the counterweight and the mass of powder used) and the inverse proportionality of speed and resistance. However, certain questions still remained obscure; among them that of the continuation of motion when the motive force had ceased to act and that of weight, linked both to resistance and to gravity. Inertia played its part in all this without anyone being able to isolate it. There was also the problem of the *quies media*, that is to say the continuation of motion at the moment when one of the components began to prevail over the other. This *quies media* was found in the circular motion engendered by a connecting-rod and crank system which had two dead centres, occurring at the moment of the change of direction of the rectilinear alternating motion of the rod.

Although ballistic researches were basically of little importance to artillery men, because the nature of the motions of the projectile and the path of the curve could to some extent be dissociated from the result, changes in methods of firing and the transition from one type of apparatus to another inevitably brought these questions into the lines of argument.

The case had even arisen in connexion with trebuchets. Parabolic fire-flight, or, as we would call it, plunging fire, was much easier when there was no precise target to hit, that is to say when it was just a matter of damaging the inside of a castle or a city. It was therefore infinitely more efficient. But in order to accomplish this it was necessary to place the engine very close to the enemy wall and therefore within reach of the arms of the enemy. Long-distance fire ensured that the gunners were out of reach of any retaliation, but it was much more difficult to control. The transition from parabolic to long-distance fire already presupposed some elementary knowledge. It was not only a matter of modifying the path of the curve, which went without saying, but also of breaking this curve down into various parts and of determining more accurately at least the first part of the curve, that is to say the part which is more directly dependent on the motive force. These shots had, or could have, a double aim: either to hit the inside of a fortress or a city or to destroy a wall. The use of cannon made long-distance firing necessary, except for bombards (mortars). The use of artillery in battle and not as siege engines came appreciably later. If it were required to hit targets inside the walls it was rapidly perceived that it was necessary to compensate for the diminution of the height of the fall of the stone ball by its weight, by transferring from parabolic firing to long-distance firing. The problem was partially resolved by the invention of bombs as substitutes for simple cannon balls. If a wall had to be hit, it was obvious that a given distance had to be covered, that it was necessary to hit a more precisely determined point at a given height and with maximum force. Problems of measurement, and in particular of the measurement of a height at a distance, acquired a certain importance; our engineers were much occupied in resolving the problem of the measurement of height at a distance and we find many references to this subject in their works, up to Leonardo da Vinci.

Trajectories of a cannon-ball by Leonardo da Vinci.

The engine masters had enough accumulated experience to understand the main elements of the problem and to establish the simple relationships which ensured approximate solutions that proved to be entirely usable and adequate. The very construction of the trebuchets shows, in their smallest details, that these different elements had been dissociated from one another. There was in fact the counterweight mass, fixed in principle (doubtless fixed for a given distance, since it was a chest filled with stones), but which could also be varied by being pulled up, and on which depended the velocity of the projectile. There was the point on the course of the sling at which the cannon ball was released, on which depended the form of the trajectory. There was finally the weight of the ball which was of importance both for its velocity and for the path of the curve. Unfortunately we do not have a firing manual for a trebuchet. But it would have contained the dimensions of the apparatus and the principal indications showing, for a trebuchet of given size, the relationship of the mass of the counterweight, the weight of the ball, and the regulations for releasing the ball; otherwise a shot would have been completely arbitrary. Even the existence of the variables that had to be determined, an existence which stems inevitably from the very conception of the engine, proves no less inevitably that a certain number of notes had been justified and that the relationships between the factors had been more or less abstractly established in such a way as to permit an elementary formulation to be made. We also know that a number of masters had a good reputation and it is difficult to admit, with such a technique, that it could have been a simple matter of manual dexterity as in ordinary craftsmanship; in this case skill without knowledge would have been unthinkable. Everything which is known of the transmission of technical knowledge at this period leads us to believe that a few fairly simple rules would have enabled these masters to obtain the effects they were looking for. We shall come across other examples of the formulation of tables, the approximation and nature of which undoubtedly corresponded to the possibilities of measurement and which show that certain phenomena were known if not explained. Correct ballistic tables were not drawn up before the nineteenth century although it is known for certain that there were good artillery men before this date.

It would be surprising if men who merely wished to be more efficient had not tried to improve their rules. And the means of achieving such a result was to try to understand better what was in fact happening. But simple measurement was not enough and other considerations, of a more abstract kind, intervened.

The practice of measurement had certainly always been in use. Given what we have said about the degree of precision required by the engineers, such measurements did not entail any major difficulties. Numbered observations, which had certainly been made by those who directed counterweight artillery, must have also been practised by the succeeding artillery men. Thus we see the artillery men of Charles VIII trying out their pieces on canvases stretched between poles on an Italian beach. It was thus possible for them, although very approximately, to trace the curves by measuring the height of the holes which appeared in the canvases placed at varying distances. It was much more difficult to assess the velocities at different points of the trajectory. It was known, however, by experience, that the velocity increased more rapidly during the first moments of the course. Theoreticians affirmed, nevertheless, that for a given projectile, there was no fixed relation between the violence of the impulse and the velocity of the movement.

From the time of Leonardo da Vinci onwards, practice had made important progress and had set up relationships, in spite of the fact that the nature of the phenomena remained ill-defined and that certain measurements, such as the exact curve of the projectile, were still unknown. Leonardo attached great importance to the phenomena of percussion, on which he discoursed at considerable length without, in fact, reaching convincing conclusions. For the artillery men, as for the scientists, the curve was composed of three parts: the straight ascending trajectory, a mixed circular trajectory when the effect of weight intervened, and, finally, a straight fall to the ground when weight predominated. As a geometrician and designer Leonardo da Vinci may have recognized intuitively, what could be seen in a jet of water, that there was no rectilinear part. Leonardo stopped short on a path that Tartaglia was to follow.

The transformation of artillery towards the end of the fifteenth century had presented new problems. Here again 'intuitions' were required to discover the most perfect solutions. These intuitions, as the example of Charles VIII's artillery men showed, were not immediate and rested on concrete, measured and therefore reasoned, observations.

The link between the initial force and the velocity of the projectile had been known for some time. The notion of velocity, more important at first for artillery men than for theoreticians, came up in connexion both with the distance of the flight and the force of the percussion. In both cases another fact intervened, the weight of the ball. Given differences of calibre, which in a certain sense corresponded to differences of weight (and also led to the fixing of the

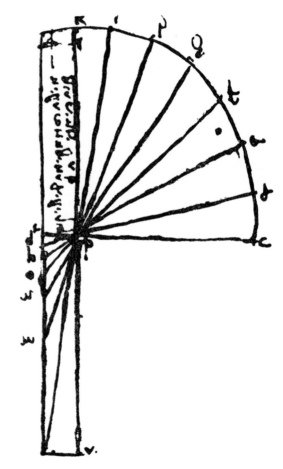

Attempt to determine the effects of percussion by Leonardo da Vinci.

limits of power), the time came when it was possible to establish the difference of power required (that is, the difference in weight of powder) to launch projectiles of different weights over the same distance. Inversely, it was possible to measure the effect of weight by using the same force and measuring the distances covered by two projectiles of different weight. By repeating these experiments with variable angles of fire, the rudiments of a firing table were obtained. It was soon found that it was advantageous to use balls of identical weight for every calibre and fixed charges of powder and to vary the distance covered only by modifying the angle of fire. Serious thinking was required before it was possible to advance from one to the other of these successive lines of reasoning, the outlines of which can be discerned at long intervals. The transition from stone balls, which are heavier, to cast-iron balls also required an increased velocity through the effect of impact. The next stage was thus the rationalization of calibres, which makes the supply of munitions easier and which appears to have constituted the great advantage of the French artillery at the beginning of the wars in Italy.

In the event the rules were bound to be numerical, that is to say the main elements of the problem had been separated. Many uncertainties undoubtedly remained, such as the lack of homogeneity of powder, wind, etc. But the main data in regard to firing had been established. There was nothing surprising in the fact, since it was of no consequence, that certain confusions remained. If Leonardo da Vinci confuses the notion of time and space this does not greatly affect the technical efficacy of his theory. We think that in this connexion there might be much to learn from the 'manuals of gunmanship' of which a certain number dating from the first half of the fifteenth century have come down to us.

Tartaglia's ballistics, as outlined in the small work with the promising title of *Nova scientia*, published in 1537, is still traditional. If our engineers had a theory, it must have been this one. He was the first, states Koyre, to submit to theoretical treatment an 'art' which up to then had been purely empirical. There were only empirical calculations to go on, but these calculations had helped the scientist to construct something else, since some of the facts had been determined, some of the ideas had been brought to greater precision and numerical relationships had supervened in the process. Also the artillery men could no longer turn their minds to abstract reasoning. But it is not impossible that they had started to do so in the prospect of a theoretical technique which was being developed. The steam machine had functioned very well and been perfected before Carnot had enunciated the general theory. But Carnot was a technician and had learned a great deal from a technique which had already tried to rationalize itself. Meditation by moonlight would not have given Tartaglia the essential bases which he derived from modest artillery men. Tartaglia, however, came up against certain propositions accepted by these men but in which he did not believe: the initial acceleration of the projectile and the increase of power of impact as a function of this acceleration. In regard to the trajectory path, he adopted the ideas already accepted by his predecessors. He only deduced that the trajectory paths of heavy objects projected above the horizon with the same inclination are proportional to their initial velocities. The work was intended for technicians because it ends with certain practical questions such as the determination of the distances and elevations of objectives, and the description of an instrument for measuring angles for the use of artillery men.

In a second work, published in 1546, Tartaglia again takes up the subject and abandons a number of ideas, in particular the rectilinear sections of trajectories. He defends this new proposal in a dialogue with an artillery man who tells him about the pseudo-experience of common sense. It was considered fair play, if one may express it so, to appear to remonstrate with a technician. Tartaglia's reasoning was basically only the reasoning of a technician, though this was partly masked by this pseudo-dialogue.

Benedetti (1530–1590) was, of all the men of the Renaissance, the nearest to modern science and the immediate predecessor of Galileo. It almost goes without saying that he was an artillery man and an engineer. He succeeded in demonstrating mathematically that the *quies media* did not exist. But he did not succeed in discarding the traditional notion of impetus which still masked many precise problems. While practice often constituted an obstacle to the proper comprehension of phenomena, false ideas also prevented technicians from obtaining a clear insight into what they were doing. Benedetti, steeped as he was in Archimedean ideas, was one of these.

Olschki places Galileo in the tradition of Renaissance artisans, builders, and engineers, in short, in that circle which we have tried to analyse and to which Galileo belonged. Galileo, moreover, acknowledged what he owed to technicians at the beginning of the first day of his *Discorsi*. It emerged from his explanations that his theoretical researches into the resistance of materials were stimulated directly by the concrete problems which arose in the arsenals of Venice. He studied especially the following problem: why the resistance of a structure does not vary proportionally to the size of the structure or the quantity of material used. Why is a large ship more fragile than a smaller ship, the proportions between the parts and materials used being the same? Koyre recognizes that the engineers and artists of the Renaissance did a great deal to destroy traditional conceptions. They tried, as we see in Leonardo da Vinci and Benedetti, to develop a new dynamic, of which many factors came from the Parisian nominalists. But Koyre declares that the mechanism of classical physics, far from being an artisan's conception, which was, indeed, the extreme view of certain historians, or the engineer's, which is less proven, is the exact opposite. He adds: if Benedetti, by far the most remarkable of Galileo's predecessors, sometimes advances beyond the level of Parisian dynamics, it is not because of his work as an engineer or as an artillery man; it is thanks to his study of Archimedes. It is, nevertheless, curious to observe that it is the engineers, such as Leonardo da Vinci, who was not perhaps the most perspicacious, Benedetti, Galileo, and Stevin, who are represented as the links in the chain which leads to classical science.

Stevin did not turn his mind to dynamics. Against this, his study of statics was much more advanced. It is, no doubt, purely Archimedean and is completely divorced from dynamics. In his *Statique*, published in 1586, Stevin deals with the equilibrium of weights, then with the centre of gravity of plain figures and solid bodies. He gives an elegant solution to the problem of the lever and then, by a new method of reasoning, the solution of the problem of the inclined plane, giving at the same time a demonstration of the impossibility of perpetual movement. He finally ends with hydrostatics, which he no doubt derived from Archimedes, but also from his own work as an engineer, making clear, after Benedetti, that he did not know the principle of hydrostatic equilibrium.

Doubtless one must not underestimate, even on the level of reflection and of scientific reasoning, the contribution of our engineers, most of whom, at least the last among them, succeeded in advancing beyond the narrow horizon of crude technique. It is not only technique which changes with them, but also modes of thought. Profiting from the immense fund of information of the generations of which they were the heirs, in the twin fields of strictly technical expertise and scientific knowledge, while limiting their interests to a few questions which were the source of classical science, they tried to weld their technique into a logical and concrete corpus of knowldge. The links between the two endeavours are obvious. The study of machines, by the indirect means of statics, the study of dynamics as a function of ballistic problems, even more than the fall of heavy bodies, the problems of hydrodynamics and hydrostatics, all indicate a common viewpoint.

We have already cited many proofs of this opinion. We would like to give other examples which are situated more squarely within the tradition we have just outlined.

We are aware of the difference that there was in the opinion of mediaeval students of physics between circular and rectilinear motion, a difference which made them fundamentally distinct from one another. The law of inertia could never have been discovered from circular motion. One of the characteristics of classical physics was to be to change the direction of this opposition and to make circular motion, violent motion and rectilinear motion natural motion, while for the physicists of the Middle Ages it was the reverse. The Aristotelian tradition, it is true, had always admitted natural rectilinear motion. The great difference between rectilinear and circular motion of the natural kind resided, for Aristotle and his successors, in the necessary finiteness of the first and the inevitable discontinuation of its trajectory if it lasted long enough. Circular motion, on the other hand, was continuous and nothing prevents it lasting indefinitely (*Physics*, VIII, 8 and 9). The opposition between these two motions was not to disappear finally before the middle of the seventeenth century. Technicians no doubt knew little about these oppositions in relation to the intrinsic nature of motion. They could even, if necessary, accept the discontinuity of rectilinear movement and the possible perpetuity of circular movement, if it had not been for friction which would slow it down.

Our engineers knew two particular cases of circular motion in machines: alternating circular motion created in clocks from a continuous rectilinear motion, that of the weights, and continuous circular motion created from an alternating rectilinear motion, that of the connecting-rod and crank. In the two cases they ended by establishing a link between circular and rectilinear motion, between natural and violent motion, by assimilating the two notions and by making of motion of whatever kind a single concept. Kinetic energy, as in the case of windmills, could be transformed into one or other of the two motions.

The solution of dead centres in the rod and crank system, which latterly engaged the attention of Benedetti, who wished to demonstrate that there was no stoppage at any such point and that paradoxically, perhaps, the motion is continuous, raised the problem of the conservation of motion, of kinetic energy, in circular motion. When the chariot reverses, its wheel is idle on its axis and continues to turn. In adapting a wheel on an axis to which one wishes to give a continuous circular motion by means of a rod and crank, one may easily pass these two dead centres. It is the driving wheels which furnish a continuous circular motion, when the initial motion derived from alternating rectilinear motion might not have the necessary continuity. It was soon seen that if the fly-wheel was very heavy, starting might be difficult, but afterwards it was much easier to maintain the motion: this was bringing mass to bear in its relationship with energy and was the discovery of inertia. The application of these components to motion was to lead to extremely ingenious machines, which are obvious proofs that all these elements were understood. It is true that no new concepts had emerged, but the day when the scientist's reasoning entered upon new paths, he was to be sustained by this whole extremely advanced technical context. Or, better still, the new ideas would only be born, according to a particular logic, in the minds of technicians whose technical experience, consciously or not, could vindicate abstract reasoning.

Processes of regulation, another large question, awareness of which dates from this period, set in action processes, one could almost say arguments, which demonstrate the extent of what could only have been at the beginning a matter of intuition. The idea itself was an old one, since it already existed, in admirable form, on the regulators of weight pendulums. The first clock-maker knew very well that the weight tended to drop at an irregular speed, though he probably did not know the law of the fall of heavy bodies. Although the invention of the escapement allowed this continuous movement to become discontinuous movement, it still had to be transformed into a uniform movement. This was the role of the regulator, which was a simple arm placed on the turning axis, with two weights at its two extremities. The escapement makes this arm move alternately first in one direction then in the other. The inertia at the beginning and end of each movement helps to regulate the swing. Here, again, mass was linked to motion. And that is why they went further: in effect, these weights were movable on the arms. By changing their position it was possible either to slow down or to accelerate the uniform movement of the axis, since the lever was being moved. In Dondi's drawing, which we reproduce, it was impossible to regulate the movement by shifting the weights. The two arms of the lever are replaced by a crown with decorated weights, appropriately called the brake crown. If all knowledge exists only to the extent that it is systematic, Dondi did not know that a weight falls with accelerated motion. But, able mechanic and perspicacious observer that he was, he knew quite well that if he wished to drive the movement of a clock with a falling weight, a brake would be required to ensure regular motion: the escapement

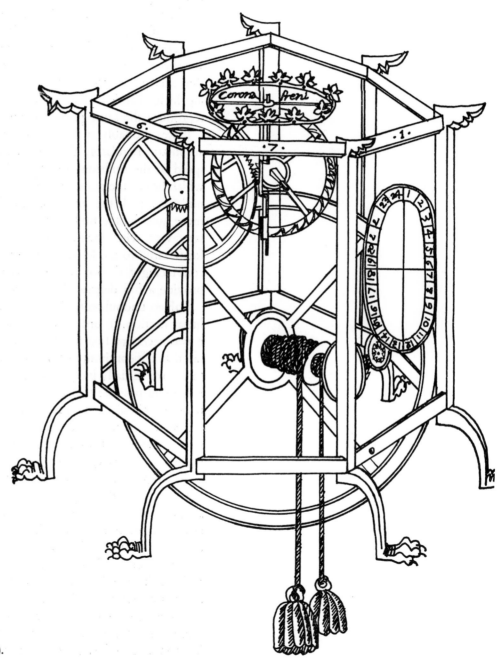

Dondi: Clockwork mechanism (1340).

by itself was not capable of transforming accelerated motion into regular motion.

This was, certainly, only a primary regulation, in which all the facts were constant. Francesco di Giorgio was to link a truly automatic regulation to a continuous circular motion. In his ball mechanism the balls, which deviate more or less from the centre by virtue of centrifugal force, which was known from experience, offered greater or lesser resistance to the motion. Inversely, the variations of the motion caused the balls to deviate automatically, thus exerting a braking effect. A man spinning on his heels and holding in his hands a chain to which a weight is attached, can easily reproduce the same phenomenon.

It was probably at the end of the fifteenth century that a simpler automatic regulator, the corn-trough, made its appearance. The speed of the millstone regulates the flow of the corn. The trough which brings the grain rubs against a square section of the axis of the millstone and the result is the jigging-distributor. By turning more quickly, the millstone will obtain more grain to grind; in the same way, when the motive force diminishes there will be less work for the mill to do. M. de Latil, who discovered this mechanism, has convincingly shown that it was a regulator but that it did not provide a full degree of compensation.

Galileo undoubtedly discovered the principle of inertia in rectilinear motion. In order to arrive at the modern concept of inertia, it was necessary first to eliminate the criterion of impetus, that is to say that the continuity of motion was related only to mass, and not to a force initially incorporated into this mass and remaining there. It is quite possible that the difference which was supposed to exist between circular and rectilinear motion prevented scientists and technicians from looking for this principle in circular motion. But it is evident that technicians, in looking for the solutions they needed, had already arrived at other concepts. Here again the efforts of the engineers must have been of some use.

Inertia existed everywhere, in the technical world, even in the simplest machines. The moment the technician came to grips with any form of motion, whether it was that of the ball fired by a cannon, or a mill grinding corn, or that engendered by a rod and crank, innumerable difficulties arose, which had not been defined and which could be confused with other mechanical difficulties, such as friction. Undoubtedly, and probably unconsciously, mass began to come into the picture. It was necessary, in order for the idea to be clearly established, that impetus should lose its quality of being incorporated in the nature of objects and that motion should become something autonomous. The technician had, perhaps, shaken off the yoke of metaphysics, but he was not capable of substituting another system of explanation.

Thus, notes Koyre, it was the effort of explaining facts of daily experience, the fact of falling, of throwing, etc., which gave rise to the reflections that led to the discovery of the law of inertia. But, curiously enough, it was not the sole or the principal cause of these reflections. The new physics was not a child of the earth alone; its home was also in the heavens, where it was to find its culmination.

It would probably be more correct to show the whole complex situation in which the 'new science', to take over the title of Tartaglia's little book, appeared. All the problems came to maturity together, which is not surprising. Astronomy reversed its ideas and everyday mechanics also abandoned its false attitudes and misguided principles. From this combination of new tendencies sprang classical physics. If it is impossible to attribute all the credit to the technicians, at least they played their part in the common development.

While the technical world was exerting its influence on scientific development, it was not unaware of the existence of this development. It also changed its modes of thoughts and its methods. The nostrum was progressively supplanted by rational theory. In all fields the attempt was made to substitute valid explanations for accepted truths. But it happens that in the technical sphere empiricism can produce effective results. It was thus less the technique itself which changed than the idea in people's minds and the explanations put forward. It was necessary to wait many generations before science, in its turn, was able, to an increasing extent, to influence the development of techniques. As early as the end of the seventeenth century, with Roberval, Huygens, and Papin, science in its turn became the servant of technical activity. Scientific reasoning became the source of technical 'perfection'. And it was at this early period that the belief first emerged – though it was later to grow in importance – that it was possible, with the aid of science, to achieve a result perfect in itself.

This development of technical ideas is striking. Our engineers were at its origin. They were no longer pure technicians and they looked for a logic outside the traditional procedures which had been transmitted from generation to generation. From them certainly dates what might be called the demystification of technique, which put technical truths within reach of everyone. This first stage, not to be confused with an analogous process in the sphere of scientific knowledge, was followed by a second period in which an attempt was made to integrate abstract scientific concepts into an already accepted system of problems and practice. This end was doggedly pursued during the whole of the sixteenth and the first half of the seventeenth century. This more or less successful course is studded with great names. In the field of agriculture, for example, the *Théâtre d'agriculture*, by Olivier de Serres, seemed, from the moment when it appeared, in 1599, more like a culmination than an innovation. Bernard Palissy's work *Recepte véritable par laquelle tous les hommes pourront apprendre à multiplier leurs thrésors*, printed at La Rochelle in 1563, belongs, however, to the tendency which wished to introduce scientific concepts into traditional techniques. And the title, which invests 'all men' with a kind of technical power, is also symptomatic.

This incursion of science, which in many cases was only pseudo-science, showed itself at different levels. It was more marked among those engineers who were directly descended from those we have studied and who were perhaps less concerned with true technical practice than with technical progress. There is probably no better example than that curious being, better known today than formerly, named Salomon de Caus (1576–1626). The titles of these works again reveal the new tendencies: *Pratique et démonstration des horloges solaires* (Paris 1624), *La perspective avec les raisons des ombres et miroirs* (London 1612), *Les raisons des forces mouvantes, avec diverses machines tant utiles que plaisantes* (Frankfurt 1615). The use of these terms is a valuable pointer in itself. Olivier de Serres had composed a 'theatre' in the manner of the mechanical engineers. Palissy still used the term 'recette' or recipe: from the beginning of the seventeenth century this was replaced by the more rational 'raison'. The change had come. The only reminders of the previous period are the 'pleasant machines' which are an echo of those games and entertainments that had so much delighted the men of the Renaissance.

Side by side with these articulate individuals, whose works were printed, and whose illustrations delighted a public more or less unfamiliar with the problems they were debating, there were the true technicians who had remained more or less artisans and who still belonged to a past age. They had also been touched by the new spirit and were soon attempting to express their achievements in scientific terms. This was a deep-seated movement which was not reflected in the printed literature of the period, but records of which are preserved in manuscript form. Matthew Baker (1530–1613), was the son of a well-known ships' carpenter. He was the first master-builder of the English navy, and was appointed in 1572. He issued numerical rules designed to ensure the building of better ships, which already show the rudiments of rationality. If the scientific justification of his plane is still embryonic, at least it marks the beginning of a quest which was to be pursued without interruption until a theory of ship-building was achieved.

All this is represented, although still imperfectly, in tables. There were tables of all kinds, which illustrates the progressive infiltration of mathematical reasoning, since the data of a table are, in spirit at any rate, no longer empirical. Tables for calculating interest were of long standing: they had indeed provided the opportunity of perfecting methods of calculation. Navigators used rudimentary trigonometrical tables to bring a ship back on to course when it had missed it for any one of a number of reasons. There are examples of these tables, known as *martelogio* tables, dating from 1436 and 1444, and it is probable that they existed in the fourteenth century, but they continued to be improved, corrected, and completed. In other fields there was also an attempt to bring out a kind of 'ready reckoner' which was scientifically compiled, so it was supposed, and provided answers to all kinds of concrete questions. Firing tables, very rudimentary these, tables of proportions for shipbuilders, musical tables, which may have led to logarithms, etc. The importance of these tables is very great in the development of science in the strict sense of the word.

At the end of the sixteenth and the beginning of the seventeenth century, the introduction of mathematics into technical activity made a further advance. From that time onwards technicians were looking not so much for approximate tables, capable of providing an answer that could be used in practice and in which the errors were negligible, as formulae which, for any given collection of facts, would enable them to achieve the one and only result they were seeking. When Simon Stevin gave himself up to calculating the force of windmills he had passed to the next stage. Not all techniques had reached that point, but they were all moving towards it. Their progressive disengagement from scientific ideas inevitably led in that direction.

These words from Bernard Palissy's work on the art of the potter, which he described in so masterly a fashion, clearly reveal the follower of Leonardo da Vinci: 'You must know that, in order to manage well a kiln full of pottery, even when it is glazed, you must control the fire by so careful a philosophy that there would be no spirit however noble which would not be much tried and often disappointed. As to the manner of filling your kiln, a singular geometry is needed ... The arts for which compass, ruler, numbers, weights and measures are needed should not be called mechanics.'

It is clear that if the universe has its physical laws and possesses its own geometry, technology must also be subject to these, since all techniques proceed from nature. If the technicians were thus able, to some extent, to set scientists on new paths which lead them to important discoveries, in return the scientists could now counsel the technicians, especially when they were unlettered men. The cycle is complete; having begun with technology we return to technology.

There was no doubt of this in the minds of the men of this important period at the end of the sixteenth century, the period of Galileo and of the law of inertia, of Mercator and his modern cartography, and of Lee and his knitting machines. Nourished by hopes that were too high and too ambitious in relation to their intellectual means, the technicians of the Renaissance and of the dawn of the classical period believed that everything was possible. Their immediate successors experienced the difficult aftermath of this and they may have been disappointed, to use Palissy's expression. They thus returned, for a short time, to more traditional concepts. Engineering science gave way to art: the description and perfection of the arts, according to the title which could still, in the middle of the eighteenth century, be given to the great technical collection of the Académie des Sciences of Paris.

The *Encyclopédie* of Diderot and d'Alembert still in many places reflected this attitude towards techniques. 'Moreover', wrote Diderot, 'it is workmanship that makes the artist and he will not learn from books how to ply his tools. The artist will only find in our work opinions that he might not have held and observations that he would not have made without long years of work. We offer to the studious reader what he would have learned from an artist if he had sought to satisfy his curiosity by watching him at work; and to the artist what it would be desirable for him to have learned from the philosopher to advance to perfection.' At this period, furthermore, the effect of balance was bringing techniques back into the realm of science and, as at the beginning of the sixteenth century, the close alliance between technician and scientist was being restored and was once again to be a rich source of instruction. But the attitude had changed, the sciences were more autonomous. Monge had founded the Ecole Polytechnique to give those technicians who had been trained in 'practical' schools between 1750 and 1780 a scientific culture that enabled them to confirm their knowledge. Just as Leonardo eagerly sought out the works of Archimedes, Monge wished to make his engineers good mathematicians and physicists.

The methods were a little different but the programme was the same and it was that defined by Descartes in a famous text that is still quoted. 'They [his speculations] have made me see that it is possible to acquire knowledge that is very useful in life; and that in place of the speculative philosophy that is taught in schools, it is possible to devise a method whereby, knowing the force and activities of fire, water, air, the stars, the skies, and all the other bodies that surround us, as clearly as we understand the various crafts of our artisans, we may use them in the same way for all the purposes for which they are suited and thus become as it were the masters and possessors of nature.'

Conclusion

Now that we have reached the end of our discussion we see before us just what we saw at the beginning: a perpetual thirst for power that compels men towards progress and the mastery of nature, as well as power over other men. The 'pleasant machines' mentioned by Salomon de Caus are no longer there and fireworks have changed their character. Mechanical exercises and festive occasions have become displays of vainglory.

All our engineers were men of war. Such statements of the obvious have the uncomfortable habit of often being true. Yet the sixteenth century had passed beyond warlike preoccupations and had constructed a complete technical system, just as it had built a new scientific system. More than their quest for deadly power, more than the amusements and the love of images, what has attracted us in these men is the difficult apprenticeship they served in a new world.

Much remains to be done before we understand the processes of their thought, before we appreciate their hesitations and grasp the nature of their ignorance and their failures. We must underline their gradual distortions of accepted truths, their difficult departures from the traditional paths, in order give them credit for having brought about a unique advance in the history of thought. This modest essay had no such ambitious aim. Its main purpose was to rehabilitate those who had been somewhat neglected and to reduce the supposed genius of others to truer proportions. But the enquiry remains open: it might bring to light other works still languishing in the dust of libraries, it might also provide a more precise analysis of the notebooks which have never been published and which are full of information. The notebooks of Francesco di Giorgio, certain Sienese manuscripts, all the treatises on artillery and the construction of clocks would certainly supply elements of great value, would give precision to notions which are still vague and would open up new perspectives. Unless – which is always possible – new commentaries are written or unpublished works discovered it does not seem that future study will greatly modify what we know about Leonardo da Vinci. But those around him deserve better than the disdain they have been shown. and this was what we wished to demonstrate.

Whether they have learned something or been entertained, we hope that our readers have not been bored and that they have felt, as we have done, the interest and pleasure of having passed a few hours in the presence of men who cannot leave us indifferent.

Bibliography

General Bibliography

TH. BECK. *Beiträge zur Maschinenbaues Geschichte* (Berlin, 1910).

G. CANESTRINI. *Arte Militare, meccanica, medievale* (Milan, 1945).

F. M. FELDHAUS. *Die Technik der Vorzeit* (Leipzig, 1914).

U. FORTI. *Storia della tecnica italiana* (Florence, 1940).

JAHNS. *Geschichte der Kriegswissenschaften*, Vol.I (Munich, 1889).

FR. KLEMM. *Technik, eine Geschichte ihrer Probleme* (Munich, 1954).

A. MIELI. *La eclosión del Rinacimiento* (Madrid, 1951).

L. OLSCHKI. *Geschichte der neusprachlichen Wissenschaftlichen Literatur*, Vol.I (Leipzig, 1919).

P. ROMOCKI. *Geschichte der Explosivstoffe* (Berlin, 1895).

G. SARTON. *Introduction to the History of Science*, Vol.III, Part II (Baltimore, 1948).

CH. SINGER. *A History of Technology*, Vol.II, (Oxford, 1956).

A. UCCELLI. *Storia della tecnica dal medioevo ai giorni nostri* (Milan, 1943).

A. P. USHER. *A History of Mechanical Inventions* (Harvard, 1954).

Chapter 1: The Weight of Tradition

Greek origins

CARRA DE VAUX. *Le livre des pneumatiques et des machines hydrauliques de Philon de Byzance* (Paris, 1902).

TH. H. MARTIN. Recherches sur la vie et les ouvrages d'Héron d'Alexandrie. *Mémoires présentés par divers savants à l'Académie des Inscriptions et Belles-Lettres*, Vol.IV (Paris, 1854).

A. DE ROCHAS. *La science des philosophes et l'art des thaumaturges dans l'Antiquité* (Paris, 1912).

A. DE ROCHAS. Traité de fortification, attaque et défense des places. *Mém. de la Société d'émulation du Doubs* (1870–1), pp.192–325.

A. DE ROCHAS. *La poliorcétique des Grecs* (Paris, 1871).

A. DAIN. *La tradition du texte d'Héron de Byzance* (Paris, 1933).

Byzantine origins

Les poliorcétiques d'Apollodore de Damas, translation by Ernest Lacoste. *Revue des Etudes grecques* (July–Sept. 1890).

Mediaeval compilations

M. BERTHELOT. Sur le Traité De rebus bellicis. *Journal des Savants* (1900), pp.171–7.

Byzance et la France médiévale, catalogue de l'exposition de la Bibliothèque nationale (Paris, 1958).

Mediaeval innovators

HAHNLOSER. *Villard de Honnecourt, Kritische Gesamtausgabe des Bauhüttenbuches* (Vienna, 1935).

J. QUICHERAT. Notice sur l'album de Villard de Honnecourt. *Revue archéologique*, Vol.VI (1849).

CHAPUIS and GELIS. *Le monde des automates* (Paris, 1928).

Chapter 2: The Weight of Civilization

CH. BLANC. *Histoire de la Renaissance en Italie* (Paris).

P. FIERENS. *La peinture flamande des origines à Metsys* (Paris, 1938).

P. FRANCASTEL. Techniques et Arts. *L'Invention humaine* (Paris, 1942).

SOCIÉTÉ D'HISTOIRE MODERNE. *Colloque sur la Renaissance*, reports of proceedings by MM. Chastel and Mollat.

R. TATON. *Histoire générale des Sciences*, Vol.I (Paris, 1957).

G. BEAUJOUAN. L'Enseignement des mathématiques à l'Université de Paris. *Mélanges Millas-Vallicrosa*, Vol.I (Barcelona, 1954), pp.93–124.

G. BEAUJOUAN. *L'Interdépendance entre la science scolastique et les techniques utilitaires* (Paris, 1957).

DE ROOVER. Aux origines d'une technique intellectuelle: la formation et l'expansion de la comptabilité à partie double. *Ann. d'Hist. éc. et soc.*, Vol.IX (1937), pp.171–93 and 270–98.

FANFANI. La préparation intellectuelle et professionelle à l'activité économique en Italie, du XIVe au XVIe siècle. *Moyen-âge* (1951), pp.326–46.

R. GANDILHON. *La politique économique de Louis XI* (Paris, 1942).

A. GIRARD. Un phénomène économique: la guerre monétaire aux XIVe et XVe siècles. *Annales d'Histoire sociale*, Vol.II (1940), pp.207–18.

R. H. HILTON. Sur une crise générale de la féodalité. *Annales*, Vol.VI (1951), pp.23–30.

E. PERROY. Les crises du XIVe siècle. *Annales*, Vol.IV (1949), pp.167–82.

M. POSTAN. Some economic evidence of declining population. *Economic History Review*.

L. FISCHER. *König Mathias Corvin und seine Bibliothek* (Vienna, 1878).

C. GUASTI. Inventario della libreria urbinate compilato nel secolo XV. *Giornale storico degli archivi toscani*, Vol.VI (1862), pp.127–47 and Vol.VII (1863), pp.44–55 and 130–54.

MUNTZ and FABRE. *La Bibliothèque du Vatican au XVe siècle* (Paris, 1887).

E. PELLEGRIN. *La Bibliothèque des Visconti et des Sforza au XVe siècle* (Paris, 1955).

CH. YRIARTE. *Rimini, études sur les lettres et les arts à la cour des Malatesta* (Paris, 1882).

B. GILLE. La naissance du système bielle-manivelle. *Techniques et civilisations*, Vol.II (1952), pp.42–6.

Chapter 3: The German School

Kyeser

B. GILLE. Etudes sur les manuscrits d'ingénieurs du XVe siècle, II, Kyeser. *Techniques et civilisations*, Vol.V (1956), pp.216–23 (with bibliography).

LOREDAN-LARCHEY. Les ribaudequins du manuscrit de Colmar. *Revue Alsacienne* (1890), p.385.

Manuscript of the Hussite War

B. GILLE. Le manuscrit dit de la guerre hussite. *Techniques et civilisations*, Vol.V (1956), pp.77–86.

The end of the German School

A. VON ESSENWEIN. *Das mittelalterliche Hausbuch* (Frankfurt, 1887).

BOSSERT and STOCK. *Das mittelalterliche Hausbuch* (Leipzig, 1912) (with a very complete bibliography).

Chapter 4: The First Italian Generation

VENTURI. *Brunelleschi* (Rome, 1923).

AL. BIRKENMAJER. Zur Lebengeschichte und wissenschaftlichen Tätigkeit von G. Fontana. *Isis*, Vol.XVII (1932), pp.34–53.

HUELSEN. Der liber instrumentorum des Giovanni Fontana. *Festgäbe für Hugo Blümner* (Zurich, 1914), pp.507–14.

H. OMONT. Un traité de physique et d'alchimie du XVᵉ siècle, en écriture cryptographique. *Bibliothèque de l'Ecole des Chartes*, Vol.LVIII (1897), pp.253–8.

L. THORNDIKE. Marianus Jacobus Taccola. *Archives internationales d'histoire des sciences* (1955), pp.7–26 (complete bibliography).

FAVARO. *Un ingegnere italiano del secolo decimoquarto* (Padua, 1914).

HORWITZ. Mariano und Valturio. *Geschichteblätter der Technik*, Vol.IX (1922), pp.38–40.

IVINS. Valturio's De re militari. *Bull. Metropolitan Museum* (1926), p.267.

E. RODAKIEWICZ. The editio princeps of Valturio's De re militari in relation to the Dresden and Münich MSS. *Maso Finiguerra*, Vol.V (1940), p.15.

P. H. MICHEL. *La pensée de L. B. Alberti* (Paris, 1930).

LAZZARONI and MONOZ. *Filarete* (Rome, 1908).

W. VON OETTINGEN. *Anton Averlino Filaretes Tractat über di Baukunst* (Vienna, 1890).

L. BELTRAMI. *La vita di Aristotele da Bologna* (1912).

Chapter 5: Francesco di Giorgio

FRANCESCO DI GIORGIO MARTINI. *Trattato dell' Architettura civile e militare.* Saluzzo and Promis (Turin, 1841).

VENTURI. *Francesco di Giorgio* (Rome, 1925).

S. BRINTON. *Francesco di Giorgio Martini of Siena* (London, 1934–5).

A. ST. WELLER. *Francesco di Giorgio Martini* (Chicago, 1943).

R. RAPINI. *Francesco di Giorgio, architetto* (Florence, 1946), with a very complete bibliography.

M. SALMI. *Disegni di Francesco di Giorgio Martini nella Collezione Chigi-Saracini* (Siena, 1947).

The bibliography of Francesco di Giorgio is very extensive, and is to be found in the above books.

Chapters 6, 7, 8: Leonardo da Vinci

Anything like a complete bibliography would be impossibly long; we only mention here those works which have been particularly useful and which have not already been listed. There are first the older works, which are still available:

G. SEAILLES, *Léonard de Vinci, l'artiste et le savant* (Paris, 1892).

E. MUNTZ. *Léonard de Vinci* (Paris, 1899).

DUHEM. *Etudes sur Léonard de Vinci* (Paris, 1906–13), 3 volumes.

ED. SOLMI. *Le fonti dei manoscritti di Leonardo da Vinci* (Turin, 1908).

There follows a list of recent researches undertaken on the occasion of the quincentenary of Leonardo's birth:

A. SARTORIS. *Léonard architecte* (Paris, 1952).

Léonard de Vinci et l'expérience scientifique au XVIᵉ siècle (Paris, 1953).

G. U. ARATA. *Leonardo architetto e urbanista* (Milan, 1953).

I. CALVI. *L'ingegneria militare di Leonardo* (Milan, 1953).

G. STROBINO. *Leonardo da Vinci e la meccanica tessile* (Milan, 1953).

L. TURSINI. *Le armi di Leonardo da Vinci* (Milan, 1953).

L. RETI. Leonardo da Vinci nella storia della macchina a vapore. *Rivista di Ingegneria* (1956–7) (and printed separately).

Chapter 9: Research and Reality

We have made use almost exclusively of the general works listed at the start of this bibliography. We have also had recourse to the following:

A. FAVE. *Etudes sur le passé et le présent de l'artillerie* (Paris, 1845–67), 6 volumes.

RITTER. *Châteaux, donjons et places fortes*, Paris (1953).

J. U. NEF. *La guerre et le progrès humain* (Paris, n.d.)

R. DION. *Histoire des levées de la Loire* (Paris, 1961).

F. RUSSO. Deux ingénieurs de la Renaissance, Besson et Ramelli. *Thalès* (1948), pp.108–12.

Chapter 10: The Dawn of Classical Science

Here again, we have made much use of the works cited at the start of the bibliography. The following works have also been frequently consulted:

A. KOYRE. *Etudes galiléennes* (Paris, 1939), 3 volumes.

R. TATON et al. *Histoire générale des sciences:*
 I.–*La science antique et médiévale* (Paris, 1957).
 II.–*La science moderne* (Paris, 1958).

A. C. CROMBIE. *Histoire des sciences de saint Augustin à Galilée* (Paris, 1959), 2 volumes.

La Science au XVIᵉ siècle, Colloque de Royaumont (Paris, 1906).

1. The German School

The primitives

1. *NUREMBERG, Germanisches Museum, No.25,801.* Paper, 134 × 200 mm. 21 ff., unbound.

2. *MUNICH, Staatsbibliothek, cod. germ. 600.* Paper, 264 × 180 mm, 22 ff., early binding.[1]

3. *VIENNA, Wappensammlung, P 5014.* Parchment, 196 × 278 mm, 119 ff., 15th century binding.[2]

4. *VIENNA, Bibl. Nat. No.3069 (phil.182).* Paper, 300 × 211 mm, 169 ff., early binding.[3]

Kyeser

5. *GÖTTINGEN, Universitätsbibliothek, cod. phil.63.* Parchment, 325 × 240 mm, 140 ff., modern binding.[4]

6. *INNSBRUCK, Ferdinandeum, MSS.16.0.7.* Paper, 310 × 213 mm, 180 ff., early binding.

Latin series

7. *COLMAR, mun. lib., No.491.* Paper, 301 × 210 mm, 79 ff.[5]

8. *DONAUESCHINGEN, Fürstenberg lib., cod. 860.* Paper, 325 × 210 mm. 125 ff., modern binding.[6]

9. *KARLSRUHE, Landesbibliothek, cod. Durlach 11.* Paper, 405 × 285 mm, 114 ff., early binding.

10. *COLOGNE, Archives mun. cod. W fo.232.* Paper, 285 × 205 mm, 96 ff., modern binding.[7]

1. SCHMELLERS, *Die deutschen Handschriften der K.Hof und Staatsbibliothek zu München*, Munich, 1866, p.98.

2. From the collections of the Archduke Ferdinand.

3. *Tabulae codicum manuscriptorum . . . in Bibliotheca Vindobonensi . . .*, Vol.II, p.190, not identified.
UNTERKIRCHER, *Inventar der Illuminierten Handschriften der Oesterr. N.B.*, Vienna, 1953, p.90, dated 1411.

4. *Verzeichnis der Handschriften im Preussischen Staat, Göttingen*, Vol. I, Berlin, 1893, pp.164–7.

5. Inserted in a Valturio. Not in the MS. catalogue.

6. BARACK, *Die Handschriften der Fürstlich-Fürstenbergischen Hofbibliothek zu Donaueschingen*, Tübingen, 1865, pp.581–2.

7. MENNE, *Die Handschriften der Archives*, Cologne, 1937, pp.202–4.

11. *CHANTILLY, Fonds Condé, No.348.* Paper, 300 × 217 mm, 153, bound with the arms of Orléans.[8]

12. *VIENNA, Nat. Bibl., No.5518 (phil.245).* Paper, 279 × 201 mm, 82 ff., unbound.[9]

13. *VIENNA, Wappensammlung, P 5342.* Paper, 325 × 218 mm, fo.66 to 167, damaged binding.

German series

14. *BESANÇON, Bibl.mun., No.1360.* Paper, 300 × 250 mm, 133 ff., early binding.[10]

15. *VIENNA, Nat. Bibl., No.3062 (phil.127).* Paper, 306 × 212 mm, 251 ff., early binding.[11]

16. *VIENNA, Nat. Bibl., No.5278 (phil.143).* Paper, 310 × 220 mm, 204 ff., modern binding.[12]

17. *STRASBOURG, Nat. Bibl., No.2259.* Paper, 280 × 203 mm, 138 ff., binding restored.[13]

18. *VIENNA, Nat. Bibl., No.2952.* Paper, 217 × 151 mm, 107 ff., modern binding.[14]

19. *GÖTTINGEN, Universitätsbibliothek, cod. phil.64.* Paper, 298 × 206 mm, 148 ff., early binding.[15]

20. *VIENNA, Nat. Bibl., No.3068 (phil.181).* Paper, 295 × 217 mm, 90 ff., early binding.[16]

Unknown – probably lost

21. *BERLIN, Arch. Etat. Major, MSS. No.117.*

Hussite MS.

22. *MUNICH, Staatsbibliothek, cod. lat.197.* Paper, 220 × 320 mm, 48 ff., modern binding.[17]

Book of mediaeval reason

23. *Von Waldburg-Wolfegg Coll.*[18]

Later copies of Kyeser

24. *ERLANGEN, Universitätsbibliothek, No.1390.* Paper, 430 × 290 mm, 305 ff., modern binding.[19]

25. *FRANKFURT, Stadtbibliothek, mun. lib. MSS.11.40.*

26. *BERLIN, Bibl.royal, cod. germ. Q 94.* Paper, 149 ff., modern binding.[20]

8. *Catalogue général des Manuscrits . . .* , Institut, Paris, 1928, p.78.

9. *Tabulae . . .* , Vol.III, Vienna, 1870, p.147; UNTERKIRCHER, *op. cit.*

10. *Catalogue général des manuscrits . . . Départements,* XLV, Paris, p.144, not identified.

11. *Tabulae . . .* , Vol.II, Vienna, 1868, p.189; UNTERKIRCHER, *op. cit.*, p.90, not identified.

12. *Tabulae . . .* , Vol.III, p.85 and UNTERKIRCHER, *op. cit.*, p.105, *id.*

13. *Catalogue général des manuscrits . . . Départements,* XLVII, Paris, 1923, p.470, not identified.

14. *Tabulae . . .* , Vol.II, p.160.

15. *Verzeichnis der Handschriften . . . . Göttingen,* Vol.II, pp.167–70.

16. *Tabulae . . .* , Vol.II, p.190, and UNTERKIRCHER, *op. cit.*, p.90, not identified.

17. HALB and LAURMANN, *Catalogus codicum latinorum bibliothecae monacensis,* Vol.I, Munich, 1868, p.31.

18. Probably lost.

19. LUTZE, *Katalog der Handschriften der U.B. Erlangen,* Vol.VI, 1936, p.104.

20. DEGERING, *Kurzes Verzeichnis der germanischen Handschriften der preussischen Staatsbibliothek,* Vol.I, Leipzig, 1925, p.11; copy of the preceding.

27. *HEIDELBERG, Universitätsbibliothek, cod. Palat. germ.787.* Paper, 291 × 220 mm, 196 ff., modern binding.[21]

28. *MUNICH, Staatsbibliothek, cod. germ.356.* Paper, 220 × 165 mm. 196 ff., modern binding.[22]

29. *MUNICH, Staatsbibliothek, cod. germ.734.* Paper, 213 × 138 mm, 234 ff., modern binding.[23]

30. *WEIMAR, Staatsbibliothek, cod. Q 342.* Parchment, 225 × 163 mm, 83 ff. unbound.[24]

Martin Mercz

31. *VADUZ, Lichtenstein lib.*

32. *MUNICH, Staatsbibliothek, cod. germ.599.* Paper, 296 × 210 mm, 101 ff., modern binding.[25]

Ulrich Bessnitzer

33. *HEIDELBERG, Universitätsbibliothek, cod. palat,germ.130.* Paper, 371 × 261 mm, 62 ff., modern binding.[26]

Friar Philibs

34. *HEIDELBERG, Universitätsbibliothek, cod. palat. germ.126.* Paper, 410 × 285 mm, 44 ff., modern binding.[27]

2. The Italian School

Taccola

fragments and notes

35. *MUNICH, Staatsbibliothek, cod. lat.197.* Paper, 220 × 300 mm, not paginated, modern binding.[28]

36. *FLORENCE, Bibl.Nat., cod. palat.766.* Paper, 299 × 225 mm, 48 ff., parchment binding.[29]

complete works

37. *PARIS, Bibl. nat., lat.7239.* Parchment, 321 × 233 mm, 163 ff.[30]

38. *VENICE, Bibl. Marciana cod. lat.XIX 3.* Paper, 290 × 430 mm, 116 ff.[31]

39. *VIENNA, Wilczek lib., No.23.172.*[32]

21. F. WILKEN, *Geschichte der Bildung, Beraubung und Vernichtung der alten Heidelbergischen Büchersammlungen,* Heidelberg, 1817, p.534.

22. SCHMELLERS, *op. cit.,* p.52.

23. SCHMELLERS, *op. cit.,* p.123.

24. There is only one badly compiled manuscript catalogue, in which the information is unreliable.

25. SCHMELLERS, *op. cit.,* p.97.

26. WILKEN, *op. cit.,* p.354.

27. WILKEN, *op. cit.,* pp.351–2.

28. HALB and LAUBMANN, *op. cit.,* p.31. The second part of the MS. cited in 23.

29. *I Codici palatini della R. Biblioteca nazionale centrale di Firenze,* Vol.II, Rome, 1890, p.296.

30. Bought at Constantinople in 1687.

31. VALENTINELLI, *Bibliotheca manuscripta ad S. Marci Venetiarum codices latini,* Vol.V, Venice, 1872, pp.194–5.

32. Disappeared during the second world war.

Fontana

40. *MUNICH, Staatsbibliothek, cod. icon.242.* Parchment, 263 × 187 mm, 70 ff., modern binding.

Valturio

Since the book has been printed we only give the accession number of the MSS.[33]

41. *OXFORD, Canonici, class. lat.185.*

42. *OXFORD, Laud., lat.116.*

43. *VATICAN, Cod. Ottob. latin 1414.*

44. *FLORENCE, Bibl. Riccard, N 794.*

45. *VATICAN, Urbin., lat.281.*

46. *PARIS, Bibl. nat., lat.7236.*

47. *MODENA, Cod. Estensis, lat.447.*

48. *VENICE, Bibl. Marciana, lat.VIII, 29.*

49. *TURIN, Bibl. Duca di Genova, cod.308.*

50. *MILAN, Bibl. Ambros. F 150 sup.*

51. *PADUA, Bibl. Chapitre, cod. D 11.*

52. *LONDON, Brit. Mus., add.24.945.*

53. *DRESDEN, Staatsbibliothek, R 28 m (carried out for Matthias Corvinus).*

54. *MUNICH, Staatsbibliothek, cod. lat.23467.*

55. *CESENA, Bibl. Malatesta, S.XXI, 1.*

56. *FLORENCE, Bibl. Laurenz., Plut.XLVI. 3,*

57. *PARIS, Bibl. nat., lat.7237.*

58. *TURIN, Bibl. Naz., cod.371.*

59. *NEW YORK, Voynich. cod.*

60. *NEW YORK, Voynich. cod.*

61. *VATICAN, Reginensis.*

62. *PARIS, Bibl. nat., lat.7238.*

Filarete

vernacular version

63. *FLORENCE, Bibl. Naz., II.I.40 (ex. Magl. XVII, 30).* Paper, 290 × 400 mm, 195 ff., 15th century binding.[34]

64. *VALENCIA,* Paper, 270 ff., no number.

65. *MILAN, Bibl. Sforza, cod. Trivulzianus, cod. 863.* Paper, 300 × 430 mm, 273 ff.

66. *FLORENCE, Bibl. Naz. cod. palat.1411.* Paper, 311 × 214 mm, 248 ff., modern binding.

33. From E. RODAKIEWICZ, *op. cit.*

34. MAZZATINTI, *Inventari dei manoscritti della Biblioteca d'Italia,* Vol.VIII, Forli, 1898, pp.51–2.

67. *VENICE, Bibl. Marciana, lat.VIII, 11.* Parchment, 300 × 490 mm, 173 ff., bound with the Corvinus arms.[35]

68. *VATICAN, cod. reginensis, lat.1886.* Paper, 290 × 420 mm, 172 ff.

69. *VATICAN, cod. Sirletanus, lat.4966.* Paper, 290 × 430 mm, 173 ff., without illustrations.

70. *VATICAN, cod. Ottobr. lat.1548.* Paper, 200 × 260 mm, 483 ff.

71. *VATICAN, cod. Ottobr. lat.1300.*

72. *MILAN, Bibl. Ambros., A 71 inf.7.*

Alberti

A systematic search for the manuscripts of the *De re aedificatoria* has never been carried out. We limit our list to two manuscripts, the first in Latin, made for Mathias Corvinus, and the second in the vernacular.

73. *MODENA, Bibl.Estense, cod. Estensis 419.*

74. *FLORENCE, Bibl. Riccardiana, No.2520.*

Ghiberti

75. *FLORENCE, Bibl. Naz., BR 228 (ex. Magl.XVII 2).* Paper, 197 × 145 mm, 219 ff., modern binding.

Neroni

76. *SIENA, Bibl. Comunale, S IV 6.* Paper, 214 × 148 mm, 66 ff., modern binding.

Francesco di Giorgio Martini

note-books

77. *FLORENCE, Uffizi, architectural drawings, 318–37.*

78. *VATICAN, Cod. Urbin. 1757.* Parchment, 81 × 59 mm, 235 ff.[36]

79. *SIENA, Bibl. Comunale, S IV 4.* Paper, 291 × 220 mm, 74 ff.

manuscript of the treatise

80. *FLORENCE, Bibl.Naz., II.I.140 (ex Strozzi 1367; ex Magl., XVII, 31).* Paper, 437 × 288 mm, 99 ff., modern binding.[37]

81. *TURIN, Bibl. Duca di Genova, No.148.* Parchment, 324 × 265 mm, 100 ff., modern binding.

82. *FLORENCE, Bibl. Laurenziana, Ashburnham 361.* Parchment, 371 × 265 mm, 54 ff., modern binding.[38]

35. VALENTINELLI, *op. cit.*, Vol.V, Venice, 1872, pp.185–8.
36. This small note-book comes from the Montefeltre Library.
37. This is followed by a Vitruvius. MAZZATINTI, *op. cit.*, p.52.
38. This incomplete MS. of the treatise bears seven notes in the handwriting of Leonardo da Vinci. It comes from Libri.

later copies of the treatise

83. *TURIN, Bibl. Naz., cod. milit.238*. Paper, 430×287 mm, fos.10 to 76.

84. *VENICE, Bibl. Marciana, it. IV 3-4*. Paper, 223×293 mm, 264 ff., 2 vols. bound together.[39]

85. *MILAN, Bibl. Ambros., cod. N 195*. Paper, 84 ff.

86. *MODENA, not found*.

collections of machine drawings

87. *TURIN, Bibl. Naz., cod. milit.383*. Parchment, 299×206 mm., 82 ff., modern binding.[40]

88. *LONDON, Brit. Mus., 113 add. 24/381*. Parchment, 87 ff.

89. *FLORENCE, Bibl. Naz., 11.111.314 (ex Magl. XVIII, 4)*. Paper, 337×235 mm, 104 ff., modern binding.[41]

90. *SIENA, Bibl. Comunale, S IV 5*. Paper, 351×257 mm, 108 ff., modern binding.

91. *SIENA, Chigi-Sarracini Coll*. Parchment, 408×292 mm, 20 ff.[42]

92. *LUCCA, Bibl. Governativa, No.2723*. Parchment and paper, 175×230 mm, 53 ff., parchment binding.[43]

93. *FLORENCE, Bibl. Naz., cod. palat.767*. Parchment, 268×176 mm, 267 h., 15th century binding.

Giuliano da San Gallo

94. *VATICAN, Cod. Barber., lat.4424*. Paper, 455×390 mm, 75 ff.[44]

95. *SIENA, Bibl. Comunale, S IV 8*. Parchment, 181×121 mm, 51 ff., modern binding.[45]

96. *ESCURIAL, cod. 28 11 12*. Copy of No.94.

97. *FLORENCE, Uffizi*. Numerous architectural drawings.

Antonio da San Gallo

98. *FLORENCE, Uffizi*.

99. *FLORENCE, Uffizi*.

100. *FLORENCE, Uffizi*.

101. *FLORENCE, Uffizi*.

Leonardo da Vinci

These works are too well known for us to need to give many details; here they are just enumerated.

102. *PARIS, Bibl. Institut, MS.A*.

103. *PARIS, Bibl. Institut, MS.B*.

39. FRATI et SEGARIZZI, *Catalogo dei Codici marciani italiani*, Vol.II, Modena, 1911, pp.5-6.
40. This MS. was executed for Emmanuel Philibert, Duke of Savoy.
41. MAZZATINTI, *op. cit.*, p.37. The author is not given in this catalogue.
42. M. SALMI, *Disegni di Francesco di Giorgio nella Collezione Chigi-Saracini*, Siena, 1947.
43. G. ARRIGHI, *Benedetto Saminiati e il maniscritto 2723 della Biblioteca governativa di Lucca*, in *Physis*, II (1960), pp.325-57.
44. Published by HUELSEN, *Il libro di Giuliano da San Gallo codice vaticano barberinano latino 4424*, Leipzig, 1910.
45. Published by FALB, Siena, 1902.